To 3116479

with best wishes,

Bill Ruckelshaus

1385872
144393

Kondor

Bill Randle

Kondor

by Bill Randle

First publication in Great Britain

Copyright © WSO Randle 1999

First edition published in 1999 by:

Independent Books
3 Leaves Green Crescent
Keston
Bromley
BR2 6DN
United Kingdom

Tel: +959 573360
Fax: +959 541129

e-mail   indbooks@globalnet.co.uk

Edited by David Tindall

Jacket design by Daniel Osborne using original artwork by:

John Larder - *'Night Attack'* and Tony Theobald - *'Herr Kreis'*

Page layout and book design: Independent Books

ISBN: 1 872836 25 9

Kondor

The events which were the inspiration for this book actually occurred and are, in many respects, based on first hand experience. However, the characters used in the story are entirely fictitious.

Publisher's Note

There is a broad use of foreign words, particularly German, in the text with appropriate translations in the glossary. This is because many German words have no completely accurate English equivalent. For instance, in the *Luftwaffe*, a *Gruppe* is by no means equal in structure or size to a Group in either British or American terms. Similarly, a rank such as *Gefreiter* falls somewhere between Private First Class and Corporal in the US Army, Private and Lance Corporal in the British Army and Leading Aircraftsman and Corporal in the RAF. Therefore, in the interests of authenticity, the proper names and terms have been retained, but will not detract from the flow of the text.

INTRODUCTION

Like so many old men with little left to do but reflect and ponder on the past, I have decided to record something of my eventful life. In fact an episode which, after all these years, still disturbs me greatly.

I am a German who has seen and experienced much in a lifetime of well over eighty years. I made a start as a professional soldier, and served faithfully for many years until the final collapse of my country. I saw many triumphs and disasters but have, for a long time, had cause to regret the part I played in the evil my nation inflicted on so many millions in its blind pursuit of power. This is why I still find myself harried with terrible memories, some of which remain as vivid today as when the actual deeds were done. Perhaps, by recording those memories, I can warn future generations of man's potential for inhumanity and evil, and seek some forgiveness for my own part in the sins of the past.

CHAPTER ONE

I shall never forget that day in the early spring of 1943, when a series of relatively routine events led to the start of what was to prove the most exciting chapter in my career as an air force officer. It was early morning, and there was still a lot to do before I could complete my night's duty as Operations Officer at one of the *Luftwaffe's* most hard-worked *Nachtjagdgeschwader*. It had been a rewarding night for our crews, in stark contrast to the plight of the poor souls who had had no option but to huddle in their air raid shelters in Essen, while the British carried out another of their heavy bombing raids. Bomber Command had tried, yet again, to hit the giant Krupp works, but their Pathfinders had been foiled on a night when the whole Ruhr had been covered with a thick ground mist. Above it, however, there had been clear skies and a half-moon, ideal for our night-fighters.

From the reports that had streamed in from the District Control Centre, Bomber Command had lost heavily, and the Me 110 nightfighters of *NJG 3* had played their part by making four kills. The last of these, a twin-engined machine, heading homewards at very low altitude, had been picked up by the radar of *Feldwebel* Deissen's aircraft as he was making a long descent back to Venlo at the end of his patrol. We had listened to him on the radio telephone as he made sure that he was not following another fighter, and then heard his triumphant *'Pauke, Pauke!'* call as he made positive identification, opened fire and shot the enemy down close to the Maas at Roermond.

Although it was strictly none of my business, I had agreed to take Deissen to the scene of the crash, where he hoped to find something to keep as a memento of his ninth victory. It was a relief to get away from the stuffiness of the Operations Room and out into the cold fresh air. It was just getting light, the moon was down, and the skies were clouding over with the approach of a cold front. I drove the duty *Kübelwagen* out of the camp with Deissen beside me and *Gefreiter* Holbach, a *Luftwaffe* policeman, sitting in the back. I knew the road to Roermond well; it was clear of traffic and we pushed along at a good speed. The sun was about to break through the low clouds as we reached Roermond. We drove into and through the cobbled centre where the market stalls were already set up and working. We then turned eastwards on to the road which led, eventually, to our Homeland.

When we were just clear of the town, and about to cross the Maas bridge, Deissen shot up in his seat, and pointed off to the right. 'There it is!', he shouted, 'down by the river.' I swung off the main road and drove along a narrow path, through an open farm gate and down across a soggy meadow, right up to the scattered remains of the aircraft. It seemed to me that the pilot had done his best to make a forced landing, maybe in the river itself, but he had come to grief in a drainage ditch after a long skidding arrival which had left bits of his machine strewn over a hundred metres or so. Both wings, the engine nacelles and the port engine were more or less in one group, while the starboard engine was rammed into the side of the broken forward section containing the cockpit and front turret. The tail section was still upright with its fin and rear-turret in place. On the riverbank, two members of a Dutch Fire Brigade were winding in hoses, while others were trying to move the fire engine which had become bogged down at the edge of the river. It was clear that someone had taken charge of the situation, and it pleased me to see a young *Oberfeldwebel* coming my way. He saluted smartly: 'Respectfully wish to report, *Herr Oberleutnant, Oberfeldwebel* Busch, *Luftwaffe* Police District 5. All the enemy crew accounted for. Three dead, one seems to be dying and there is one uninjured. There are no bombs left, but all the machine gun ammunition remains. All fires extinguished and the wreckage has been damped down. The aircraft is a Wellington Mark Three, and the markings on it tell me it is from No. 115 Squadron, based at Mildenhall in Suffolk. I am just about to clear all these Dutch spectators away ... your orders, *Herr Oberleutnant*?' I was impressed with the man's obvious efficiency and bright manner, and showed my appreciation: 'Excellent, thank you indeed. You've done well. Do carry on with your duties. I won't get in your way, but there is just one thing.' I pointed at Deissen, who was already inside the main part of the wreckage and searching amongst the bits and pieces.

'That's the pilot who shot this one down. He is looking for a souvenir. We would very much like just to look around and, in my case, I would like to have a few words with the survivor.'

The *Oberfeldwebel* nodded his assent, saluted and made off towards a knot of curious Dutch people grouped at the top of the meadow.

I began my examination of the crash by going first to what was left of the rear-turret, which was still attached by its mountings to the starboard side of the fuselage. What I found made me feel sick. Inside were the decapitated and smashed remains of the rear-gunner who had been hit squarely, I thought, by a cannon shell. The smell of viscera and blood was awful. I quickly moved on. Two bodies were laid out on blankets alongside a Dutch ambulance. From their aircrew badges, it was clear they were the navigator and the wireless operator. As I studied them, a tired-looking doctor stepped down from the ambulance, wiping blood from his hands.

'There's very little I can do for the poor creature in there,' he said, pointing back over his shoulder, 'but I would like to try my best to make him more comfortable at our hospital in the town. He is unconscious and quite unable to speak. I can assure you that he is no use or danger to you.'

Perhaps not, I thought, feeling a little guilty at doubting the doctor's words, but then, who could ever trust these people to be entirely honest with us?

'Of course, I understand,' I said, 'but I am sure you know it is my duty at least to have a look at him.'

The body inside was that of the pilot. He was loosely strapped to a stretcher and was covered in blood. From the look of the damage to his face, he must have been wearing his flying goggles pulled down over his eyes, presumably to protect them during the crash landing. These had been eased out of his crushed face, and he was fighting desperately for breath through a tube which had been thrust into his windpipe. He was certainly very far gone, and was already taking on the pale blue pallor of approaching death. I turned to the Dutchman.

'I have seen more than enough. You were quite right. Do please carry on with your work, Doctor.'

I got down from the ambulance; the doors were closed and it was driven off slowly across the meadow and up on to the road into Roermond. At this point I was rejoined by the *Oberfeldwebel* and, together, we went to have a look at the only survivor, the bomb-aimer. He made a truly pathetic picture, sitting on the damp grass with head bowed, a blanket around his shoulders, drawing continuously on the stub of a cigarette. He was a small man, dark skinned and older than the usual Bomber Command aircrew. I asked the *Oberfeldwebel* whether the prisoner spoke or understood German.

'Not as far as I know,' he answered, turning up his nose. 'Judging by the smell of him, I think this hero has been scared shitless. I had the Dutch medicos look him over and, although they spoke to him both in English and in Dutch, he said not a word.'

The continuous bird-like movements of the head and hands of this wretched man fascinated me as he glanced furtively at all around him. He was obviously terrified and, as all good interrogators know, this was the time when he could be made to talk. I decided to try but, first, I had to get him away from the carnage around us: I told the *Oberfeldwebel* what I had in mind.

'I have seen enough, and we should be on our way back. I shall take the prisoner with me for questioning. You see, not only am I the *Geschwader* Intelligence Officer, but I speak good English. This man is absolutely ripe and ready for interrogation, after which he is all yours. You need not worry about security. We are all armed.'

The *Oberfeldwebel* seemed a little taken aback. He did not like what I had said.

'But *Herr Oberleutnant,* you must know it is not possible for you to take this prisoner with you. He is the responsibility of the *Luftwaffe* Police. This is not correct procedure. I cannot ...'

At that very moment, our attention was drawn to the noisy arrival of a gleaming black Horch staff car, which drove right through some lingering Dutch spectators at the top of the meadow, sounding its horn, and was now heading down towards us.

'Oh no,' groaned the *Oberfeldwebel,* 'I knew they were somewhere around here, although I didn't expect them to interfere with us but, no matter.' He straightened up: clearly the arrival of the car had helped him to a decision. 'The *Luftwaffe* was here first, and everything to do with this crash is our responsibility. In the circumstances, *Herr Oberleutnant,* I must agree that it would be better if you did take this man with you to Venlo. Please do that; I will be there this afternoon to collect him.'

That was certainly the right thing to do. In any case, I did not want to become involved in the rights and wrongs of what had to be done with shot-down Britishers. That was none of my business. I turned and scowled at the wretched bomb-aimer, then shouted to Holbach to take the man up to the *Kübelwagen,* where they should wait for me. Holbach hauled the prisoner to his feet, made him put his hands on his head, prodded him with his *Schmeisser,* and had him doubling up the slope past the approaching Horch.

The occupants of the staff car ignored us for a while as it cruised along the length of the crash site before drawing up alongside us. Two smartly dressed officers got out. The senior was wearing the grey-green uniform of the *SD,* with a leather top-coat draped over his shoulders. He made a languid yet commanding picture as he stood in front of us, fastidiously smoking a cheroot. I felt an instinctive dislike at once for this man, with his superior and disdainful attitude. The other was much younger and was dressed in the black uniform of the *SS.* Observing a rank far senior to mine, I saluted the *SD* officer and told him that everything was under control, that all the necessary tasks had been completed and that the only survivor was on his way to Venlo for questioning.

'So I see... and that is good, *Oberleutnant.* Do feel free to carry on with anything you have left to do. By the way, my name is Leisendahl. We are on our way back to Sittard after a good night's business. We saw the commotion down here from up on the main road and just thought we would like to take a look.' He peered at me and smiled: 'You do not mind if we look around, do you? After all, this job is just as much ours as it is yours ... although, perhaps, we are a little better at it.'

'Of course, *Herr Sturmbannführer.* In any case, we are just about to leave. If I can be of any assistance, please tell me.' He stubbed out his cheroot and beckoned me to follow him. We went first to look at the corpses, at which point we were joined by Deissen, whom I introduced as the victor of the combat. Leisendahl did not bother to congratulate him, but seemed more interested in an ornamental rabbit's foot which Deissen had found in the navigator's compartment. I noticed that Deissen had acquired something else of a little more value, as he was now wearing one of the excellent British navigators' wrist-watches, most likely taken from the dead body. We left Deissen to continue his searches, and strolled on: Leisendahl then decided to confide in me.

'We have done well, clearing up after these damned *Terrorflieger.* A few hours ago, I found three of them, part of the crew of a Halifax, all very happy to give themselves up, even to us. I am sure that the rest of that bunch will be rounded up soon, but I hope they don't get any ideas about using the Dutch to help with an escape.' He stopped to light another cheroot, looking at me all the time.

'If they do, then they will probably meet the same fate that awaits a Dutch farmer and his family; some fools we also found during the night. They were actually hiding a *Terrorflieger,* and had him dressed as one of their farm hands.' He swore quietly to himself.

'It is strange, you know, my dear *Oberleutnant*, what these people will do, even when they know full well what the consequences are if they are caught.'

What he said was true. In every part of the Greater *Reich*, there were notices posted in every town and village, making it abundantly clear that the penalty for helping a *Terrorflieger* was death. I wondered if the same fate would befall the British airman who had been caught with the Dutch farmer.

'In the case of the airman,' I asked, 'will he not, in due course, end up in a prisoner-of-war camp? Surely, he would simply be doing his duty to escape, just as we would in the *Luftwaffe*?' I seemed to have nettled Leisendahl. He was annoyed, and glared at me.

'Do you not realise that any enemy found wearing anything other than a recognised uniform can, under the terms of the Geneva

Convention, be treated as a spy? All these so-called evaders who are being helped to get back to England are doing so in disguise. Yes, in disguise, *Oberleutnant,* and then they can come back and continue with their terror campaign. No, this particular type of subversion has to be dealt with ruthlessly... and this we can do whilst keeping well within the bounds of International Law.'

Changing the subject, he asked whether there was any chance that someone could have parachuted from the Wellington. I told him I thought it would be a remote possibility, because four of the parachutes were still in their racks and the remains of the rear-gunner were on top of the fifth. With that, Leisendahl said he had seen enough. He stayed a few more minutes, and then drove off without any form of farewell, pausing only alongside our *Kübelwagen* at the top of the meadow, where he got out to harangue our prisoner before finally driving away.

I had also finished, so, after checking with the *Oberfeldwebel,* Deissen and I made our way back to the *Kübelwagen,* where our captive was still standing, hands on head, trembling and shaking, quite unconcerned with the large spreading stain now wetting his trousers. The encounter with the *Gestapo* had reduced him to a pathetic state, and it was my intention to keep him, at least for a while, as terrified as I could. I glared at him, turned up my nose, and spat on the ground.

'I want him put in the front with me: I shall just have to endure the smell,' I told Holbach. 'You will sit behind him and watch his every move. If he makes a dash for it,' and I laughed, 'shoot him.'

Holbach roughly pushed the bomb-aimer into the front seat, cocked his *Schmeisser* for good measure, and got in behind him. Deissen jumped in next to him, holding his nose and trying hard to keep a straight face. I scowled again at the foul-smelling man, and now intended to make sure that he did not understand German. Looking him straight in the face I said with measured coldness, *'Sie jämmerliches englisches Schwein! Wie ich Sie verachte! Wir hätten besser getan, Sie mit Ihren Kameraden dort drüben auszulegen! Ich hoffe, Sie werden in der Hölle verrotten! Oder, noch besser, ich überreiche Sie zur Gestapo!'* He looked beseechingly at me, like a stricken animal. I was certain he had not understood a word, but had been taken aback by the hatred in my face and voice. His head slumped to his chest. Now was certainly the time for his interrogation to begin. I sat there looking at him and said nothing for a few moments. Then I put my hand under his chin, raised his head and, looking him straight in the eyes, spoke again - but this time in perfect English, 'Things are never as bad as they seem, old boy. You've had a rough time; you look as though you could do with a cigarette.' I offered him a Caporal from an opened packet. 'I must apologise for these foul-smelling things, but we do have some difficulty in getting Players these days.'

The man was dumbstruck. His jaw dropped and his eyes widened in astonishment. As though transfixed, he slowly took the offered cigarette, which I lit with my *Luftwaffe* presentation lighter.

'Well, my dear fellow, you are a lucky one, in fact doubly so. You have not only escaped the chop, but we managed to get to you before our super-efficient *Gestapo* could grab you. I am sure you know what that could have meant. They probably told you back at the squadron that the *Gestapo* treat you as terror-flyers; in fact, as war criminals to be strung up or shot. But then, they do not understand us airmen. By the way, I am *Oberleutnant* Wilhelm Rath, or as you might say in your RAF, Flying Officer Bill Rath. What's your name?'

The man was beginning to respond to me. He was trying to pull himself together, and had found his tongue, '1394552 Sergeant W A Coleman... Sir.' He replied hesitantly.

'Does that mean you are called Bill, as well?'

'Yes Sir', he nodded, 'the oldest one in our family is always William or Thomas. It's been...' He stopped abruptly, no doubt remembering words of advice given about conduct after capture. I had to play him carefully.

'Oh yes, I know as well as you do about what you must and must not say when you meet us. But no one here is going to interrogate you. Believe me, I am just an ordinary flyer. I am not up to the tricks of the trade used by those you will no doubt meet before long. All I want to do is have a chat with you, and practise my English. If I can, I want to help a fellow airman, even though I know I shouldn't. All I have to do is take you back to my station, where we can get you cleaned up and fed and ... by the way ... it happens to be a night-fighter base, the very place from where that chap sitting behind you shot you down.' Coleman squirmed around in his seat to look at Deissen, smiling at him in an almost benevolent way.

'I am sure that your family will want to know you are safe. Maybe your mother or, perhaps, your wife? I can easily arrange for them to be told; we do that through the International Red Cross in Switzerland. I just hope we can talk a little, because I don't get many opportunities to speak English these days. You see, I actually went to school in England, to a public school in Yorkshire. Where did you go to school?'

Coleman sighed deeply, leant back into his seat and slowly drew on his Bleu. He blew out the smoke, looking ahead into the distance. 'I suppose I was lucky', he said, speaking slowly. 'I grew up on a farm in Dorset and went to what we call a Church School. I won a scholarship to Dorchester Grammar School, where I did well and got my School Certificate. I'm sure I would've done better if I had gone to a public school, like you, but that was not possible for the likes of me.'

I knew that I had hooked my fish. He was coming under my control, relaxed and very much at ease. All I had to do was keep him talking. I started the *Kübelwagen,* and drove back onto the main road and into Roermond. Coleman was now asking me questions, about exactly where he was and how far was it to my station? We entered Roermond and drove through the now crowded market place, where we caused something of a stir when some Dutchmen ironically cheered us and one fool actually shouted 'Good luck, Tommy.' Back on the Venlo road, I settled down to drive at a modest speed. With the help of a leading question here and there, Sergeant Coleman regaled us with his opinions on many things, including politics and the small part he played in the war. He abjectly avowed that he had not been in favour of Bomber Command's area bombing policy and that, in any case, as a mere sergeant, it had nothing to do with him. He did what he was told to do; obey orders.

He went to some lengths to explain that he had not been on the terror fire raids to Lübeck and Rostock, and certainly not in the thousand bomber raid on Köln. By now, however, he was beginning to brag. He said that his particular Wellington had been the first on the squadron modified to carry the 4,000 lb 'blockbuster', a tricky weapon to manage and to drop accurately; but then, what did it matter if it was a little off target when its power was so great? He went on, without any prompting, to volunteer the information that the casualty rate on his squadron was so high that, despite continual reinforcement, there had been only four crews available for the Essen raid. His crew had been very lucky until now, and had made twenty-seven trips over Germany, with only three more needed to complete their first tour of operations. And so we chatted as I drove back to Venlo. I was disgusted with Coleman, a man full of excuses and with little moral backbone. He had thrown discretion aside, and seemed to think it mattered little what he said to us. He prattled on about conditions in England, saying that the *Luftwaffe* night blitz had failed and then, with ridiculous bravado, that Britain would never give in.

He was still holding forth in this way as we drew up at the guardroom, and Holbach took the cretin away to be locked up. I had been on duty for eighteen hours and was dead-beat. Duty bound, I reported to Operations and, promising to submit a full report on Sergeant Coleman as soon as possible, went to my room in the Officers' Mess. There, I took a shower and literally scrubbed myself to get rid of the pervading smell of the Englishman. A little refreshed, I ate a late breakfast alone, an excellent meal prepared for me in the English style, something I continued to prefer. I was spreading marmalade on my toast when a steward quietly informed me that I was wanted in the *Kommodor's* office.

I was on the verge of dozing off, but I finished my meal and walked across to the *Geschwaderkommodor's* office at the rear of the temporary hangar on the edge of the airfield. I was not kept waiting: I entered, and saluted my old *Legion Kondor* friend, *Major* Kurt Winter, who was seated, waiting, at his desk.

'Good to see you, Wilhelm,' he said, 'I know you have been working hard and have done well, but I have some important news for you. It could be good news... at least I think so. Do sit down.' I took a seat and accepted a cigarette. Winter leant forward across the desk and lit it for me. I sat back to prepare myself for the worst.

'You are on your way, Wilhelm, I am afraid. I am truly sorry to lose you, but I have orders here for you to report to Berlin as quickly as possible. I have tried to find out what it's all about, but I come up against a security screen every time. I cannot find out whether it has anything to do with your constant requests to get back to flying. All they tell me is that I have to send you post-haste to the *Luftfahrtministerium* where, no doubt, all will be made clear.' He looked apologetically at me.

'Sorry to rush you like this, but you must be packed and cleared by mid-day. There is a Siebel diverted in here from Wildenrath, just for you, so make sure you catch it.' I felt overwhelmed by it all, but far too tired to argue or ask questions. Winter was on his feet with arm outstretched in farewell. I took his firm hand.

'God be with you, my dear Wilhelm. Have a good trip, and all that you hope for in the posting. I trust that we can keep in touch and, maybe one day, we can serve together again. *Hals- und Beinbruck!*'

With that salutation still ringing in my ears, I made my way back to my quarters and packed, my mind racing as I wondered what could be behind all this. An aircraft diverted to collect me? Surely not. I was ready on time, and watched as the dumpy Siebel joined the circuit and landed, taxi-ing close to Operations. The pilot did not shut down the engines and his navigator, an *Unteroffizier* in his oil stained *Fliegerkombi* and *Feldmütze,* opened the rear door and sprinted across the grass towards the building. I picked up my bags as he came through the door. '*Oberleutnant* Rath?', he asked, as he flicked up a rather perfunctory salute. I nodded, and he turned on his heel and opened the door for me to follow. Taking one of my bags, he led the way back to the aircraft and gestured for me to take any of the seats; the aircraft was, indeed, empty. As I tightened the seat harness, the *Unteroffizier* replaced his *Feldmütze* with a flying helmet, plugged the communications jack plug into a socket, and spoke to the pilot. As he stowed my bags in a rack at the front of the aircraft, we began to move off towards the end of the runway. Swinging the aircraft into wind, the pilot per-

formed his routine power and magneto checks and, before I could ori-
entate myself, there came the full-power roar of the engines and I felt
the tail lift quickly as we began the take-off run.

Making myself as comfortable as I could, I began to mull things
over in my mind. What a curious turn of events this was for me. What
would this new posting hold? Why had an aircraft been diverted, just to
collect me? I was desperately tired, but my mind raced. How complicated my journey to this point in my life had been, and how diverse were the
influences which had shaped me.

CHAPTER TWO

I was born in Burislav, into a family which had flourished in that part of Silesia for over a hundred years. My father, Philip Albrecht Rath, a banker, married my English mother, Edith Carey, in Hampstead, London in 1898 when he was a junior clerk serving in his bank's London office. This was at a time when relations between Germany and Great Britain could hardly have been better. My parents had four children, the first three all being born in Breslau (now Wroclaw, Poland). Their eldest son, Karl Wilhelm, was born in 1901; their daughter Emily Charlotte in 1902, and their second son, Albrecht Johan, in 1904. I was born in 1913, when Germany was in the throes of mobilising for war with Russia. My father was called to the colours in July 1914, as a *Leutnant der Reserve* in the Hirschberger *Jäger* Battalion 'Von Neumann'. When war broke out, his regiment became part of the 8th Army, soon in action against the Russians advancing into Galacia and East Prussia. He fought at Tannenberg, where his bravery and leadership were brought to the attention of General Paul von Hindenburg. He was wounded but quickly recovered, returning to his regiment in time to fight in the Battle of the Masurian Lakes a few months later. Despite his utter devotion to duty at the front, he saw to it that, as the Russians advanced, his family was safely evacuated from Silesia and re-established in Berlin.

In every respect, my father was a fine soldier. His bearing and appearance were striking; indeed, the military life should have been his profession from the start. He proved himself in many campaigns, mostly on the Western Front, where he fought as an officer of the Bavarian Army at such places as Ypres, Neuve Chapelle, Arras, Cambrai and, finally, in defence of the Hindenburg Line. He returned only twice to Berlin on furlough, and the only other times my mother saw him were when he was in hospital recovering from wounds. In all, he was wounded five more times, and ended the war with the rank of *Hauptmann* and the rare distinction, for an infantry officer, of being awarded Germany's highest honour, the *Pour Le Mérite*.

My mother must have led a very lonely life, but she did well, single-handed, to raise our family. As a born Englishwoman, she was naturally torn between love for her family and a basic loyalty to her mother country. She had a strong personality, a perfect foil for my father, and she quickly made herself settle into life in suburban Berlin where, somewhat surprisingly, she was accepted as the loyal wife of a gallant German hero. She did her best to ignore the rights and wrongs of the conflict, devoting her life to her children and helping others. She took up voluntary nursing at one of Berlin's military hospitals, and became involved in various welfare organisations, including the International Red Cross. As the war progressed, she found herself increasingly bewildered by the ferocity and callousness of the fighting. She believed that the U-boat campaign, aimed at starving the British into surrender, might almost be acceptable as an act of war. However, the indiscriminate bombing of London and other parts of England by Zeppelins and heavy bombers was, to her, totally incomprehensible and utterly abhorrent.

My brothers and sister naturally held very different opinions, and did their best to help in any way possible with Germany's war effort. Admiring my father, my brothers could not wait to get into uniform and emulate his deeds. Karl joined the Army on his 17th birthday, and was soon in action. Unfortunately, he was killed fighting gallantly in Ludendorf's great push into France in March 1918. By now, my mother was showing the aggravated effects of four long years of war, openly praying for it to end and, as was discovered later, hoping, one day, to leave the country she had once grown to love.

I was, of course, far too young to remember much of the Great War or of my father's return to the family. Such few memories were clouded with the atmosphere of our nation's defeat and the pathetic lifestyle which then existed in Berlin. We were beset with the problems which followed the betrayal of our Army by the *'Novemberverbrecher'* - those who had accepted the defeat of Germany by agreeing to the Armistice in November 1918 - and by those who wanted Bolshevism to replace the rule of the Kaiser. Berlin was in turmoil. Armed men, supported by field guns and armoured cars, and operating in the name of the Revolutionary Soldiers' Council, were on the streets. They, in turn, were opposed by the newly constituted *Freikorps*. All around us was the detritus of a lost war: the wounded, the blinded, the amputees, all made the worse by lack of food and employment.

My father's brilliant war record counted for little. Although he still had to maintain contact with the Army, he was able to take up his career again as a banker in a responsible position at a major branch in Berlin. Amongst his former comrades, he was recognised as a leader and a hero, and very soon had drawn together disillusioned and aimless ex-Servicemen who were searching for some purpose in life in a turbulent country which they loved, yet which now seemed to have no place for them.

He became increasingly interested in their problems and, inevitably, in local politics. He did, however, try to keep in the background and, in doing so, turned our home into an ex-Servicemen's meeting place. Often, I was allowed to sit quietly in a corner, listening to stories of how soldiers lived and fought in the trenches, the battles that had been won and lost, and what was so desperately wrong with government in Germany. Father then began to spend more time away from home. He travelled now and then to Bavaria to meet many old friends from his former Regiment; I well remember him returning from one such visit to Munich in early 1920, to tell us that he had met a truly remarkable man who had served with him as a *Gefreiter* in the Regiment during the last year of the war. His name was Adolf Hitler, and he was organising a vital new political group called the National Socialist Workers' Party.

My father had long since resumed his rightful place as head of the family, and we welcomed his authority and guiding hand. My brother Albrecht finished his secondary education in grand style, gaining a scholarship to Munich University to study Economics and Politics. Emily, my sister, had married a young pilot from the former Imperial Air Service and was living in Baden Baden, where her husband was now studying to become a dentist.

My education had been, so far, entirely under the control and influence of my mother. I was fluently bilingual, since she had always instructed me in both German and English. I received most of my basic learning at a private nursery school, where I was considered to be reasonably intelligent. I read and wrote well, and showed a flair for arithmetic and practically anything that could be learned by heart. My father, however, was not at all happy with this arrangement, and I remember heated arguments between him and my mother. He thought I was becoming too much of a mother's boy - in fact, in danger of becoming a cissy. My father won the tussle in the end and, on my seventh birthday, told me that I was a fortunate fellow indeed to have been accepted as a weekly boarder at a *Internat* for officers' sons in Spandau, not far from where we were living. I had no idea what this meant, only that my mother was upset about something which she thought was too regimented and hard for someone so young.

I did not like the dramatic change of events at all. I would have to be away from my home from Sunday night to midday the following Saturday. I began with a tearful first week, longing to be at home under the protection and love of my mother. Contact with home during the week was forbidden, and the resident Matron quickly went to work on me and asserted her influence, not by mothering me, but by steadily instilling in me a sense of duty and a sincere respect for my parents. She convinced me that I was indeed lucky to be getting such a fine start in life.

The regime at the school was Spartan. We stood apart from other children in our uniforms and student caps. Everything we did was governed by rules; if we transgressed, then we were physically punished. The teachers were formidable people, and we responded to them fearfully and with respect. They taught us emphatically and systematically, almost by numbers, but we found this something which we all could understand. Strong emphasis was placed on physical education, sports, competition and drill. We were kept in during the week, and I was one of the few lucky ones able to see the outer world for a few hours. During the time at home, I had to deal with a lot of homework but, always, mother was at hand to help and guide me.

I saw less and less of my father. His interest in politics had increased, and he now spent all his weekends away from home. He joined the *NSDAP* (National Socialist German Workers' Party) in 1921, just after the Allies had presented Germany with a crushing bill for reparations. This put the *Weimar* Republic into serious difficulties as it struggled with the demands of the political extremes on the right and the left. My father's involvement in the Party grew steadily and yet, somehow, he was still able to deal with his duties at the bank. However, in early 1923, when the *Mark* was losing its value on the international exchanges, and when French troops occupied the Ruhr, he resigned from the bank, telling us that his future would be entirely political.

Germany's economy was now being destroyed as inflation turned into hyper-inflation and the *Mark* became worthless. Our life savings and those of most around us were wiped out. I do not know how we managed but, at least, I was able to continue at the *Internat*. Someone, certainly not my father, was paying the bills, and I believe this help was coming from my mother's relatives in England. My mother fought hard to keep the home together. At weekends, I could see how desperate things had become. I did my best to help, and would often go with her to scavenge on the tips for coal, and travelled everywhere, always on foot, in search of food.

In the autumn of 1923, when a State of Emergency was proclaimed throughout Germany, my father shocked us with the news that he was leaving us to live in Bavaria. He showed little concern for us, and certainly no remorse, even being adamant that we should not follow him. He was now a *Kommandeur* in the *Sturmabteilung* - the Storm Troopers - effectively a private army of the Nazi Party. On 9th November, he took part in the *Bügerbräu Keller* - Beer Hall - *Putsch* in Munich, standing alongside General Ludendorf and Adolf Hitler at the barbed wire barricades in the centre of the city when *Reichswehr* soldiers opened fire. My father was badly wounded in the leg but, fortunately, was dragged away to safety from a street littered with the dead and wounded.

Relations between my father and mother then worsened. They had not been good ever since his return from the war, and he was now something of a stranger to us. Our existence in Berlin was absolutely wretched. My mother was getting no financial support at all, and depended entirely upon gifts from her relatives in England. My father was in hiding somewhere in Bavaria, recovering from his wound and, because of the failure of the Beer Hall *Putsch* and the fact that Adolf Hitler was now in gaol, there seemed little likelihood that he would be returning to live in Berlin.

My mother's kin were now very concerned, and urged that something definite should be done. My uncle, John Carey, came to Berlin in May 1924, as I was later to discover, to entreat my mother to make a break with the sorry state of affairs in Germany, and to return with him to England. She travelled with him to Bavaria, where the matter was discussed with my father, and the outcome was that, a few weeks later, she told me it had been agreed that I should leave school at once and go with her to live in England, at least until the situation in Germany had greatly improved.

CHAPTER THREE

My mother had married at an early age, and at the time we moved to England she was in her mid-forties but still very active and forceful. It had been more than ten years since she had last been in England, but it did not take her long for us to be settled in a small detached house near the Careys' home in Hampstead. She quickly adjusted to the very noticeable differences in life around us, and began her search for financial independence. She had been unable to bring anything of value from Germany, and was entirely dependent on the charity of her friends.

After a few months in London, we moved to Oxford, where my mother had secured not only a position as governess with a titled Roman Catholic family, but also as a part-time teacher of German. I attended what was called a Church School where, after a while spent getting used to English working class prejudices and backwardness, I found myself well ahead of my fellows in practically all subjects. Fortunately, although slightly over age, I was permitted to sit a State examination which allowed me to take up a place at a Grammar School.

Finding a better school was not easy, although my mother had established good relations with the educational authorities in the Oxford area. Also, I knew that she had asked my uncle to help. Then, one late summer evening in 1925, she returned home from work, happy with the surprising news that I had been accepted at an excellent Roman Catholic public school in Yorkshire, and that I would start there as a boarder at the beginning of the autumn term in September.

After my harsh primary schooling in Germany, and the privations of our life in Berlin, I had developed a marked measure of personal independence. I went to my new school with a feeling of expectancy, almost pleasure, knowing that I could benefit from something I had gained by my own ability. I had many reasons to remind me that I was in a foreign country, but my mother's influence had been so strong that I fitted easily into my new life. Academically, I was ahead of most and, physically, I was in good shape. I looked forward to the challenges of a new style of learning and getting to grips with such new games as fives, cricket and rugby.

For most of the first year, there had to be some assimilation of my habits and speech. I was 'adopted' by my housemaster's wife, who did her best to make me feel at home and to adapt to life as a boarder. I was easily able to follow lessons and, by the end of the first term, had begun to emerge as a good student. At first, I found some difficulty in coming to terms with the bullying and the denigration of Germany by the sons of the victorious British, but this soon came to an end.

I progressed well. Games were my forte; particularly rugby and athletics. I was selected for, first, the School's Junior XV, and then the Senior. I was *Victor Ludorum* at athletics in both 1928 and 1929. My best subjects were physics, mathematics and history. I was extremely good at accurately remembering facts, even the unimportant. My hobbies and pastimes were creative and usually connected with aviation. I could recount the names and victories of all the German, British, French, Austro-Hungarian, Belgian, Italian, Russian and American aces of the Great War, right down to the score of ten. I knew such worthless details as the dates of accession of the British monarchs since Saxon days, and those of the German States from the early Middle Ages. I formed an aircraft modelling club which drew around me others similarly interested. Often, at weekends, we cycled to various parts of Yorkshire to watch aeroplanes flying from small airfields and, sometimes, just from fields. If we had the necessary five shillings, then we went aloft in fascinating machines, most of which had been left over from the War.

Between terms I went back to Oxford, where being with mother was always enjoyable and stimulating, but I still kept in touch by letter with my father and my brother and sister. My father took pains in trying to explain how things had greatly improved in Germany, and how the time was coming when the nation would find a leader strong enough to take positive control, and so lead Germany back to its proper place in world affairs.

I made my first visit back to Germany between the Summer and Autumn terms in 1927. Mother and I travelled by train to Munich, where we met my father and Albrecht and, after a week of constant excitement, went on to Baden Baden to see Emily, now the mother of four children. I had expected some rapprochement between my parents, but there were no signs of emotion, just the impression that they were friends. I was sub-sequently allowed to make an annual visit to Germany on my own, and I always stayed with my father.

At school I was doing very well indeed. I had been appointed a prefect while still in the Fifth Form and was made Head Prefect during my first year in the Sixth, at a time when I also became Head of House. I gained the School Certificate with exemption of matriculation to London University and then, after two years in the Sixth, the Higher Schools Certificate together with an Exhibition to Oxford University. I had reached a stage where I knew that important decisions would soon have to be made about the nature of my future life. I could remain in England and reap the benefits of an excellent education and, perhaps, even end up as a British citizen, or I could face up to my heritage, make a clean break and, as a German, return to the land which I knew I really loved.

My visits to Germany had become more frequent, at a time when the country, like all other industrial nations, had been brought almost to a standstill by the effects of the Wall Street crash in America. This cor-nerstone of Germany's prosperity, where most of its loans were secured, had collapsed with horrendous results. Millions were made unemployed as large firms and small businesses went under. I saw at first hand the misery of my fellow countrymen, most of whom were mystified and searching for guidance to a way out of their troubles. My sheltered, pleas-ant and untroubled five years in England had dulled my latent patriotism but, after a visit to my father in September 1930, when he explained his work with the National Socialist Party - the Nazis - it was rekindled, and indeed, fanned into flame with thoughts of what had to be done to help my Fatherland.

Although I had always known that my mother had foreseen the possibility of my ending the close ties with her, I was surprised at the vehemence of her reaction when I told her I had decided to return to Germany. She was deeply upset, almost distraught. She pleaded with me, called me a fool to forego the advantages of an Oxford education and wondered why, in any case, I did not stay with her long enough to get my degree and, perhaps, the cherished Oxford doctorate. I am sure she knew that my heart was not in England but with the land of my birth. I asked her to return to Germany with me, knowing full well that she would say no. She had long since told me that her marriage had foundered in Berlin, where my father's obsession with politics had driven the family apart.

My father was, of course, extremely pleased. His political militarism was the centre of his existence. He had aged well, keeping himself wonderfully fit. I found him someone to admire and respect. Albrecht, my brother, was now living with him and was an active supporter of National Socialism, also working to unite the people and to restore something of the old Germany.

CHAPTER FOUR

I arrived in Berlin on the day the election results made the National Socialist Workers' Party the second largest political group in Germany. I could clearly see an exciting and fulfilling time ahead if I joined in the work of my father and brother. My father, however, had very different ideas. He was adamant in his view that my education was incomplete and un-German, and that something had to be done to remedy matters. He decided that the best solution would be for me to take a degree at a good German university: accordingly, and doubtless due to his influence, I was entered as an undergraduate at the old university in the beautiful city of Heidelberg.

I took up my studies there when the country was in the hands of the aged and senile President von Hindenburg, who had lost control of an inept and divided government. There were five million wage-earners out of work, the great farming industry was in chaos and the middle classes again faced ruin. Something drastic had to be done to save Germany, and the elections of July 1932 showed the way ahead, with the *Nazis* gaining 230 out of 608 seats in the *Reichstag*. I could not understand why, at such an eventful time in our history, my father thought that three years in the remote calm of Heidelberg could in any way help me fashion the type of life I intended to lead in the restoration of my country. Nonetheless, as a dutiful son, I buckled down, studied and played hard, and earned a good degree.

As undergraduates, we did our best to ignore the diversions around our university but, increasingly, we were drawn into the political turmoil sweeping the country. There were continuous rallies of the Party; torchlight parades; amplified broadcasting of news from street corners and vans, and uniforms were being widely worn as a mark of political identity. Some of these changes I found disturbing. The *SA*, the Brownshirts, now had orders from the Party to break up opposition rallies, particularly those of the Social Democrats and any with a liberal leaning. As students, we were unhappy about the suppression of Social Democratic newspapers and other liberal journals but, when Hitler was appointed Chancellor on 30th January 1933 and the Third *Reich* came to power, I decided, without any pressure from the family, that the time had come for me to play my part, and this I would do by joining the newly formed *Wehrmacht* - the Armed Forces of the *Reich*.

My father and mother were reunited for a short time at the formal degree awarding ceremony held in November 1934, just two days before the great Nuremberg Rally. I shall never forget my mother's surprise and ill-concealed dismay when she saw my father dressed in the black parade uniform of the *Schutzstaffel*, Hitler's recently formed Elite Guard . He was an *Obergruppenführer SS,* and paraded with his Great War decorations on his chest and the *Pour Le Mérite* at his throat. She was confused and depressed at the military trappings around her, and by the hurried departure of my father for Nuremberg immediately the ceremony finished. She went back to England a sad and forlorn figure, to live on for only another four months. It was as though this frail, lonely, yet still beautiful lady had lost all reason for living. I had never realised just how much she had grown to dislike Germany and, in particular, my father. She was buried in the Carey family plot at Highgate on a beautiful spring morning in 1935, mourned by her English relatives. I was the only representative there from her immediate family.

Now, with the blessing of a first-class education, I was able to turn to my chosen career. Whilst at Heidelberg, I had fostered my deep interest in flying. I had qualified as a glider pilot and had spent much time and money flying in various light aircraft: I had no doubt that what I wanted to do was to serve in the newly-born *Luftwaffe.*

I had already been accepted for interview as an airman cadet by the time I had said farewell to my mother at her graveside. The way ahead had been prepared for me by my father, who had close connections with many government officials in Berlin. I passed through the initial stages with ease, being tested for flying aptitude and the necessary mental and physical qualities for pilot training. My health was excellent and all my sporting achievements, both in England and at Heidelberg, had been noted. I had been asked why I wanted to fly under military orders, and had given the expected pat answers: I explained that I had always wanted to fly and, quite honestly, to serve my country.

During the second day of the interviews, I was surprised to be taken from the *Luftwaffe* Headquarters to another government department, which I later discovered dealt with intelligence matters and had a connection with the *Geheime Staatspolizei* - the secret state police, often referred to as the *Gestapo*. There I was interviewed by an extremely well educated civilian, who talked to me at length in perfect, unaccented English. He seemed fascinated with the details of my upbringing and schooling in Yorkshire, and asked many questions about the towns and cities in England, the Parliamentary procedures, the English way of life, and what I thought of the English as a race. He even had me reading passages from Shakespeare. He finished by asking me how I would react if, at some time in the future, the *Reich* were placed in the unfortunate position of having to go to war, once again, with the British. I did not hesitate with my reply, which no doubt told this polished interviewer that I had been waiting for him to ask that very question. Later, my father told me that the *Gestapo* conducted such interviews as a matter of routine.

I was accepted for training as a pilot in February 1935, and reported to Wildpark-Werder, Potsdam, for initial training. This was undoubtedly a place where the aim was to knock us into shape. There was not an aircraft to be seen, and our existence centred on hard work in a military barracks which had, sometime in the past, been the depot of an Hussar Regiment. Reveille was sounded at 05.00 hours, very quickly followed by a parade, an inspection, and a three-kilometre run. We then dashed back to our dormitory to shower, shave and dress in working uniform. Within the next thirty minutes, we had to eat breakfast and then line up on the parade ground for an hour's infantry drill. After that, we began our studies in the classroom where, in time, we learned about the rules and regulations of the *Wehrmacht,* the basics of life in the *Luftwaffe,* the use of the Morse Code, navigation and map-reading. We dwelt on such diverse subjects as the newly established decorations of the Third *Reich,* German history, medical problems associated with venereal disease and, above all, the code of honour of a German officer.

Drill and lectures alternated throughout the day and ended at 1900 hours. In our Students' Mess, we were allowed an hour for dinner, after which there was written work to be completed, before 'Lights Out' at 22.00 hours. Discipline was strict at all times, and we saluted everyone on the Directing Staff from *Gefreiter* upwards, no matter where we met them, even in the lavatories.

There were a few who could not cope with the restrictive pressure. They were usually the older ones, who had joined the Air Force as a second thought after first making an attempt at a profession or a business. The parade ground was where we first saw their reaction - usually when they skirmished with the strict drillmasters and received short shrift. Those who had difficulty in distinguishing left from right got special attention, and it was not long before we were able to settle down and pull together as a team. The enforced confinement to camp did lead to some transgressions, but only for a while. There were proctors, of a sort, in the nearby town, most likely *Gestapo* for all we knew, and we were soon made to realise that there was nothing to be gained by dwelling in the beer gardens, or trying to satisfy our lust with the fair sex.

For six weeks we worked hard and learned a lot. Only seven of the course fell by the wayside. We finished as a very smart unit, much healthier than when we had arrived, and all looking forward to what was next to come. We were given seven days leave, and then ordered, in batches of twenty, to one of three different elementary flying schools.

I spent my furlough with my sister, whose husband now had a thriving dental practice in Baden Baden. She was pleased to see me, and her family made me very welcome. It was an ideal place for me to unwind and, at first, all I wanted to do was to walk for hours in the woods and over the hills around this charming town. After a few days, however, I began to get bored, and became impatient to return to the excitement of Service life. Therefore, on the sixth day, I cut my leave short, said goodbye to Emily and boarded the train for the long journey to Pütnitz.

As I had expected, the atmosphere at Elementary Flying School was decidedly different. The strict regime of discipline was maintained, and every day we spent some time on the drill square, but now we were, at last, among aeroplanes. There were two types of training aircraft; the Fieseler biplane in which we would do our primary work, and the Arado monoplane, intended to see us through the advanced stages and on to graduation. In batches of three, we were allocated to the men who would be our mentors throughout our stay.

I was fortunate indeed to become the pupil of a very experienced pilot, a rather pudgy, jocular Silesian, *Oberleutnant* Adolf Loewe. He was an extrovert, with outspoken views on practically every subject under the sun. Although only thirty-six years old, he had served on the Western Front with *Jasta 11,* and had flown both the Fokker D7 and the triplane DR1. He had a total of 15 kills and, in addition to the Iron Cross First Class, had been awarded the Knight's Cross with Swords of the Royal House of Hohenzollern. My first flight with 'Fats' Loewe will always remain in my memory. His instructions through the speaking tube were unhurried, clear and precise. Very soon, he let me take control and talked me through the basic handling movements. Then it was his turn and, with a curt, 'I've got it, just sit tight and relax,' he gave me all the thrills of looping the loop, rolling in every direction, including vertically, and finishing with an eight-turn spin right into the circuit pattern of the airfield.

I was sent solo after just five hours of dual instruction. This was followed by a succession of solo flights, after which my aerobatics training began. Although I did enjoy this excitement, I had to admit that it was beyond me to be able to react instinctively. When flying with 'Fats', I could manage to follow his orders and promptings but, on my own, there was nothing at all natural about my clumsy efforts at aerobatics.

I did well at ground school and, at the halfway stage examinations, came top of the course. I converted easily to the more nimble and faster Arado, and was soon away on cross-country flights, and picking up the skills of formation flying and the use of weapons. I still had trouble, however, with my aerobatics.

Life at Pütnitz was relatively relaxed, and we easily accepted the happy, hardworking routine which would lead us to graduation and the award of the *Flugzeugführerabzeichen* - the pilot's badge. There was ample off-duty time, and most of us were able to establish friendly contacts with people and families in the neighbourhood. We indulged in occasional excesses, usually when we overstayed our welcome in the *Biergarten* but, in the main, we behaved ourselves. This was not, however, the case with our student course leader, who was summarily dismissed, when found to be suffering from syphilis.

For various reasons, fifteen of the course failed to graduate. I finished third on merit, which guaranteed me officer status. In the final interview with the School *Kommandant,* my abilities and potential were reviewed, together with my obvious failings which, in fact, damned any chance of my ever becoming a fighter pilot. Written in bold letters on my logbook assessment certificate were the words: 'Ability as pilot ... Average. Analytical ability ... Only fair.'

The pilots' badges were presented on a snow-covered parade ground, on 15th December 1935, by an old *Luftwaffe General* whose name now escapes me. The parade was a masterpiece. We marched as well as the Prussian Guards, at the end advancing with arms at the present, and coming to a crashing halt in review order as the band thundered our glorious *'Deutschland Über Alles.'* We then marched off to the swinging tune of my favourite Bavarian *'Defeilee Marsch',* to dismiss and meet the visiting dignitaries, friends and relatives, who included both my father and my brother Albrecht.

CHAPTER FIVE

This time, I spent my leave with my father, who had just married the handsome widow of a junior member of the Prussian aristocracy. They were living in some style in Berlin, where I was made most welcome in their villa on the edge of the Bodensee. It was during this time that my father suggested I should keep a diary because of the great days which lay ahead for Germany, a time when I would undoubtedly have a part to play. This was what he had done from his early days in the Great War. He showed me three carefully written books which described his experiences right up to the present day. They fascinated me; not only for his graphic accounts of stirring events, but for his narrative style, which was appreciated by many, in due course, when he published his memoirs.

Confirmation of my rank came through during this leave, together with orders to report to Lechfeld for operational training. From a call to a friend of my father in the *Luftfahrtministerium*, I was disappointed to learn that Lechfeld was where bomber-transport pilots and crews were trained on the venerable Junkers 52, the old *'Tante Ju'*, an aircraft in use with most European airlines, including even the British. The operational training was not difficult, and was confined mainly to getting to know the peculiarities of this strong and reliable metal aircraft, used primarily as a bomber. It was also capable of doubling-up as a transport aircraft in which a wide range of supplies and loads were carried, and from which gliders could be towed and parachutists dropped. It could even operate on snow, using a ski undercarriage, and from water when equipped with floats.

At the end of the second week, we were crewed as a team of two pilots, a navigator, an engineer and a crewman. The last-mentioned had the responsibility of positioning the various loads which could be crammed into *Tante Ju's* cavernous body, and the management of the parachutists when they were dropped. If necessary, he could also function as a bomb-aimer. My ability to fly well at night, and in bad weather, improved tremendously whilst at Lechfeld. I lost all fear of having to rely entirely on instruments in cloud, mist or fog, no doubt helped very much by the services of an excellent navigator, who was superb at finding our way home and bringing us back directly over the airfield in the worst of all weathers.

There was a laudatory comment in my log book at the end of the course. It stated that *Leutnant* Rath was 'Above average as a multi-engined pilot and equivalent in ability to a Commercial B Airline rating.' The assessment of my instrument flying was given as excellent.

The next step was a posting in July 1936 to *Staffel J88* at Wertheim am Main which, on arrival, we found buzzing with the news of the start of the Spanish Civil War. We soon settled down to work with other crews as inexperienced as we were. We practised the carrying of heavy loads over long distances and, at mid-point in the flight, took photographs of supposed targets or, occasionally, dropped small practice bombs. We dropped real bombs into Army training areas, always under simulated operational conditions, which meant, among other things, that we had to fly with the under-turret lowered. The turbulence caused by this protuberance was so bad that it was almost impossible to make a steady bombing run.

The politics of this time provided us with plenty to do. The economy had recovered, and there was a general feeling of optimism. Unemployment had been practically wiped out by the use of national labour schemes, and the country was thriving under firm leadership. National Socialism was showing the world that the fortunes of Germany were in the ascendant and that, very soon, we would again be taking a lead as a major power. Our *Staffel* was constantly called upon to show the flag, and we made numerous ceremonial flights over places in the *Reich*, coinciding with the holding of Party rallies and parades.

It was by no means a surprise when, in late July 1936, three of our aircraft were ordered to fly to Tetuan in Morocco to assist in the transportation of General Franco's army to the Spanish mainland. After this was done, the aircraft remained in Spain and were used in support of the Nationalist forces. It began to look as though Germany was about to play a part in the liberation of Spain from Communism, and this was confirmed when German warships took up positions around the Spanish coasts to assist in the evacuation of German nationals and other refugees. There was no lack of volunteers among us wanting to serve in Spain. Most of us wanted to grasp the opportunity of learning our trade. In Spain, there would be every chance to gain operational experience if Germany were to be drawn into the conflict. That hope was soon realised. One early morning in October 1936, our *Staffelkapitän* read out the operational order for *'Winterübung Rügen',* which committed our *Staffel* to service in the *'Legion Kondor'* alongside the Nationalists. We were to become part of a bomber *Gruppe* comprising three Junkers 52 *Staffeln*, supported by our own fighter and reconnaissance aircraft, and we were going to war.

The move to Spain was difficult but interesting. Because of the belligerent attitude of France, it was not possible to transport our vital equipment or personnel overland. All our ground crews and administrative staff, together with servicing equipment, spare parts, weapons, ammunition, vehicles and fuel had to be moved by sea, and this began in September. Our freighters sailed without escort, and were met by our Navy when they reached Spanish waters. Everybody and everything was safely ashore in Vigo by early November.

The bomber *Gruppe* formed at Lechfeld, whence we flew in small groups to Ciampino, near Rome. We then went on to Sardinia, crossed over the Balearic Islands and finished our journey at Seville. We had to thank the Italians for some excellent assistance. In addition to allowing us to refuel in Italy, they posted their warships along the length of our Mediterranean route to help us with our navigation by acting as direction finding beacons. We were soon in action. The entire bomber *Gruppe* of thirty-four Junkers 52s attacked the seaport of Cartagena, where most of the Spanish fleet was at anchor. We did considerable damage and put the port out of action for several months. We did not lose a single aircraft, although there was some anti-aircraft fire.

I was now caught up in a fascinating and exciting new life. We learned something every day, being kept continually on the move as we followed the advance of the Nationalist forces through the Seville, Salamanca and Avila areas. We had also been given the responsibility for the weekly courier run from Seville to Berlin, carrying official reports and personal mail and, sometimes, casualties who required the better treatment which was available in Germany.

On the operational side, we found our Junkers 52s far too slow, and also vulnerable when attacked by the nimble Russian fighters. We were escorted on all daytime flights by the old-fashioned Heinkel 51 biplanes and, together, we were a poor match for the latest Soviet Il-15s and 16s, used to such good effect by the Republicans. Thankfully, early in 1937, we were told that the dear old *Tante Ju* would soon be replaced by the new Heinkel 111, and the aged Heinkel fighters by the brilliant Messerschmitt *Bf* 109. This, however, had not happened by the time our *Staffel* took part in a raid which, to this day, is held up as an example of how we Germans love to indulge in wilful destruction.

Together with Spanish Nationalist and Italian aircraft, we had been bombing enemy fortified positions on the northern front as the Republicans retreated to the northeast. We followed their beaten armies, step by step, as they fell back across the desolate, mountainous country towards Bilbao. Guernica, a small town in a valley just ten kilometres from the coast and only thirty kilometres from Bilbao, was identified as a vital road junction which led to a bridge over the river Mundaca, one that could be defended strongly by the retreating Basques. This Guernica bottleneck was, indeed, a classic target for attack from the air.

On 27th April 1937, three *Staffeln* of Junkers 52s were ordered to attack the bridge across the Mundaca, with the roads running through Guernica and leading to the bridge being the secondary target. Four of the new Heinkel 111s were to act as pathfinders, and fighter protection would be provided by the newly arrived Messerschmitt *Bf* 109s. Ten of the old Heinkel 51 fighters would follow and carry out low level ground attacks.

Our *Staffel* flew in the third formation of this aerial armada. Visibility was very good, and we could see well ahead of us, up the valley, as the Heinkels dropped their bombs, missing the bridge entirely. Then, as we drew nearer, the first large formation of Junkers 52s bombed but, by the time we arrived over the target, the whole area had become obscured by dust and smoke. We were unable to identify anything, and had no alternative but to drop our loads as best we could into the centre of the ever increasing haze. We held our formation as we flew over the town, and then turned to head back over the wooded tops of the hills. When abeam Guernica, the Heinkel fighters began to ground strafe. An enormous cloud of smoke and dust now covered the town and, through it, many burning buildings could be seen. We had achieved absolute surprise and had met little opposition; in fact, throughout the run-up to the target, and afterwards, I had not seen any anti-aircraft fire.

We flew on to land at Burgos, where we attended a routine debriefing, and the commanding general told us that the Nationalists were very pleased with our work. These congratulations were soon marred by the incredible international condemnation which began that very day. We were kept on the ground for days while the rights and wrongs of what we had done were argued across the world. We learned, to our dismay, that the bridge had not been hit, nor had the adjacent arms and small munitions factories, but we had killed 2,000 out of a total population of 8,000. What really hit hard was the accusation that the *Legion Kondor* had been experimenting, and was simply studying the effects of massed bombing on cities and population centres.

Our *Staffel* did not bomb again after the Guernica raid. This was not because of the international uproar, but because more Heinkel 111s, Dornier 17s and even the wonderful Junkers 88s were arriving every day. As a result, we had been relegated to a purely transport role. Try as I might, I was unable to get a transfer to the new bomber *Gruppen* in any capacity whatsoever. I became dispirited as a result, particularly as I had become wrapped up in the tactics and problems of this civil war which, to my mind, heralded a much bigger clash to come, between National Socialism and Communism. Spain was the testing ground for these ideologies, and Germany, Russia and Italy were taking every opportunity to try out and develop their military equipment and theories.

For the next few months, all we did was tied up with the routine resupply and support of the Nationalists on the Northern Front. Twice, I was lucky to be given the weekly courier flight to Berlin. Then, in February 1938, my service with the *Legion Kondor* came to an end, and I was posted to the staff of the *Oberbefehlshaber der Luftwaffe* in Berlin. I considered this move very unfair. I had recently been promoted to *Oberleutnant* and was a young, operationally experienced bomber pilot with every right to expect another flying appointment. However, when I arrived in Berlin, I was pleased to learn that the posting was only temporary, and that I had been selected for particular duties which matched my talents. These duties should be completed in a matter of months, after which I would return to active flying duty.

CHAPTER SIX

My new place of work was to be in the *Luftwaffe* Intelligence Bureau, which was not at Headquarters, but in a section of the *Reichsluftfahrtministerium*, the huge new grey building in the *Wilhelm Strasse*. There, I had the task of analysing British and American aeronautical reports, not as an aviation specialist or scientist, but accurately to translate the documents. Now and then, I would sit in as interpreter at meetings where our engineers had discussions with foreign aviators and scientists. I quickly regained my fluency in English, and was pleased to find myself drawn into English-speaking circles in the city. I was becoming a useful person to know, and this applied very much so in my dealings with the staff at the British Embassy. This fruitful liaison was happening at a time when Germany was involved in the crucial reunification with Austria, and also with the vexing problem of liberating our nationals in the Sudetenland. My services and advice were in constant demand to translate matters and, more often, to explain my country's emphatic and just points of view.

Twice during this attachment I made visits to England, something I was encouraged to do by my superiors. My reason for these visits was, of course, to visit my relatives, but I was briefed to keep my eyes open and to note anything of interest.

I found many things changed since my days in the country as a schoolboy. My younger relatives engaged me in rounds of carefree social events, all of little consequence and most with the sole purpose of having a good time. On the other hand, I found those of my mother's generation very reserved in my company; sceptical and curious, almost withdrawn from me. Time and time again, the conversation would come around to 'What do the German people really think of *Herr* Hitler?' or 'Could he be trusted to carry out his plans?' or, and this was the most disconcerting, 'Heaven forbid that there should ever be another war between our two countries.' There was constant talk of the need for peace, and nothing brought this home more forcibly than when I went with my uncle to a Peace Rally in Trafalgar Square addressed by trade unionists and politicians, including the redoubtable Bertrand Russell. There were thousands cramming the Square, and the keynote was that peace was absolutely essential, 'no matter what the cost.'

Another time, after a visit to Highgate to see my mother's grave, I was caught up in a clash between the British Blackshirts and Communists in Tottenham. Whilst waiting for a bus, I had been attracted to an open market place where Sir Oswald Mosley was addressing a largely hostile audience on the merits of democratic national socialism. A riot developed when the Blackshirts tried to form up for a march to the East End. I had to struggle hard to get away from the fight, but not before I had been hit by a heavy object. I picked it up, intending to throw it back, only to find it was a large potato embedded with razor blades.

During the second visit, I retraced my steps to my old school in Yorkshire, where I found everything looking just the same as when I had left it on my return to Germany. Almost all the masters were still there, and time seemed to have stood still. I strolled around the grounds and playing fields remembering the happy days, saw my name in gilt on the Honours Board, and took tea with the Headmaster in the Common Room. Yet again the conversation turned to my country's politics and, once more, the fervent hope was expressed for peace in Europe. He was concerned that Britain had decided to rearm, and asked me if I had ever read Hitler's *'Mein Kampf'*. I told him that I had not done so. In fact, I avowed that it held no interest for me. He was surprised at this, and asked me if I knew that *Herr* Hitler was predicting the eradication of both Judaism and the Communists, so that a Greater German *Reich,* whatever that was, would last for a thousand years. Against such words, there was no answer. Sitting there in my former home from home, I felt completely out of place and just wanted to be on my way. Such British points of view were indeed hard to understand.

I saw little evidence of British rearmament in my travels around the country. Compared with the hustle and bustle in Germany, England appeared to be sleeping. Nothing confirmed this more clearly than when I accepted an invitation to spend a day at the Royal Air Force station at Mildenhall, where one of my English cousins, John Carey, was a Flying Officer with a bomber squadron. I naturally cleared the invitation with my Embassy, which was only too pleased for me to accept, and asked me to report anything 'interesting'.

The visit was enjoyable, but of little value. I was treated as an honoured guest, surviving a seemingly endless Guest Night rounded off by a dreary speech by the Station Commander who, in 1917, had been a pilot in 100 Squadron of the Royal Flying Corps: he claimed that this had been the first night bomber squadron on the Western Front. I was shown everything of which John's squadron seemed so proud; the Operations Room, the engineering workshops and the assembly of their antiquated Handley Page Heyford biplane bombers.

There was no reason for me to call again at the Embassy when I returned to London. I had learned nothing, and everything I had seen was well written-up in such magazines as 'Popular Flying' and 'Aeroplane' which, in any case, were on sale in the bookshops in Germany. I was concerned, however, with the misunderstandings I had experienced. Until now, I had given little thought to where my chosen profession was leading me. The differences between my native and adopted countries were now marked, and widening. Few of those I had met in England had any idea of the remarkable progress made in Germany since the early Thirties, or of the many problems which had been solved to make a better life for all Germans. This had been the goal of National Socialism from the start, and it would continue, without recourse to war, until Germany was restored to her proper place in the world. The casual politics of capitalism did not suit us, and we would deal with Communism and international Judaism in our own way. In a revitalised country, with avenues opening everywhere on remarkable technological advances, with standards improving in every respect, the way forward was surely as we had so emphatically decided at our democratic national elections.

CHAPTER SEVEN

I was delighted to be returned to flying duties in May 1938. After a short refresher course, I quickly settled down as a pilot with *Kampfgeschwader 'Legion Kondor'*, which was equipped with the Heinkel 111 at a time when we were concerned with the fate of our nationals living in Czechoslovakia. The Czechs had begun to mobilise and Britain, France and Russia were taking sides. I was not very impressed with the 'Pact of Steel' which bound us to our Italian friends but, fortunately, the French and British Governments came to understand our rights and, in September, agreed that our people in the Sudeten area of Czechoslovakia should be set free.

We were involved in this liberation. The *Kampfgeschwader* was put on alert to prepare for any hostile Czech reaction. As it turned out, all went well, and our troops crossed the Czech border to be greeted by cheering crowds. The entry in my logbook for 3rd October read:

'Flew protective armed patrols over *Wehrmacht* formations in German Sudetenland. No opposition. A great day.'

The *Luftwaffe* was developing into a fighting force without parallel. Our aircraft were better designed than the French, Russian, American or British. We were proud of our abilities and position in the life of Germany, yet tended to set ourselves apart from everyday life, taking little interest in politics and what was happening around us in Germany. It was only when something directly concerned us that we bothered to take notice, and this happened dramatically in early November, just after we had taken part in a victory parade held for the liberation of the Sudetenland.

During the night of 9th November, the Brownshirts went on the rampage against the Jews in what became known as *Kristallnacht*. They burned synagogues, destroyed and looted Jewish shops, buildings and homes and, in some places, actually killed those who resisted. Our national wireless and newspapers reported the event as a spontaneous expression of moral outrage by the German people for the killing of a minor German official in our Embassy in Paris by a young German Jew. What had really happened was that the persecution of the Jews had, at last, been brought out into the open.

We all knew that strong anti-Semitism had always been just below the surface in Germany. Our *Führer* had made no secret of his hatred of Judaism, or of his belief that the Jews were the root cause of much of the financial trouble which he had overcome in his drive to eliminate unemployment and create work. Whether he was right to attack the Jews in this way, however, seemed doubtful, to say the least.

The return of my navigator from a short leave of absence brought me face to face with the consequences of this outrage. *Leutnant* Eric Schumann had been staying at his family's home in Plauen, where his father was a well-respected Jewish doctor married to a Gentile. During *Kristallnacht,* Schumann had defended his family at the risk of his life. Both his mother and father had been badly beaten and his father's medical office had been set on fire and destroyed. The mayhem had only been stopped when the local police belatedly intervened. It was as though a curtain had been drawn aside to reveal a madness which astounded me, something which had never entered my mind or had been thought possible. In my case, my contacts with Jewish people had always been good, and some were even my friends, both in Germany and England.

Schumann had already decided what he would have to do. His father's practice was ruined; his patients were now too afraid to attend his makeshift temporary clinic. As the Government had taken no action, there would surely be more trouble to come. He saw no future for the Jews in Germany and felt it was his duty to help his family in any way possible and to get them resettled in a friendly country. There was, of course, nothing I could do to help. Surprisingly, my navigator became 'odd man out' on his return, as if a stigma were attached to him. It was a relief to me, as his pilot, when Schumann suddenly left us. Later, I learned that, together with his family, he had managed to get out of Germany and they were now starting a new life in England.

In March 1939, it became essential for Germany to occupy Czechoslovakia so as to bring some sort of order back into that disturbed country. We flew to Prague, where we stayed for just a week. This time there were no cheering crowds; we were not welcomed into this former part of the old Austro-Hungarian Empire. I could not fathom the lack of understanding in the blank expressions we saw on the faces of people we passed in the streets of this beautiful capital city. I had a feeling that something was wrong; that perhaps, somehow, an error of judgment had been made this time by the *Führer.*

When we got back to Germany, few of us had much doubt that our leader would have to use all his vision and diplomatic skills in the months which lay ahead. He averted any possible trouble with Russia by signing a non-intervention pact, but still had to placate the French and the peace-loving British. How much longer would they stand aside to allow us to right the wrongs of the hated *Versailles Diktat*? The signs were not good, because there had to be resolution of our problems with Poland. The facts that our Reserve Forces were called up for 'summer training' and that we now flew daily on operational exercises with the *Wehrmacht* began to worry me.

There was a diversion of sorts on 6th June 1939, when we formally put an end to our successful intervention in Spain. I took part in our 'Day of Victory' in Berlin when, wearing my Spanish Cross with Swords and *Kondor* campaign medal, I marched with *Legion Kondor's* 18,000 volunteers along the *Via Triumphalis,* and then parade-marched through the Brandenburg Gate and past the *Führer.*

By now, we had become used to preparations for action, and to standbys at operational readiness. On 21st August, our base was placed under strict security, and we began to made ready to move, as rumour had it, 'to deal with those dreadful Poles' - the ones in the Polish Corridor. Two days later, the whole *Kampfgeschwader* flew to a temporary airfield just fifty kilometres from the Polish border opposite Danzig. On the way, we passed over convoy after convoy of troops and equipment on the *Autobahnen,* and arrived to share the airfield with a gaggle of more than fifty Junkers Ju 87 dive-bombers.

That evening, we attended a general briefing, where we were told by an Army general that something was going to be done to resolve the situation along and inside the Polish border, where German families were being ill-treated and had, in some cases, become the victims of atrocities. Diplomatic representations had been made to the Poles, but no answers or apologies had been received. There was always the possibility of adverse French and British reaction and, for this reason, the battleships *Deutschland* and *Graf Spee* were already on station and the U-boat fleet had put to sea.

We were on the brink of war. I found myself in a distinct minority, as I could not see how France and Britain could possibly stand aside if we moved against Poland. I knew enough about my British friends to realise that they would honour their treaty of mutual assistance with Poland if we maintained our present policies. They could not, this time, accept our Leader's 'final demand'. We had played a poor hand over Czechoslovakia, and now the international poker game was ended. On 27th August, the Government announced the rationing of food, shoes, soap, textiles and coal. The newspapers were full of reports of extreme provocation by the Poles, and even gave the impression that Poland was about to attack Germany. This we knew to be arrant nonsense, but the die had been cast, and we were ready and prepared to do our duty.

We received the operation order for the offensive against Poland on 31st August, 1939. Early the next day, every available aircraft took off to strike at Polish targets. Our *Kampfgeschwader* was detailed to bomb two airfields about one hundred and fifty kilometres inside Poland, where we caught scores of light aircraft, probably fighters, lined up on the ground. After dropping our bombs we were able to go down and machine-gun what was left. My log book lists at least two sorties a day for the next week, mainly flown against airfield targets, troop concentrations and vehicle parks. One, almost comic, diversion was the machine-gunning of Polish cavalry, caught in the open, galloping, troop upon troop, across open country, armed with lances. There was also a single entry crediting my crew with the shooting down of a PZL fighter, by no means exceptional because the *Luftwaffe* dominated the air over Poland. This lone aircraft, already smoking from damage inflicted by our fighter screen, vainly persisted in attacking our large formation and, as it passed beneath our machine, was shot down by my under-gunner.

We were then switched to attacks on the capital city of Warsaw. At first we bombed specific targets but, after a day or two, we were ordered systematically to lay waste to the whole area, with the intention of forcing the Poles, fighting in the city, to surrender. This was at a time when the Russians had crossed into Poland from the east, and it was imperative to bring about the Polish surrender as quickly as possible before the Russians got too far.

As is now well know, Polish resistance collapsed soon after the Russians intervened. We moved our base to Cracow, and there dealt with a few isolated incidents at the time of the final Polish surrender. We then returned to Germany, an event which was absolutely fantastic, something on the lines of a Roman triumph. We may have miscalculated on the politics which had brought France and Britain into the war, but now we were supremely confident. We had resources and capabilities which put Germany ahead of any other country. With our borders with Russia secured, and Italy on our side because of the Pact of Steel, most of us thought it was only a question of time before a negotiated peace settlement would return Europe to peace.

CHAPTER EIGHT

This seemed to be borne out in the following months, when a lull developed in the war. We spent our time in building up our strength and practising the tactics we had so quickly learned in Poland, particularly in the use of close support for the *Panzers* and storm troops. There were many rumours that peace proposals had been suggested by the British, backed by strong anti-war movements in both France and Britain. The Polish campaign had been an outstanding success; the *Wehrmacht* had swept everything before it, and the part played by the *Luftwaffe* had been decisive. We had taken control of the air from the very start, and had quickly destroyed the Polish Air Force. Our dive-bombing *Stukas* had dealt devastatingly with pin-point targets of all kinds, while we, the bigger boys, had wiped out everything we had been ordered to bomb, including practically the whole of Warsaw.

I was not very happy about my part in this destruction and the moral issues involved, but such afterthoughts were of little concern at the time. I had acquitted myself well. My crew was now a first-class unit and, together, we had actually enjoyed our war. Then, to cap it all, I was awarded the Iron Cross Second Class. We did no strategic bombing during the lull. We did make a few raids on the static front-line positions along the French Maginot Line, and had a few brushes with French Moranes and British Hurricanes, but usually just as spectators watching the fun as the enemy was seen off by our superior *Bf* 109s. Then, during April, tell-tale signs of preparations for the next move began to appear. Although we had no idea in what form or where this would happen, it was made clear that we were going to strike first, before the enemy stirred themselves.

We took no part in the operations necessary to forestall any British involvement in either Denmark or Norway. We remained at readiness throughout that time until, at dawn on 10th May 1940, we were off to play our part in the *Blitzkrieg,* which began with our rapid thrust into the Netherlands and Belgium. The capture of the port of Rotterdam in a glider coup was brilliant, and had been made possible by my former colleagues flying the reliable *Tante Ju's* towing the gliders. Similarly, carefully planned parachute drops led to the capture of The Hague and Amsterdam. We began to give close support to the *Wehrmacht* as they rapidly pushed across Belgium and into France, our targets being mostly those of instant opportunity as we dealt with the retreating Allied armies. The targets were so numerous that we often went out singly, or in pairs, and concentrated on attacking temporary airstrips or bases as the rapidly shrinking French Air Force and British 'Advanced Air Striking Force' began to fall apart.

I had a certain admiration for the British fighter force, which did its best in slow and under-gunned Hurricanes, and the utmost sympathy for the poor crews of the light bomber force in their out-dated and out-classed Fairey Battles. Nothing brought this home more forcibly than when, on 21st May, together with another Heinkel, we bombed an airstrip near Abbeville just as two Battles were trying to land. Our fighter escort was well above us, dealing with a few Hurricanes, as we came in to drop our loads on aircraft on the ground. Suddenly, I found a Battle in front of me, its wheels and flaps lowered. My front-gunner shot it down in flames. I then saw the other Battle, also trying to land, and got onto its tail. We were shooting merrily away at it when one of our heroes in a *Bf* 109 nipped in front of us and blew the Battle to pieces.

I suppose I got my just deserts a few days later, when attacking an RAF airstrip which was in the process of being evacuated. All the aircraft had gone, and a few lorries were being loaded with men and stores. I dropped my bombs around these, and then flew low across the airstrip, machine-gunning anything in sight. I happened to see two British airmen running out of a makeshift building, carrying a Bren gun between them: as I came around the second time, they had the gun set up and in action, with one man firing, using his comrade's bent back as a support. Instinctively, I ducked down behind the instrument panel as I saw them, and then we were hit by a good burst of bullets. One went through the canopy directly in front of me, while most hit the port engine. As I climbed away, the engine stopped dead and burst into flames, leaving me with little option but to get down as quickly as possible. I managed to make a reasonably decent wheels-up landing in a sloping meadow bordered by a road jammed with columns of retreating soldiers, refugees and vehicles.

There had been no time for us to take up crash positions, but luckily we all got out uninjured, and were smartly away from the machine before it exploded and was engulfed in flames. There was no time for us to gather up any equipment as we ran off towards nearby woods, screened from the soldiers on the top road by the flames and smoke from our burning aircraft. A few shots came our way, but no one apparently thought it worthwhile to bother to take us prisoner. We pushed on, well into the woods. The pine trees must have been planted about ten years previously, and then neglected. The undergrowth between them was thick and, in places, almost impenetrable. We reached the plantation centre and, realising there had been no pursuit, set up camp. With the *Blitzkrieg* going so well, the best course of action was simply to make ourselves comfortable, hide, and wait until our soldiers arrived. We stayed in the woods for the best part of two days, until we heard the approach of many tanks and came out to greet the forward elements of one of our *Panzer* regiments.

We were soon back with our *Kampfgeschwader,* and quickly operational again. In all, we completed thirty-three sorties during this period, including four against the beaten and demoralised British Army on the beaches at Dunkirk. I could claim that I had shot down one aircraft, and had been shot down myself and successfully avoided capture. It was for all this, I suppose, that I was again decorated with the Iron Cross although, this time, First Class.

After the surrender of Paris, followed by that of the French nation, we were sent back to Gilze Rijen in the Netherlands to replenish and rest. We had every reason to be proud of ourselves. The French, Belgian and Dutch armies had been destroyed, and the British army was in no condition to fight on. More than one and a quarter million enemy troops had been taken prisoner, including thousands from the Dunkirk debacle.

I had again enjoyed the fighting, but was somewhat uneasy about some of our actions during the course of the *Blitzkrieg*. It had been a hideous mistake to bomb the open city of Rotterdam, killing more than a thousand people who were on the streets an hour after the Dutch had actually surrendered. It would be a long time before were forgiven for that atrocity. Although Paris had saved herself, and our bomber force had been kept in check thereafter, we had already dealt brutally with Warsaw. No matter how I reasoned, the possibilities of my becoming involved in something similar in the future were only too real. Churchill had now made it clear that there was no chance of a negotiated peace, and that the British would fight on. The only alternative left was to smash them into surrender; and how would we do that?

Peace in Europe would not come easily, and only then with the defeat of the British. I lived in hope that, after a few knocks to show our overwhelming superiority, they would seek an honourable way out, long before we were forced to use the full might of the *Reich*. I began to worry myself with this theory, knowing that, given the slightest chance, I would avoid bombing my adopted country. But such thoughts were always kept at bay by my oath as a German officer, and by my intention to serve the *Reich* faithfully until I was no longer needed. In July 1940, my *Kampfgeschwader* moved to a fine airfield near Abbeville in Northern France as a unit of *Luftflotte 3,* standing ready to support Operation 'Seelöwe', the invasion of England. The day was drawing nearer when I would have to face up to the real possibility of fighting on English soil, and even against my own relatives. I could not see the Careys, with whom I had much in common, giving up easily; like all other British people, they would fight to the bitter end.

Our preparations for the forthcoming campaign were impressive. All available airfields in Northern France, and some in Belgium and the Netherlands, were filling with fighter and bomber aircraft, manned by experienced crews who had everywhere dominated the skies for the past nine months. The airfields developed into huge supply dumps, closely guarded by the Army against the remote possibility of sabotage by the defeated French and Belgians. Strangely, there was little evidence of the build-up of the strength of the *Wehrmacht* and the means whereby they would cross the Channel. No doubt that was merely a matter of timing because, first and foremost, the *Luftwaffe* had to wrest control of the air from the British to make it possible for our troops safely to cross. There was little doubt that the remnants of the defeated British Army could be swept aside, but we were not so sure of the capabilities of the Royal Navy and the Royal Air Force. The lack of ability of the latter had often been mentioned, but we were now facing a new situation: the British had their backs to the wall.

At regular briefings we got to know details of the establishment and disposition of all RAF airfields in the south of England, the capabilities and limitations of the British defences, including the fighter force and, in particular, the Spitfire, which had been met in combat for the first time over Dunkirk. We were told that our first priority, in what was to be called the *Kanalkampf,* would be the interruption and eventual elimination of the coastal shipping passing through the Channel. With that, there would naturally have to be attacks on the ports of Dover, Portsmouth, Southampton, Portland and Poole. After that first phase, which would sound out the capabilities of British Fighter Command, radar sites would be destroyed and the last hurdle would be tackled, by attacking RAF airfields. Their destruction would enable us to establish air supremacy over the whole of South East England. Happily, throughout these briefings, there was no mention or hint of attacks against the civilian population.

I took part in the very first raid of the *Kanalkampf* on 9th July 1940, when a large formation, including our Heinkels, attacked shipping in the Thames Estuary. We approached undetected, using cloud cover from the trailing edge of a cold front. All went well, and I felt secure within this formation, protected by our *Zerstörer* and *Bf* 109s. Several small flights of Hurricanes did try to get at us, but their efforts were uncoordinated and only felt on the fringe of our formation. In the far distance, we were able to see London under the clearing skies, and it gave me some comfort to know that the large population there would not be affected in any way by what we were doing.

The attacks on Channel shipping and the ports along the coast went on for about three weeks. The accurate bombing was left to the *Stukas* while we, with our much heavier bomb loads, concentrated on port installations and ships at anchor. This combination worked well when we attacked Portland harbour. The *Stukas* sank a warship and other small craft, while we put the port itself out of action. Unfortunately, the *Stukas* had a limited range and were vulnerable to fighter attack. Their losses began to mount as the Hurricanes, once clear of the escorting *Bf* 109s, found the *Stukas* easy victims. By the time we could begin our attacks on the RAF airfields, it had become necessary to withdraw the

Stuka Staffeln from the front line.

We nearly always flew with excellent and tight fighter escort. Our first inland targets were the RAF airfields and radar sites along the coasts of Sussex and Kent: Tangmere, Thorney Island, Hawkinge and Manston. The nature of our fighting had begun to change. It was no longer anything like the struggle in the air over Poland or during the *Blitzkrieg*. The British were beginning to show their mettle, and were fighting hard to protect their homeland. They managed to keep their radar chain in operation, no matter how often we attacked it, and this meant that the RAF was able to anticipate our arrival and know our strength.

We now had to be on constant alert and ready to fight all the way from the coasts to the targets, defending ourselves against ever-increasing numbers of fighter aircraft. These were usually Hurricanes although, now and then, we ran into the more efficient Spitfire. We had made fourteen raids on airfields in South East England, and three on bases further afield, at Middle Wallop, Yeovil and near Bath. By the middle of August the pace was beginning to tell on me. Twice I had returned to base badly damaged; once on one engine, and the other time with lost hydraulic power, which meant another 'wheels-up' landing. I lost my navigator, who was killed alongside me when a Hurricane made a suicidal head-on attack. I was slightly wounded in the neck but, further back in the aircraft, one of my gunners sustained terrible injuries to the stomach and chest.

It was at this point that I found things beginning to worry me. The two replacements in the crew were inexperienced strangers, and I had lost that wonderful camaraderie which had sustained us through so many perils. I was becoming jittery and apprehensive, really afraid of what was coming next. My imagination was affecting my reason and, strangely enough, despite all the operational flying I had done, I now feared that I was going to die, to be killed in a most horrible fashion. Fear is insidious: it can destroy judgement, freeze reflexes, lead to mistakes and, worst of all, it is contagious. I fought hard to keep it hidden but, in so doing, began to draw apart from my new crew and to feel very much alone.

I do not think this new-found failing of mine was very noticeable. I kept to myself somewhat more than formerly, and often restored my spirits with a drink, a stiff one, once the flying was done. Superstition began to play a part, even though limited to small things such as kicking the tail wheel three times before each take-off, and eternally 'touching wood'. We were now at a vital stage in the battle. We were getting on top of the RAF, despite their courage and resourcefulness. We were beginning to win as we daily pulverised their airfields. I took part in the successful raids on Biggin Hill, and knew this to be true. Afterwards, we were shown reconnaissance photographs which revealed that many of the vital British fighter airfields were already out of action, and could be destroyed completely if we kept up the attacks a little longer. It seemed only a matter of time before RAF Fighter Command would be unable to refuel and rearm at most of its principal bases.

This constant pounding of the RAF airfields stopped suddenly on 29th August. No doubt some of us were pleased at the possibility of a short rest from operations but, as the lull continued day after day, we became concerned that something had gone wrong, and that the British would be working feverishly to rebuild and refurbish their airfields. They would no doubt be wondering, just as we were, why they had been allowed to 'get off the hook'.

The answer came, most dramatically, on 2nd September. Apparently, during the night of 27th August, a few bombs had been dropped, entirely by mistake, on a London suburb near Croydon. In retaliation, Churchill had ordered RAF Bomber Command to make a raid on Berlin, the following night. This was carried out quite effectively by a small force, despite all assurances by *Reichsmarschall* Hermann Goering that the British had little worthwhile strategic bombing capability, certainly not enough to strike at the very heart of Germany. The *Führer* had been furious, and had taken temporary control of the *Luftflotte* in order to make plans for a dramatic next move. This was revealed at a special briefing during the evening of 6th September, when we were astonished to learn that, on the direct order of the *Führer,* the whole might of both *Luftflotte* 2 and 3 would be used to teach the British a lesson. London would be attacked in retaliation for the bombing of Berlin.

The moment I had always dreaded had arrived. For ages now, I had deluded myself with the belief that, somehow, such a dreadful thing could not possibly happen. I sat through the briefing with my mind in turmoil. I was shocked, almost stunned, at the prospect of taking part in the destruction of something which was, oddly enough, dear to me. I wondered how I could find a way of not taking part. I even considered the extreme action of simply getting up and walking out to report myself sick ... sick of everything I knew I would soon be ordered to do.

I was brought back to reality by the firm voice of the *Kommandeur,* who brought the briefing to an end: 'See you bright and early tomorrow. This is the big one. Good luck, gentlemen.'

I did not eat with my fellow officers that evening; instead, I went to my room hoping to find some relief from my desperate confusion; any excuse, I suppose, for not doing my duty as a German officer. After several schnapps, I opened a bottle of Cognac and began to drink myself stupid: eventually, I slept, but it was a sleep mixed up with awful images of death and corruption, even of my own burial alongside the worm-eaten body of my mother. Airman Holsten woke me with my usual cup of coffee, not the least surprised to find me lying fully clothed on the floor. My aching head cleared a little, after I had vomited in the spew basin. I showered and scrubbed myself, shaved, dressed and walked to the Mess, where I actually devoured a good breakfast, all my thoughts numbed by the effects of a first-class hangover.

I joined my crew at the final briefing in the Operations Room, where the extreme feeling of trepidation returned. Strangely enough, I was a little relieved when we were told the specific targets for our *Kampfgeschwader* were the docks at Silvertown and the surrounding warehouses and shipping. Surely, that was a legitimate military target? Would not the civilians in the area be well-warned of our approach, and have ample time to get down into the shelters? These thoughts relaxed me, and I even began to respond a little to the general feeling of bravado and excitement around me as we trooped out to collect our parachutes and board the trucks taking us to our aircraft.

Once settled in the cockpit, I was swept with waves of real panic. I hardly knew what to do next as I tried to gather my thoughts for the routine of starting engines. I did things automatically, without thinking. My head ached, my pulse was racing and I began to become breathless. I felt, in fact, very unwell; so much so, that my navigator came forward to ask if I was ill. I merely looked blankly at him and shook my head. I knew that nothing could possibly postpone the inevitable. The discipline of years of flying finally got me through the engine starting, the preflight checks and vital actions for take-off. I began to settle down, and was almost myself by the time we had taxied out to join the procession of heavily-laden aircraft moving up to the take-off point.

We took off smoothly, and I took up my usual position in the *Staffel's* formation as we climbed away to join the much larger one comprising the *Gruppen*. By the time we reached the French coast, we had formed into an armada of Heinkels, Dorniers and Junkers, flying layer upon layer northwards towards the eastern coast of Kent, no doubt giving the British radar the impression that we were on our way to attack some target on the east coast, a long way from London.

Our large fighter escort joined us, and we levelled out to fly between layers of stratus hiding us from sight from the ground. We then made a full ninety degree turn to port, and began our run westwards into the Thames Estuary and so on towards London. The layered clouds began to break below us as we neared Gravesend, where some parts of our formation were nibbled at by a few Hurricanes. These attacks had little effect, and we continued on our way without hindrance until, ahead of us, and in excellent visibility, we could see the beginning of a raid which was about to change the whole future of the air war against England. The anti-aircraft guns then opened fire. They were easily finding our height, but seemingly having little real effect. Our *Kampfgeschwader* sailed into the thick of it; we could see the shells bursting all around us, then hear them above the roar of our engines and, finally, smell the cordite. Suddenly, a yellow-nosed *Bf* 109, minus its tail unit, plunged vertically through our group. I could actually see the pilot struggling to get out of the doomed machine as it flashed by.

The first wave of aircraft, well ahead of us, had already dropped its bombs, and the growing area of fire and smoke from ruined buildings, warehouses and homes on either side of the river was coming clearly into view. As we flew nearer, we could see the bombs bursting and then, to my horror, I noticed that a very large number were falling far from the target, causing a general extension of destruction away from the docks. Some areas south of the Thames were ablaze, and the raid was spreading towards the City of London and even beyond. Soon we would be smashing the homes, burning the buildings, and killing the innocents who lived in them.

It was then that I lost my head. The waves of dreadful panic returned, and I became absolutely terrified. My hands froze on the controls, and I started to babble to myself; louder and louder into the switched-on intercom. My alarming behaviour brought an anguished call from the navigator. 'What's wrong? Are you wounded?', but I kept on with my ravings and began to mutter in English such words as: 'Dear God, sweet Jesus,' and, 'Blood, blood, blood.' Now greatly alarmed, Schiller, my navigator, came forward, and tried at first shaking me by my shoulder. When he saw this had no effect, he smashed his fist into my masked face, again and again, until I screamed back at him. 'No, no. We must not kill the innocent. This is hell. No, no. We cannot bomb!' I was then overcome with an immense feeling of relief at the very moment we should have been dropping our bombs. All became quiet. The crew said nothing as we kept our place in the formation, with bombs from the other aircraft falling all around us. Schiller then took command of the aircraft. He reached forward, opened the bomb doors and jettisoned our load into the inferno below.

The return to base was dreamlike. We turned with the armada to fly over southern London and out across Kent. We were attacked repeatedly on the way, although it meant little to me. We fought our way to the coast, and out onto our homeward course over the sea. There we picked up a new fighter escort, and flew home without further incident. No one had spoken to me on the way back. After landing, I remained in the cockpit until the crew had left, walking away without even a backward glance at me. I got down with every intention of following them to the Operations Room, but changed my mind, and went directly to the Adjutant's office, where I asked the astonished man to place me under arrest.

I cannot forget the shame of the next few hours. My *Kommodore* had known me well for almost four years, and there was even a bond of friendship between us. The utter shock of his reaction to my behaviour when I was escorted into his office, still in my flying gear, was unforgettable. 'You know what I have to do with you, Rath, don't you? I have to remove the cancer you represent from this *Geschwader* at once. You will be kept under arrest, away from here, until you are court martialled ... and I hope they damned well shoot you. Now, for Christ's sake, get out of my sight!'

The expected Court Martial did not take place. I was kept under close arrest for four days, while a sympathetic *Hauptmann* from *Hauptquartier, Luftflotte 3,* compiled a draft summary of evidence. This he found difficult to do, because I was unable logically to explain what I had done. I said nothing about my constant brooding over my partial English upbringing, while he was unable to construct a charge of cowardice. After all, I had done well in Spain, Poland and during the campaign through the Low Countries and into France. Also, I had operated without a break, over England, from the very beginning of the *Kanalkampf* right up to the time of that fateful raid on London. *Hauptmann* Baaker, perhaps wrongly, confided in me that he could not build a case of operational stress, fatigue or even the onset of mental illness; in fact, on the fourth day, he admitted he could not substantiate a major charge against me.

No one visited me during this time. My name had been removed from the *Kampfgeschwader's* establishment, just as if I had been a fatal casualty. Then, without any warning or explanation, I was flown to Berlin, still under close arrest, and handed over to the *Wehrmacht* medical facility at Spandau. For the next few days I had no idea of what was in store for me. There were some straightforward medical examinations and interviews, some with psychiatrists. I was then released from close arrest, which enabled me to receive visitors, the first of whom was my father, now an *SS Standartenführer.* He admitted that he could not understand my behaviour, but he was sure I was no coward. He promised that he would do everything possible to get me back to flying duty, a good chance indeed now that the *Kanalkampf* was coming to an end and Operation *Seelöwe* had been postponed. This surely meant there would soon be other operational areas in which I could serve to redeem my good name.

I finally appeared before a Board at the *Oberbefehlshaber der Luftwaffe* on 31st October 1940. It was presided over by a dapper, bald-headed *Oberst,* a veteran of the Great War, with two much younger officers sitting as members, one a *Hauptmann* with the *Ritterkreuz.* I was asked at the outset whether I was prepared to accept the Board's findings and to abide by their decisions. What could I say but: 'Yes, of course,

Herr Oberst.'?

I was then told to sit, and the President opened the proceedings by saying that there would be no Court Martial, but that that decision in no way diminished the gravity of my offence. I had put the safety of my crew at risk by disobeying an order. Because of this, it was difficult for the Board to see how I could possibly be relied upon in the future to carry out flying duties as an officer in the *Luftwaffe*. Did I have anything to say? The die was cast. I had lost my flying career and had only myself to blame. I feared the worst, but stood rigidly to attention, facing the Board squarely, and replied: 'No, *Herr Oberst.'*

'*Oberleutnant* Wilhelm Rath,' began the Preident, 'it is the decision of this Board that you will lose your flying status and, in future, carry out ground duties of an administrative nature. In mitigation, because of your earlier services, you will be allowed to retain your rank, badges and decorations.' Then, leaning towards me and piercing me with his gaze, he went on: 'Off the record, Rath, you are a very lucky man. Anyone else making such a fool of himself would have been cashiered and sent as a common soldier to a penal battalion. You must have some very influential friends, somewhere.'

I left the room in a daze. It seemed that everything I had lived for had been lost. I felt empty and sorry for myself, wondering if there was any point in appealing against the decision and asking for my just deserts which, at least, would enable me to clear myself of this disgrace. But I did not. I hung my head and did nothing. My father, however, was pleased with the Board's findings. He would not admit to having exerted influence, although it seemed obvious to me, but he gave me some good advice. Germany would soon be on the brink of new victories, in places I had never even considered. In the present ever-changing political world, the war would last long enough for me to benefit. Sooner or later, I would return to flying, but the only way to do so was by staying in the *Luftwaffe* and obeying orders.

My next appointment was no surprise. Because of my linguistic ability, I was posted back to the *Wilhelm Strasse,* to the small branch within the *Luftfahrtministerium* which dealt with the interception of British mail and general English correspondence, the examination of documents taken from dead and captured British airmen, the translation of recorded interceptions of British conversations, and of captured notices and orders. I accepted this tedious and laborious task as the first stage of my penance, and did my very best to acquit myself well. Things improved somewhat when I was transferred to a new radio installation built underground near Nordhorn, and was given the job of monitoring British radio-telephone broadcasts.

I began work there in August 1941, when the British were making an effort to step up their bombing offensive by flying daily sweeps over Northern France and the Low Countries. I found myself well-suited to this work, and very soon settled down to something of a make-believe existence. As I listened intently to the various orders and instructions on the RT, I could easily imagine myself sitting with the aircrews in the cockpits of their machines. With the RAF fighters, radio silence was often broken as soon as they began their attacks, or were themselves attacked by our fighter aircraft. The light bombers, on the other hand, always made it possible for me to follow the build-up and the course of the attack, once the formation leader began to issue his orders after crossing our coasts. The night bombers were another matter.

In early 1942, Bomber Command, under new leadership, adopted its area bombing policy, and we made a start on the compilation of target intelligence from the careless use of RT by the bomber crews. We heard a lot of often pointless conversation, which began early in the day, when pilots were air-testing their machines. This chattering continued while the bomber force was taking off and assembling over bases in Yorkshire and Lincolnshire. The conversation included trivial items, such as: 'Starting starboard outer'; 'The girls are going to miss us at Betty's Bar tonight'; 'The bloody Navy is firing at us again; fire the colours of the day'; as well as valuable intelligence such as: 'Good God, not Doodleburg again, poor sods,' which told us at once that Duisburg would be the target for that night.

The crews kept silent as they crossed the North Sea and flew on into Germany. We heard nothing more until the target was reached. Then, sometimes, we heard banter but, more often, orders being given from one aircraft to others, usually about the dropping of target marker flares. Not much of intelligence value was being gathered, but the disturbing fact was that, despite ever-increasing losses, there did not seem much wrong with the morale of Bomber Command.

I was not backward in criticism or offering advice, and always worked at trying to get myself more actively involved in the war. The limited intelligence we were getting from the intercept programme could have been obtained just as easily (and perhaps even more efficiently) by civilians - maybe women. I must have succeeded in finally making this point, or perhaps my superiors became fed-up with my tiresome arguments because, after eight months underground at Nordhorn, I was posted back to the *Luftwaffe*, not as a flyer, but as an operations officer at the *Nachtjagdgeschwader* base at Venlo in the Netherlands.

It was from there that I was to undertake a really desperate venture which was to dominate what was left of my wartime career. It was something in which I was to feel no pride, only remorse for what I had to do. This is the subject of the remaining part of this story, which I have set down as accurately and faithfully as possible; indeed, I find it strange that, after all these long years, I can still clearly remember every aspect of all that happened to me.

All this lay before me in the unknown but, minute by minute, I came closer to what would be my fate, as the Siebel carried me across Germany, once more on my way to Berlin.

CHAPTER NINE

Eventually I must have fallen asleep, because I woke with a start, my pilot's instincts registering the increase of pitch and power as we approached to land at Gatow. As the engines stopped turning, and the *Unteroffizier* dragged my bags from the rack, I glanced out of the window to see a black Mercedes sweep up, an *SS* pennant fluttering on the wing. As I stepped onto the tarmac, a smart young *SS* officer was already standing by the aircraft, and we exchanged salutes. He ordered the crewman to put my bags in the car, and formally asked for my orders and papers, which he treated to a cursory glance before leading the way to the car.

We drove into town in virtual silence, eventually making our way down *Unter Den Linden* where, to my complete surprise, we turned off just before the Brandenburg Gate, stopping outside the prestigious Hotel Adlon. I was completely lost in the mystery of everything, and mutely followed the *SS Untersturmführer* into Berlin's most famous hotel to discover that arrangements had been made for me to spend the night there. I was shown to a fine double room, en suite, on the second floor, where he handed me the key.

'*Herr Oberleutnant*, if there is anything you want, you have only to ring and ask. You are our guest here for the moment. I shall return tomorrow at 08.00 hours to be your duty escort.'

It was impossible for me to make any sense of what was happening. Although my only contact so far had been with this man, I was too far gone to bother with reasons. Instead, I decided to relax and make the best of things for as long as I could. First and foremost I yearned for a good, deep, hot bath... and then, as I was, remarkably, a guest, I was going to enjoy the best dinner that the Adlon could provide. After that... well, I needed to catch up with a lot of sleep.

I was wallowing in a huge, wonderful iron bath, half asleep, my mind very much at ease with the world, when a persistent knocking on the bathroom door penetrated my torpor. No doubt a steward, I thought. '*Herein*', I called.

'I think not, *Herr Oberleutnant,*' a cultured female voice replied. 'I will wait here until you have finished your bath.'

I quickly got out and towelled myself. Putting on my dressing gown, I went into the lounge where, sitting at ease on a chaise-longue, was a strikingly attractive young officer of the Women's Auxiliary Force. She rose and smilingly saluted me in my undress.

'I am reporting for temporary duty as your aide. I have been told to see to your requirements, and to make arrangements for anything you would like to do in Berlin this evening.'

Disturbing thoughts of what I would like to do with this ravishing creature immediately came to mind. She stood there, taking in the humour of the situation, and then, with a broad grin, dashed my lascivious hopes with her words:

'I can get tickets for the opera or the ballet if you wish but, perhaps, *Herr Oberleutnant*' she said hopefully, 'you might like to visit a cabaret or even one of our better night clubs.'

This was getting out of hand. I had to find some reality in this beguiling situation.

'First, young lady, and not so fast, please tell me what this is all about. Who has sent you... and who are you?'

'My name is Greta, *Herr Oberleutnant*, and that is all I am permitted to tell you. I work for the people you will meet tomorrow.'

I was quite out of my depth. I had heard rumours that there were "professional escorts", but I had never met one. In any case, this meeting had been set up by someone especially for me, and it would be discourteous, to say the least, if I turned her away. Greta's fresh looks and obvious goodwill greatly appealed to me, and I had to make up my mind as she waited, almost standing to attention, holding what seemed to be an overnight bag.

'You must forgive me, Greta, but it has been a very long day, and all this is almost too much for me to understand. Yes, without a doubt, the idea of seeing something of Berlin in your company greatly appeals to me. First, however you have caught me in the middle of getting ready for dinner downstairs. Would you care to join me ... and, by the way, my name is Wilhelm, if you please.' She smiled and put down her bag.

'If that's what you would prefer, sir - I'm sorry, Wilhelm. I am indeed pleased to meet you, and I accept your invitation to dinner with pleasure. Can I change somewhere? I do not think that a lady in uniform is proper for dinner at the Adlon.'

I readily agreed, and pointed to the bathroom. Soon I heard the shower running. I went to the well-stocked drinks cabinet and took out a bottle of Moët, which someone had already put on ice. I opened it carefully, and poured two glasses, feeling really on top of the world, with the devil inside me urging that I should take Greta's glass into the bathroom. But reason prevailed. I wanted nothing to harm my extremely good fortune and expectations of what could lie ahead. I drank my glass and, instead, busied myself with dressing in my best uniform. Greta reappeared, clad in a striking saffron evening dress, superbly setting off her blonde hair, which was now loose about her shoulders. She was wearing discreet and obviously expensive jewellery, and I could not miss the subtle use of Chanel. I offered her the champagne, which she quickly drank.

'I am ready, Wilhelm. Shall we go?'

Indeed so, my dear young lady, I thought. She had me enthralled, and I was blissfully content with everything.

The dinner at the Adlon was excellent. Greta let me order both the food and wine from an extensive menu and a varied wine list. The service was careful and discreet. We took our time, and I was surprised to find just how much we had in common. I called for the account at around ten o'clock, only to be told that it had already been settled. All thoughts of a night on the town had long since vanished. Without a word, apart from my thanks to the maitre d'hotel, we went up to my room, where I soon began to learn something of the real meaning of *'aide de camp'*...

So far, my visit to Berlin had been most enjoyable. Greta had already left when I awoke from a deep and satisfying sleep, refreshed and ready to face whatever lay ahead. I shaved, showered and again put on my best uniform, and then went down to relish my favourite breakfast, a taste acquired from my time in England, eggs, bacon and plenty of toast. I had finished and was ready to leave, when the *SS* officer who had met me at Gatow arrived, and told me, in a rather off-

hand manner, that I was to report to the *Luftfahrtministerium* by nine
o'clock and, because it was only a short distance from the Adlon, and
I was in good time, I would no doubt prefer the pleasure of walking
there. I objected to this affront, but the officious youngster told me
that he was merely obeying instructions.

I left the Hotel Adlon a little perturbed: I had not liked the
young *SS* man's arrogant attitude, particularly as he was junior to me
in rank and had not, as far as I could ascertain, had any front line
experience. As I stepped out onto *Unter Den Linden,* I resolved to
speak to his superiors at the earliest opportunity, *SS* or not. Turning
right in the *Wilhelm Strasse* I walked on past Ministry buildings, the
Auswärtiges Amt and the old President's Palace, the tolling of a
Matins bell in a nearby church reminding me that it was Sunday. I
continued to turn things over in my mind as I walked, until I was
roused from my reverie by the blast of a police whistle as I was about
to step off the kerb to cross *Voss Strasse*. Glancing to my right, I saw
a large black Mercedes sweep out of the *Reichskanzlei* towards me.
The policeman stopped the traffic in the *Wilhelm Strasse* as the car
turned right, heading down towards the *Anhalter Bahnhof.*

Walking on, I crossed *Leipziger Strasse* and entered the
Luftfahrtministerium by the pedestrian entrance, where an elderly
sentry at the security desk checked my papers and rang for an escort,
who took me up to the familiar third floor, where I had once worked
in the Intelligence Department. He stopped at a door labelled '*Major*
H Kurz', and went in with my visitor's permit, leaving me standing
outside. After a minute or so, a voice called, *'Herein.'* I drew myself
up, marched smartly into the office, saluted, and held myself at attention in front of an overweight, bald-headed *Major* of about forty, who
did not bother to look up at me or acknowledge my salute. He carried
on with a noisy search through a jumble of papers and folders on his
desk, then glanced at his watch.

'*Oberleutnant* Rath, I presume; just on time, I see. Do sit
down. There is no ceremony here. I will be with you in a minute.'

I sat down in a leather chair in front of him, and ventured to
ask if I could smoke.

'If you must, then do so by all means,' replied Kurz. 'I don't smoke myself. I find it a dirty habit, yet you flying types seem to smoke yourselves to death, like chimneys.'

I removed my cap, lit up a Bleu, and sat back to survey the scene. I noticed that Kurz was wearing General Staff badges on his lapels. A long term staff officer, I supposed, with precious little idea of the operational world outside. I then saw that he had finished his search, and was holding up a blue confidential folder, clearly marked 'Wilhelm Rath'. He opened it, ruffled through a few of the enclosures, and then put it down with a sigh.

'It is difficult to see why they have bothered to send you to me in any case.'

He sniffed, screwed up his face, leant back in his chair, took out a huge handkerchief and violently blew his nose twice. Very carefully, he folded the dank square of material and put it away.

'You know, Rath, I am just a post office. It seems that all I have to do is check a few details and then pass you on. Mere formalities, nothing more.'

He returned to my folder, turning page after page of what must have been a reasonably full account of my career. I was relieved to know that this man had nothing directly to do with my future, and allowed myself to hope that it would not again be somewhere within the Intelligence Department.

Kurz then appeared to have found something interesting in my file. He stroked his chin and looked quizzically across at me.

'It appears that you are some sort of paragon,' he observed wryly: 'as far as this paper shows, there are only two of you in the *Luftwaffe* with the right qualities for this special intelligence job. The requirements set out by the personnel people are most precise, and you might like to know that you have been short-listed, not only because of your operational record, but also for your excellent knowledge of the English language and of the British themselves.'

This was not at all what I had expected to hear. Kurz had highlighted the very same attributes which had condemned me to my earlier tasks, both in this very headquarters and at Nordhorn. I interrupted him, resentfully.

'With every respect, *Major*, I don't understand you. I was

rushed away from my *Geschwader* yesterday for some important reason; at least, so I was told. There must be some mistake. I am not trained for staff duties.'

Kurz was surprised at my effrontery and rebuked me.

'*Oberleutnant*, there is no mistake.' He pointed to a page in the folder. 'You know that you will do as ordered. It says here that you have been especially chosen and, to satisfy your self-esteem, there is an interesting footnote. If you are selected, and complete the task for which you have been chosen, then you will be returned to operational flying duties. For the present, that is that. I will now place you under strict orders of secrecy, and you will complete these necessary clearances.'

He passed two forms across the desk for me to read and sign, while he carried on browsing through my file. The first of the forms gave me access to secret papers and material, while the other was a declaration that I would never disclose details of my work with any of the *Reich* intelligence organisations. I signed both forms. Kurz counter-signed and stamped them.

'There can't be many like you serving the *Reich*,' said Kurz, holding up another page of my history. 'Born in Silesia in 1913, I see. That was a good start... but then you were practically raised in England. You must have spent at least ten years in that decadent country before you returned to Germany. No wonder your knowledge of England is so good. Did you ever go back there after you joined the *Luftwaffe*?'

This was none of Kurz's business, but I answered, 'Yes, at every opportunity. My mother was English and I have many English relatives.'

He then quickly scanned a document, pulled it from the folder and waved it in front of me: he seemed very pleased.

'Heavens above! This is most illuminating. It looks like a transcript of your Court Martial. Good God, what an event. How did you get away with it? Any other bastard with shell shock, or whatever it was you had, would have been packed off to make good on the Eastern Front. But then, you are an officer, so I suppose they gave you the choice of the firing squad, the rope or the axe.'

He was almost beside himself with his attempts to be funny, and laughed sardonically.

'You must have good friends in the right places, Rath.'

This sadist was enjoying himself at my expense. I could hardly contain my anger and disgust. Why was this document in my records, in any case? The decision not to court martial me had been irrevocable, and I had been released from that threat in this very Headquarters. I had to keep my temper. As politely as possible, I replied,

'I do think that an officer with your great experience might have taken the trouble to read correctly, *Major* Kurz. I was not court martialled, as you can easily see, and you have no right to be critical of me, or to gloat.'

To Hell with his superior rank. I leant forward and fixed him with my gaze; I wanted to goad him in return.

'It is true that I was not punished in a way you seem to think fit but even you, sitting here in the safety of your office, should realise that, by suspending me from flying, I was punished in the worst possible way: I was stopped from fighting for my country.'

My furious retort clearly had the desired effect. He went red in the face, guiltily shook his head and said he was sorry. He was visibly shaken by my anger, and sensible enough to say no more. He got to his feet, held out my orders, and signified that the interview was over by slowly closing my folder. I got up to leave, and all he finally had to say was that transport had been arranged to take me to an interview with a certain *Herr* Kreis at precisely mid-day. A car would be waiting for me at the vehicular entrance to the Ministry, and it would be about an hour's trip.

Even the weather now added to my anxiety and sense of foreboding. The early morning promise of thunder had developed into a hurricane-like line squall. As I waited for my transportation in the entrance to the *Luftfahrtministerium,* a blinding fork of lightning flashed down right in front of me, followed within seconds by an enormous thunderclap. The rain, already heavy, was now falling in torrents. Soon after, a *Wehrmacht Kübelwagen,* with top and sides battened down, drew up at the foot of the entrance steps and a muffled driver splashed up to me through the downpour. It was the same young *Untersturmführer* I had already seen twice before and, once again, I felt resentment. Surely, on a day like this, something better than a *Kübelwagen* could have been provided.

Huddled inside, I saw little as we drove across Berlin with wipers working overtime to clear the flooded windscreen. We stopped only once, when caught in a queue slowly making its way past a heavy lifting crane still at work on a bombed apartment building. My *SS* escort tried to joke about the futile attempts of the British bombers to hit anything of importance in the city, but I kept quiet: I was in no mood for such vapid conversation.

The rain had eased considerably when we arrived at what appeared to be a heavily guarded barracks. There were many *SS* uniforms to be seen, mixed with those of the *Gestapo*, the *Abwehr* and even the *Kriegsmarine* and the *Luftwaffe.* My guess was that we were in some sort of Combined Headquarters. My first contacts were with the *SS.* I was taken to a control point, where I was given a visitor's pass and had my orders checked. Then I was led upstairs, into a complex of offices which could only be entered through an *SS* guarded section. There I was told to sit down and wait. A clock somewhere was striking three when I was taken to an outer office. A smart middle-aged woman, probably a secretary, was seated at a desk just outside what I took to be *Herr* Kreis's office. I showed her my papers. She spoke to someone on a desk intercom and I was told to go in.

I entered smartly, not knowing what or whom to expect. I was completely unprepared when I found myself standing to attention before a smallish, grey-haired man, wearing rimless spectacles and dressed in the grey-green uniform of an *SS Obersturmbannführer.* I saluted him. He rose slowly from his chair, took a cigarette from his mouth and gave me a careless Hitler salute. He held me with his steel-blue eyes. 'Welcome, *Oberleutnant* Rath. Do take a seat. May I see your orders?'

The surprise of coming face to face with a senior *SS* officer had left me speechless. I handed him my written orders, security clearances and pass, and took a seat in a steel-framed chair in front of his desk.

I studied him as he went through my documents. He drew steadily on his cigarette which, by its smell, was French. He was a veteran of the Great War, evident by the campaign medals on his chest and the black and white ribbon of the *Kaiser's* Iron Cross in his top button hole: the chevron on his sleeve denoted long service in the *SS*. I felt very ill at ease at the prospect of an interview by a senior officer of the omnipotent *SS*. I had to say something: '*Herr Obersturmbannführer*, is there not some mistake?' In my confusion, I got to my feet, fumbling for words.

'What is it you want from me? By whose authority was I brought here? What's going on?'

He looked up at me with an air of quiet resignation: 'Did you not have these orders written for you by the *Luftfahrtministerium*? Were you not asked to report to me personally at mid-day today? Did not a *Major* Kurz explain things to you? From the pained expression on your face, perhaps not... but, no matter. I see I must do some explaining. Well... for a start, I am *Obersturmbannführer* Kreis of the *Geheime Staatspolizei,* and here is my authority,' and he produced the fob-like shield, 'Do please sit down.'

Things were going from bad to worse. I felt in awe enough of a senior *SS* man, but still more so of the *Gestapo,* that most feared of the security services. 'Rath, I can see you are confused. As you will observe, I saw front line service in the last war and, like your own father, I saw the future in the *Führer* and the *NSDAP*. My previous training in the Army stood me in good stead, and I rose quickly through the ranks of the *SS*. As to my position here, some of us are seconded to the *Gestapo* from our own units and, of course, the rank structure is the same. However, because I retain my links with the *SS,* I can wear uniform if I choose.'

Leaning back in his chair, Kreis stretched his legs languidly under the desk as he exhaled cigarette smoke, letting his words sink in. After just the right pause he continued:

'My dear *Oberleutnant*, I quite understand how strange all this must seem to you but, when you have heard what I have to say, I am sure you will agree I had little choice but to treat you in this manner.

First, let me assure you that you are not under any sort of surveillance, nor have you been brought here to answer for any misdemeanour. You are under no obligations whatsoever, and there are no threats or possibilities of new charges of any sort being brought against you by the *Luftwaffe*. We all fully understand your earnest desire to return to an active flying career. My part in this is to show you how that can be done, by helping us in a most important enterprise. If you can do this, then you will be able to resume, in fact advance, your full career in the *Luftwaffe.*'

I was beginning to feel a little better. The quiet, almost benign attitude of Kreis was a comfort to my confused mind, in which, uppermost, was the worry that I seemed to be involved with the dreaded *Gestapo*. I asked Kreis why this was so.

'The reason, dear Rath, is quite simple. Your country is in need of your particular services. No... don't look so surprised. Please have the goodness to let me explain. I speak with the authority of *Admiral* Canaris, head of the *Abwehr,* which deals with all current operational intelligence activities and which, incidentally, has top-level liaison with the *Luftwaffe.* For some time now we have been grappling, most unsuccessfully, with a serious operational situation. In various ways, it has involved every intelligence organisation in the *Reich.* We now have a plan drawn up which could resolve this problem. It has been fully approved, and all are agreed that it will best be handled by the *Gestapo*. Work has already begun, and we are now recruiting volunteers to take part. You, and only one other, have been nominated by the *Luftwaffe* to work with us - that is, if you are found suitable - and to stay with us until the job has been completed.'

He lit another cigarette, all the while keeping his eyes on me.

'You have been selected because of your expert knowledge of bombing operations, both ours and those of the British. You know a lot about how the enemy thinks, works and fights; also, more than most, about their language, customs and mannerisms. We are not going to ask you to do anything that you do not fully understand or wish to do, but your attachment to us begins now, and it is for me to explain things and to answer your questions.'

He stopped, expecting me to say something, but I had no words. His eyes pierced me.

'If you decide not to work with us, then you will be perfectly free to go, but not back to Venlo. Your new posting would be decided by the *Luftwaffe.* I know there are those who would still like to make something of your untidy affair during the *Kanalkampf.*'

I realised that he had deliberately brought up my past simply to provoke some reaction from me. This time, I had something to say.

'So, that's it! I am to be blackmailed into working with you. What a pathetic way to get volunteers. Work for us or else...'

Kreis cut me short. His face brightened. He had deliberately stung me into a reaction. He leant towards me and almost spat his words in my face.

'Just how naïve can you be? However, at least you seem to have woken up and have something to say. My dear *Oberleutnant*, we have no intention of changing decisions which were made long ago, confirmed, and then forgotten. The only thing which concerns me is that, in the end, I shall be able to convince you of the rightness of this plan of ours, so that you will willingly want to join us in striking a decisive blow for our country.'

With that, his mood changed. He had made his point, and knew that I was impressed. He changed the subject.

'Are we looking after you properly at the Adlon?'

'Perfectly,' I said. 'Very well indeed, *Herr Obersturmbann-führer*. Nothing could be better, and I thank you. I have no idea why I should have merited such attention.'

'Quite so. All that will be made clear to you soon, but first I have a few details to check.'

He opened a drawer in his desk and took out a folder. From it, he began to recount my personal history, everything I had done or experienced since my school days in England. Many passages he read aloud, and then questioned the reasons for what I had done. There were many things I had forgotten, such as visits to my old school and the RAF Station at Mildenhall. Why had I gone to peace meetings in London, and to Blackshirt rallies? How would the British Blackshirt Party fit into the scheme of things once the war was won? He touched upon my service in Spain, and was very interested in why I had been decorated with the Iron Cross. He said that he knew my father who, by the way, was in command of *SS Einsatzgruppen* somewhere on the Eastern Front. Then, as I had anticipated, he came to the fateful events of 7th September 1940, when I had aborted my bombing sortie over London.

'You know, Rath, I do believe I can understand why you took such dramatic action. Nevertheless, that was more than two years ago, and so much has changed since then; I am sure that you, too, have changed. Do you think you would do the same again, given the chance?'

The question had never left my mind since my release from the threat of court martial. So much had happened since, and the war had changed from what I had once thought would be quick and certain victory into a remorseless world-wide struggle. I had believed the bombing of London to be an atrocity, but now the British were doing exactly the same to the towns and cities of my Homeland. In fact, the leader of Bomber Command had said something about Germany, having sown the seeds of destruction, having now to reap the whirlwind of retribution. All questions of morality and thoughts of Christianity had long since gone. The crimes now being committed were excused as inevitable but necessary counter-measures.

'*Herr Obersturmbannführer,* I must be honest with you. I worry about the barbarity and the inhuman things that are being done, and I feel there is nothing I can do these days which makes much sense. I *think* I could bring myself to bomb London, but I am not sure. After all, I am German, and I bombed without reason at Guernica, Warsaw and other places. What does another mistake matter?'

I knew I had very little personal point to make and that, if I went on, I would make less and less sense. The Britishness in me was still there, but had diminished greatly. I had become more concerned than ever with the idea that Germany would win, so that we could put an end, as quickly as possible, to the damage and destruction being done to the Fatherland.

'My service with our night-fighters in the Netherlands has cleared my mind of many doubts. I have a revulsion of the British policy of destroying our cities, and killing our people, in a pointless attempt to destroy the morale of the German worker and the means whereby our soldiers can fight.'

Any doubts I had once had were put aside. I had never before put my true thoughts so emphatically into words.

'Yes,... and I hope I make this clear. If it would in any way stop the British killing our women and children, then I would drop bombs on them, even on London.'

Kreis remained silent, letting me listen to the echo of what I had said. He closed the folder.

'I like what you have told me, although I am left with some doubts. However, let us leave the matter there for the moment. Your attachment with us is provisional, and dependent entirely upon your willingness to join us. You will be given ample time to make up your mind, as it is vital that you are a willing volunteer. A pressed man would surely fail when things prove difficult. So be it. Let us go downstairs for coffee. Then, I have some rather special reading for you.'

The task given to me was daunting. Kreis had arranged for me to occupy a desk in the *SS* guarded section, which he had piled with reports, summaries, enquiries into military operations, the use of equipment, and so on. He told me that the mass of reading was in chronological sequence and that I should start at the beginning and read each item in turn, to the very end.

I was only too well aware of much of the material contained in the earlier documents, having already seen it during my duties at Nordhorn and Venlo. There were reams on British intentions, and the particular problems of their poor relations with Russia, in particular the latter's insistence on the opening of a second front in Europe, which the British were incapable of doing. I was very interested in the unexpurgated summary of the *Kanalkampf,* and the reasons why we had not seized the opportunity to invade England after her armies had been so decisively beaten. Apparently, even if we had gained control of the skies over the Channel, it would have been well-nigh impossible to get the *Wehrmacht* across the water onto the beaches in Kent and Sussex. It seemed that the boats and barges carrying the troops and their heavy equipment could only sail or be towed in a very calm sea state, such as was seldom found in the Channel for any length of time in the autumn. Why, then, had the *Kriegsmarine* not been forthright, and declared Operation *Seelöwe* a non-starter from the very beginning?

I read about the ability of our night-fighter defences, and the corresponding British counter-measures and bombing developments. New navigation equipment was explained in detail, and there was an intriguing account of their Pathfinder Force. Where all this information had come from was not explained although, in places, it was reasonably clear that it had been divulged by captured aircrew during detailed interrogation. On the other hand, some of it, by its very nature, could only have come from sources in Britain itself. Then there was a Joint Intelligence Summary of British area bombing, and the shattering results of what had already happened. The use of heavy incendiary and blockbuster bombs had, in many cases, been absolutely devastating, yet our industrial and civilian morale was bearing up well. There was also the other side of the coin - the British losses. I found it hard to understand how the British could accept and sustain such heavy casualties.

I was allowed to take my time with the reading, and to make notes of questions to put to Kreis, who dropped in, now and then, to see how I was progressing. I came to the end late on the second day, when I read a pink folder marked for the eyes only of the *Geheime Staatspolizei*. In an opening summary of Bomber Command casualties, it was recorded that, in addition to those killed or taken prisoner, an ever-increasing number of aircrew were managing to evade capture and get back to England. Ever since 1941, evaders had been making their way into Spain, Switzerland and Sweden. At first it had been a trickle, no more than two or three a month. However, as the bomber offensive against Germany had intensified, the trickle had developed into a steady stream of fit and experienced airmen returning to their squadrons, from where they could resume the bombing of Germany.

The key to this disturbing phenomenon was the remarkable success of clandestine escape routes, operated by Resistance organisations, and linked with British Intelligence. The operating method of a route was described: just how the airmen were found and collected; how they were hidden in 'safe houses', and then spirited away along the routes to a neutral country. There had been a few successes against these escape organisations, but it had never been possible to strike at the very heart of one. Losses were soon made good by the dedicated people in control, and security was always quickly re-established. There had been attempts to penetrate these routes by using the collaborators who abounded in the Low Countries and in France but, generally speaking, the fundamental security of such organisations remained impenetrable. Any transgression, or suspected fault or error, was ruthlessly punished and, in the course of counter-intelligence operations, quite a number of *Gestapo* agents had simply vanished from the scene and been presumed dead.

The folder closed with the unanswered question of what should or could be done to wipe out this pernicious aid to the British. As I put it down, I wondered if, somehow, I was being recruited to take part in whatever plan there was in hand to deal with these escape routes. If this were indeed so, then I simply had no idea how I could make any kind of contribution. The next day, I had my second interview with Kreis, who asked me whether I had found anything of particular interest in the mass of information I had been given to read. I told him candidly that, as an intelligence officer, I had already read many of the reports, although there were certain aspects that were indeed revelations to me. As we talked, he must have noticed a lack of enthusiasm creeping into my replies to his questions, and asked me why. I told him outright about the thoughts which had been nagging at me ever since my arrival; that I had no idea at all of how I could be put to work with the *Gestapo*.

It was evident that Kreis had been expecting such a question:

'My dear Rath, whether you come to work for us or any other organisation is quite beside the point, for the moment. What I have to do is to determine whether you are suited for a certain important task involving some risk, and a stern challenge to a man of courage and intelligence. I have to go about this carefully, step by step, because, in the end, if I present the problem correctly, the ideal man will undoubtedly volunteer to join us.'

He was watching me closely, studying my reaction.

'I can see that, at least, I have made some impression. From this moment on, it is up to me to develop your interest. In good time, I know that you will readily make your own decision, one way or the other. Meanwhile, there is much to get on with.'

Kreis got up and I stood with him, expecting new instructions, but was totally unprepared for his next words.

'I get the impression that you would benefit from a little insight into what the British are really doing... just how much carnage and distress they create with their bombing offensive. I shall therefore give you the opportunity to take part in one of their terror raids.'

CHAPTER TEN

The Junkers 88 in which I was to fly had been specially adapted. The night-fighter radar had been removed, together with all the armament. These had been replaced by additional electronic equipment, and the bomb bay had been modified to hold ten powerful parachute flares. Room had been made for me to sit beside the pilot. Behind sat the other two members of the crew, the navigator and an electronics officer.

I had arrived at Geilenkirchen only a few hours earlier, just in time to attend the nightly briefing of an unusual and newly-formed *Staffel* which called itself the 'Lamplighters'. The British had been monitored throughout the day, as they had carried out hundreds of air tests in preparation for possible operations that night. As usual, they were at their careless best with their radio telephone transmissions and banter. Whether they would operate at all depended upon weather conditions which, for the moment, were dominated by a vast depression moving south-eastwards, already leaving the Ruhr with clear skies. If the British were to attack, then it would certainly be somewhere within the Ruhr valley.

We had been sitting at readiness in the aircraft for the best part of an hour. The engines had been run up, checked. and shut down. I was able to listen in to the electronics officer's contact with Nordhorn control as we waited for the signal to get airborne. At last we received news of the likelihood of a raid. There was a cryptic message about the build-up of a large force of the enemy over the North Sea, followed by the order to start engines. This was quickly done, and we taxied out together with two other '88s which would work with us. Our task would be to find and then stay with the expected bomber stream, dropping parachute flares at suitable intervals from above it, thereby assisting our fighter aircraft in making interceptions, especially those from specially adapted *'Wilde Sau'* day-fighter *Staffeln*.

Once airborne, we were vectored northwards towards the Frisians. Nordhorn then confirmed the identification of a very large force, already funnelling into a 20 kilometre-wide stream, which was expected to cross the Dutch coast and then to pass inland over Zwolle.

We were at 6,500 metres, and still climbing, when the searchlight barrier on the coast lit up, and we were able to see the first anti-aircraft fire. We were then told that the target was expected to be somewhere in the Ruhr, and that the first of our night-fighters would soon be in their patrol-box positions.

We had one Junkers ahead of us, and the other about 50 kilometres astern, when we dropped our first flare from a height of about 7,000 metres. We saw nothing at all in its illumination, and it was then that Nordhorn suggested we were too far west of the stream, so we altered course. We dropped the second flare from a lower altitude five minutes later, and found ourselves right in the midst of a swarm of enemy bombers. Looking down, I could see many large aircraft. Two Lancasters and a Wellington stood out in the blinding light, and lower down were others which could be easily seen in dark outline.

Our third flare ignited at the very moment one of our *Bf* 110s opened fire on a Wellington. The Wellington was already in a deep diving turn, and the illumination allowed our night-fighter to adjust and follow the enemy into the dive. As the Wellington pulled out of the corkscrew to climb back up, a burst of cannon fire shot it down. We were now well into the Ruhr. Ahead of us, the whole valley, as far as one could see, had begun to lighten in the glare of the searchlights, the bursting of anti-aircraft shells and the burning of dummy target fires. Even at this early stage, the fires were attracting some bombs, no doubt those of the more faint-hearted. Then the mighty Ruhr barrage opened up in full force. Hundreds of twinkling explosions helped to dispel the darkness. Nordhorn radioed that the target was Dortmund, and that the enemy Pathfinders had already marked the area.

We had dropped our last flare long before we saw the ground markers of the Pathfinder Force ahead of us. We were flying above and well clear of the vast battle below, heading towards Dortmund itself. I remembered that, at briefing, my pilot had been asked to show me as much as possible of the raid, and it was now clear that he would do so by flying right across the target. The electronics officer had found the radio frequency being used by the Pathfinder Master Bomber, and we were able to listen to the orders being given by this experienced airman.

'Master Bomber to Main Force. You are not bombing on my

markers. You are bombing short. Bomb on the green markers. Ignore everything else. I am now going to re-mark.'

The scene below was like something from Dante's Inferno. The ground appeared to be entirely covered in flames. Houses, buildings, woods and the very countryside itself were ablaze. Thousands of explosions from incendiary and high explosive bombs sparkled across this devastation. Searchlights, like octopi, reached out and grasped bombers in their tentacles, coned them, and held them long enough for the anti-aircraft guns to concentrate their fire and blow them apart. At that very moment, there were four such searchlight cones, each with a central blue beam, dealing with their victims.

'Master Bomber to Main Force. I have re-marked the aiming point. Ignore everything but the green markers. Let's not waste our effort.'

We were now passing over stricken Dortmund. We had descended 500 metres or so, and could even hear the noise of bursting anti-aircraft shells. A Lancaster suddenly appeared, drifting across our path from left to right, unaware of our presence just above. Lower down, a *Wilde Sau Bf* 109 was shot down while exchanging fire with a four-engined bomber. There were many other conflicts. Bombers were going down in the searchlight beams, the day fighters were ignoring our flak and ripping into the enemy. Now and then, there would be a huge explosion as a bomber blew up, to leave myriad bits of burning wreckage falling slowly to earth. I saw the burning remains of one aircraft actually engulf each of the opened parachutes of three members of its crew, who had managed, somehow, to get out of their doomed machine just before it had exploded.

'Master Bomber to Main Force. You are creeping back again. Bomb on the greens. Bomb on the greens. Ignore everything else.'

Despite the British blood in my veins, I felt revulsion at the utter ruthlessness of what the RAF was doing to my fellow Germans. I was watching a battle in which no quarter was being given or taken. There was nothing but inhuman brutality. The stoic fighting abilities of the British were beyond belief, but then, what Hell was being endured by the poor souls on the ground. We were indeed feeling the promised whirlwind of retribution, and undoubtedly paying a terrible price.

There was a strong tail-wind at our altitude, which carried us quickly across Dortmund and into darker skies. We left the fury and flames behind us, while the survivors of the bomber stream turned away and headed back to England. They had a long way to go, and would have to fight for their lives every inch of the way. The special *Staffel* would continue with its flare-dropping, and our night-fighters would attack until the enemy was well clear of our coasts. Nordhorn directed that we should return to Geilenkirchen. We lost altitude, and let down into a prescribed pattern which kept us clear of enemy activity, landing without incident. I thanked the Junkers crew for the privilege of flying with them, and sat with them during a short debriefing. It had been a remarkable experience for me. I had witnessed something I had found to be almost beyond belief. Yet this incredible battle was being fought, time and time again, relentlessly and without any let-up. How could the British keep up such an effort and accept such heavy casualties?

I had begun to see things a little more clearly. The reasons why we were locked in this gigantic struggle were of little importance. The British were showing their traditional hatred of us and, this time, were set to destroy us. They were going to repay us for what we had done to them and, in so doing, try to win the war by bombing us into submission. All that mattered now was that we should win, and as soon as possible. Somehow, I had to play a more active part, to become involved in the actual fighting. I had to stop hiding behind a desk and, if I could not fight again in the air, then perhaps there was some other way.

CHAPTER ELEVEN

I was having breakfast when Kreis greeted me and, rather foolishly, asked if I had enjoyed my flight. I was in no mood for idle chatter, so just knodded, and carried on eating. Kreis stood behind me, waiting impatiently.

'When you have finished your meal,' he said sharply, 'we have some work to do. There are still things I want you to see. I want you to have a look at what your British friends have done to Dortmund.'

That was the last thing I wanted to do: I had seen all I wanted to from a vantage point 6,000 metres above the city, and that was sufficient for me. I tried to decline the invitation.

'No thank you, *Herr Obersturmbannführer*. I have already seen enough.'

'I think not, my friend,' he replied. 'I'll be the judge of that. You have not yet seen what really matters. I am going to insist ... now, come on ... let's have no more argument. You will find that things look so very different when you visit the scene of the crime.'

It took us quite a while to get to Dortmund, even though Kreis's imposing staff car gave us some priority. As we neared the city, we were held up by convoy after convoy and, now and then, by the damage caused by random bombing. We began to encounter refugees, leaving with whatever possessions they could carry. Many were in lorries, and a few were using private cars, but most were on foot, pushing carts, bicycles and even loaded perambulators. At the very outskirts of the city, we were stopped at a roadblock operated by the *Kettenhunde*. Here, Kreis had to argue, and then use his rank and position to get permission to proceed further. We were told that this unusual restriction was necessary because the raid had been a very bad one, and there were hundreds of refugees to be evacuated, while rescue teams were arriving from as far as 100 kilometres away.

We were allowed to drive on, but were soon stopped again by the damage to the roads and by the congestion. The British had laid waste to a large part of the north and east of the city. The Pathfinder Master Bomber had evidently not succeeded in getting his main force to concentrate on his target markers. We left the staff car and walked on, picking our way over the rubble and damage of what had formerly been the main roads. Utter devastation faced us. The heavy bombs had literally blown houses and buildings flat. Everywhere the demolition and rescue teams were hard at work, burrowing into the debris in their search for survivors.

We then came to an area where incendiary bombs had fallen in such numbers that a miniature fire-storm had developed, engulfing blocks of buildings, shops and dwellings. Fire brigades were still at work in this charred wasteland, and the rescue teams were looking for bodies and remains. Without a doubt, no one had survived this inferno. The heat had been so great that the very tar on the roads had melted into burning streams and, here and there, charred bodies could be seen fused into the now congealed mess. A little further on, we came to a roadside mortuary where there were at least fifty bodies, brought up from a deep shelter in which they had been asphyxiated. The agonies of their deaths could be all too clearly seen in their faces. It was then that I was unashamedly sick, while Kreis watched me, impassively.

We eventually got through the badly blitzed area, and walked on towards the city centre. This had also been badly hit in a few places, and fires in some of the larger buildings were still being damped down. We found the Rescue Headquarters, where Kreis asked if there was anything we could do to help. The desperately overworked Army *Major* in charge at first ignored Kreis but then, recognising the uniform, wearily held out a piece of paper. He suggested that the *Gestapo* might be interested, as it listed British casualties found in the city, some of whom could be seen, if necessary.

One four-engined bomber had exploded, with its bomb load, right inside the Hoesch steelworks. A pilot had been found sitting bemused in the main city park, under the shrouds of his parachute. Before he could be brought in, some youngsters had beaten him to death. Another Britisher had been strung up on a lamp-post by enraged civilians, and there were rumours that others had been killed by being thrown into the fires.

Kreis reacted as though this purgatory were but a daily occurrence to him. He showed no emotion, and seemed unconcerned by the appalling sights around us. It became clear to me that his only real interest was in educating me in the hellishness of war, which he was doing in an almost schoolmasterly way, by simply drawing my attention to this and that, and letting me dwell on the horrors of what I saw.

The past twelve hours had been, to say the least, a sobering and totally unexpected experience. I had never before seen such carnage at close range. My view had always been remote, seen from the cockpit of an aircraft far above what was happening below. The memories of what Kreis was now showing me, what I heard and smelt, would stay with me for ever. There was no conversation as we drove back to Geilenkirchen. Kreis left me to myself, to ponder and worry about the future. I knew that what I had seen would somehow influence the decision I would have to make, but could not yet envisage what that might be. The silence continued during the flight back to Tempelhof, until Kreis's parting words.

'Your honeymoon at the Adlon is over. You will be moving tomorrow, so make the most of your last night there. Then, I hope, we can make up our minds about what we are going to do.'

My removal from the Adlon was made at an unearthly hour, before the hotel had really begun its day's work. I was driven to quarters in the former Prussian Guards barracks at Spandau, where I was told that Kreis wanted to see me at 09.30 hours precisely. He was signing papers as I entered his office, approached his desk and saluted him. He continued with his work without looking up.

'Pray be seated. I shall only be a few more moments, and then you will have my full attention.'

I took the seat in front of his desk, settled down, and tried to compose myself. I was worried, and hoped that I was not in for another unwelcome surprise. Kreis rang a bell. An orderly came in and took away the signed documents. Kreis then rose and went to a cabinet, from which he took two glasses and a bottle.

'No need to get up, Rath. I know it's early in the day, but I trust you will join me. I can well recommend my favourite Calvados. I am lucky enough to get it regularly from our gallant friends in France.'

'Thank you, *Herr Obersturmbannführer;* I like it too. I used to drink it before the war, when I was studying French at Rheims.'

He poured two glasses, and brought them over. He sat down, putting the glasses on the desk in front of him, then leant down and took out a dossier from a drawer.

'Now, to business. It is time to make your decision. By the end of the day... or sooner... I have to know whether you will be willing to serve with us or will want to return to your unit, forgetting everything we have been doing since your arrival in Berlin. I stress again that there will be no compulsion. I want you to listen to a proposal, and consider it carefully. I hope that you will then volunteer for a dangerous yet rewarding task for which you seem very well suited. If you decide against it, and want to go back to your duties with the *Luftwaffe*, that decision will not be held against you. Your only loss will be that you will not return to flying duties. Do you understand?'

'Yes, I understand, *Herr Obersturmbannführer.*'

'I hope so,' said Kreis, leaning towards me and fixing me with his steel-blue eyes. 'I do hope so.' He pushed my glass towards me, took up his own and settled back in his chair.

'Now, you would be a fool indeed if you had not already deduced that what I have to say concerns these British terror raids. We, in the *Geheime Staatspolizei*, have been trying our best for a long time to make some contribution towards bringing them to an end. This we must do in the only way open to us, by working on the ground in counter-intelligence operations. Now, our immediate task, set by those above us, is to remove something best regarded as a cancer... one of such malignancy that drastic surgery is called for.'

He paused to take a sip from his glass.

'This threat is something new in warfare. It is concerned with the active clandestine traffic in shot-down British airmen. We have tried to find, break down and destroy the means whereby the *Terrorflieger* are returned to safety. You have read about these escape routes, and about our use of French, Belgian and Dutch collaborators in attempts to destroy them. We have even established bogus escape routes, but these are, unfortunately, limited to the rounding-up of the airmen. Our detailed interrogation of those Resistance people we have managed to capture has given us little to work on, apart from the fact that the escape routes are something special. They are, in themselves, intelligence organisations which work entirely independently of others. They keep very much to themselves, to ensure they have the utmost security for their operations.'

He drank again from his glass.

'So... having done our best... and failed, we have carefully reviewed our work and have found what we believe to be the only solution. The Joint Intelligence Bureau has agreed to a carefully planned operation aimed at penetrating one or more of the principal escape routes.'

He was watching me intently, sensing that I already had some idea of what he was about to say.

'We are going to infiltrate these routes ourselves and, once there, we shall let them take us all the way, finishing in a neutral country, just as they do with the British. The information and knowledge we gather on the way will enable us to destroy the whole organisation from within.'

I think Kreis had expected me to be surprised, but I was simply wondering why such a plan had not been used before. I finished my Calvados, while he awaited my response.

'Surely, such an idea must have been considered already?' I asked, putting down my glass.

'No, it hasn't, certainly not in the way we intend to do it this time. We did try last year, using a couple of English-speaking Dutch *Waffen SS* as agents, but they failed miserably.'

'How was that?' I asked.

'Their disguises and cover stories were seen through almost at once. We had failed to train them well enough to pass as members of the RAF. Disguise and everything else must be perfect. These people work closely with British Intelligence, and know as much as we do about the RAF. They take no chances.'

'What happened to the Dutchmen?'

'We found them both hanging from trees outside the *Kommandandeur's* office in Bergen-op-Zoom,' Kreis told me, averting his eyes.

Looking up, he continued:

'However, this exercise clearly demonstrated what was wrong. We had rushed the Dutchmen through some inadequate training, and had overlooked things about the British which gave the game away.'

Some game, I thought, almost certain now that I knew what Kreis wanted of me.

'And how does all this concern me, *Herr Obersturmbannführer?*'

He looked straight at me, with a knowing expression on his face, but said nothing.

'Do you really expect me, of all people, to become some sort of a spy?' I asked, 'To pretend that I am a Britisher... a *Terrorflieger*... and then get myself accepted by the fanatics who run these organisations?'

He nodded.

'I do indeed, and I can show you just how easily someone of your talent and ability can do so. I am absolutely sure that, if you let us train you to do the job, you will become as convinced as we are that you can succeed. Just allow us to show you how the job can be done. Then, if at the end of the training period you are not certain of your capability, you can drop the idea and feel free to leave us... again without penalty of any sort.'

The time had come for me to decide. I could not avoid the issue any longer: Kreis was reading me like a book.

'If you want time to think, so be it,' he said. 'But let us be realistic, my friend. If you really want to serve your country in a better way, and this you would be doing if you joined us, then there is time enough for you to make up your mind during the training period. Our volunteers... oh yes, there will have to be others... must be enthusiastic and utterly dedicated. The rewards for what you will achieve can be great. Not only will you deal a death blow to this ruinous subversion but, undoubtedly, there will be some advancement in the degree of those decorations of yours.'

I was fascinated by the guile of the man. He could read my mind, anticipate thoughts and, I believed, get his way in the end. He was a truly cunning individual. He knew full well that he had hooked me, and that I was about to agree to something which, only a few days ago, I would have considered outrageous.

'*Herr Obersturmbannführer*, you must forgive me for my hesitancy, but events here have taken me entirely by surprise. You know that I would welcome the opportunity of active service again. Therefore, provided I can leave my decision until the end of the training programme, so as to resolve some of the doubts that still linger in my mind, I accept.'

Kreis rose to his feet and offered his hand, which I shook firmly.

'I am delighted, my dear Wilhelm. I think we have both made good decisions. Now we can make a start. This afternoon you will meet your fellow classmates, those who have already been selected.'

CHAPTER TWELVE

There were four of us, seated in comfortable chairs arranged in a semi-circle, in front of an empty fireplace in a room near Kreis's office. He had greeted each of us on arrival, but had made no introductions, nor had we spoken to each other. Kreis stood in front of us, his back to the fireplace.

'I have met you all singly, and you are each aware of the purpose of this enterprise. From now on, you will be subject to the strictest security, which means, I am afraid, that you will spend a lot of your time in quarters until we move to the active part of your training. Each of you has been carefully selected. You are all from different backgrounds, and I doubt whether you have much in common with each other. For obvious reasons, however, we shall keep your identities a secret and, from this moment on, you will use these cover names.'

Turning to each of us in turn, he gave us our new names. A short, rather greasy-looking individual, with close-set eyes and a receding chin, was given the name of Albert Smith. Another, about thirty-five years of age, with a well-bred, almost aristocratic bearing, dressed in an officer's brown uniform without insignia, was to be called Thomas Jones. Then there was a tall, smart *Luftwaffe Feldwebel* of the Anti-Aircraft Command, to be named George Brown, while, outranking the others, I became William Roberts.

'One matter of uniformity,' added Kreis. 'While you are training, you will be attached temporarily to the *SS*. Your pay and allowances will be equal to those of an *Obersturmführer.* I want you to wear *SS* uniform but, because of the need for utmost security, you will not be able to enjoy many of their privileges.'

He then switched effortlessly to English. 'Also, from now on, we will speak in English at all times.'

His English was good, grammatically correct, but with a typically German accent.

'For the rest of the day, I want you to get used to this practice by speaking amongst yourselves. Later in the afternoon, we shall issue you with your uniforms. Any questions?'

'When do the pubs open?', Smith tried to joke. The rest of us remained silent, seeing nothing funny in the remark.

Our training began in earnest the next morning. We started with lectures and talks on British subjects, most of them political. At the end of each session, there was a group discussion, prompted by Kreis. From the start, it was clear that Smith was going to be the odd man out. He was glib, and always ready with something to say, yet it was often irrelevant, easily exposing his lack of basic education.

Our lecturers were often British. One fascinating speaker was a novelist who had chosen to stay behind after the fall of Paris. He had been specially flown to Berlin, just to talk to us on the British way of life. There was another, a supercilious defector working with the Ministry of Propaganda, who often made broadcasts to the British Isles, and seemed to have connections with German Intelligence. I found myself easily slipping back into English ways of speaking and reasoning. I wondered why Kreis had selected the man Smith, as it was difficult to see what he had to offer. Smith had confided in me that he had been on the run since before Dunkirk, in both Occupied and Unoccupied France, where he claimed he had worked for Germany against the French Resistance. He was surprisingly ignorant of things British, and only came into his own when talking about the East End of London. He spoke badly, and his use of language was coarse. He constantly moaned about his past service in the British Army, and of his 'bloody toffee-nosed' officers: I disliked him intensely.

We then moved on to military matters, beginning with talks on the broad capabilities of both sides, where and how we were fighting, what weapons were being used and how Germany would finally win the war. An Italian Bersagliari captain held back nothing about the British successes in Somaliland and North Africa. He described the British soldier as dogged, determined and licentious, always fighting in the belief that no nation on earth was as good as Britain, but having no appreciation whatsoever of the finer things in life, such as food, wine, music and how to please a woman.

From these general aspects, we moved on to the particular, the Royal Air Force. It was obviously necessary to learn as much as possible about the Service, so that we could attain the general knowledge level of most British aircrew. This time we had no Britisher to lecture us, but were very well served by members of the Intelligence staff at *Luftwaffe* Headquarters. Starting from the top, the Air Ministry, the Commands, Groups and Stations were explained, and then we came to Bomber Command. Again, we dealt with the command structure, right down to airman level, and discussed the stations, training fields, aircraft and equipment.

It was only at this point that we discovered there were in fact two Britishers in our group. This came about when, in answer to a question, the quiet, well-bred Thomas Jones revealed that he had actually been a pilot in the Advanced Air Striking Force based in France. In May 1940, while trying to get back to England and away from the *Blitzkrieg,* he had been shot down and captured. He had been against the war from the start, and had tried hard to avoid having to fight against Germany. He had made these sentiments known when he was taken to Germany as a prisoner and, after some time at the *Dulag Luft* Interrogation Centre, he was given work in the Foreign Office in Berlin, translating documents and evaluating British wireless broadcasts. Kreis got Jones to talk about the Royal Air Force. I soon gained the impression of an intelligent junior officer, a good speaker, but someone basically flawed by having little backbone or any desire to become involved in the harsher things of life. How he had come to be a turncoat was beyond me and, here again, I failed to see how the man could be of any value to Kreis's plan.

On the other hand, I began to warm to George Brown. He was good-looking, smart and bright. He disliked all things British, and made this clear to both Smith and Jones. He had been born and brought up in the United States as the eldest son of a first generation German-American family, which had gone to Detroit from Hamburg just after the Great War. He spoke English well, but with a marked American accent, having been educated at Stanford University where he had gained a Master's Degree. He had then been employed by the German shipping line which, in those days, plied between New York and Bremerhaven. His hate of the British had been born in him, and fostered by Britain's reaction to what Germany had been forced to do in order to right the wrongs of the Treaty of Versailles and thereby facilitate her recovery. In 1936, during one of his regular visits to Bremerhaven, he had decided to remain in Germany. He had become a German citizen in 1938 when he had joined the *Luftwaffe,* hoping to be trained as a pilot. In this he had failed and, at the outbreak of war, had been transferred to the Anti-Aircraft Command and thereafter stationed in the Ruhr. Kreis must have had little difficulty in getting Brown to volunteer.

A talk by an officer from *Dulag Luft* was a revelation. The expertise of this detailed interrogation centre was the reason for a wealth of up-to-date information being extracted from hundreds of captured British airmen, who streamed through the place at Obereusel, near Frankfurt. Most of the intelligence had been gained by quite straightforward techniques, such as I had used on Sergeant Coleman back at Roermond, namely the use of threats, the imposition of fear, and taking advantage of a man's mental state when under stress. This expert went on to explain the use of hidden microphones, those whom the British called 'stool pigeons', and the unintentional completion of bogus information forms. He surprised me when he told us that the British were well aware of these methods, and were, in fact, themselves masters of such techniques. Also - and this was important - all British aircrew operating over Germany were now briefed on what to expect when taken prisoner, and how best to combat interrogation.

From information gathered at *Dulag Luft,* it was possible for a *Luftwaffe Hauptmann* to take us through a typical Bomber Command briefing. Thomas Jones was surprised to learn how much had changed since his capture, just over two years ago. The address by the Station Commander, disclosure of the target and tactics to be used, specific briefings by wireless, navigation and gunnery officers, the all-important weather forecast, and the airfields to be used for diversions on return, were all dealt with in detail. We were told of the Intelligence Officer's contribution, which covered all aspects of security, how to behave when taken prisoner, and how to go about contacting the escape routes, all summed up in the familiar exhortation... 'it is your duty to evade capture and to return to your unit.'

This officer went on to demonstrate British evasion and escape aids. He showed us a range of miniature compasses, which were carried hidden on the person. Many of these were truly ingenious. Some were contained in cuff-links, studs, pencils, pens and even in trouser fly-buttons and shoe-laces. But it was the evasion material which interested us most. Contained in a flat tin box, which fitted into the breast pocket of an airman's battledress, was a collection of odds and ends for use immediately after landing, and sufficient for a few days' walking. The contents were laid out for us to see and examine. There were silk maps of the areas to be overflown, banknotes in French, Belgian and Dutch currencies, benzedrine tablets for heightened awareness, and Horlicks tablets - supposedly to provide energy. I could not resist interrupting at this point, explaining that all the Horlicks advertising I had seen in England stressed that the tablets were the best thing for getting a good night's sleep!

Then we saw a plastic water bag and Halazone purifying tablets, a fishing line, but no bait, sewing needles and thread and, for good measure, two more miniature compasses. Apparently, it was the opinion of *Luftwaffe* Headquarters that the kit had been designed for only limited use, to get a man started on his evasion, to decide on a plan, to get up on his feet and make a start on the long walk home. The discussion which followed soon turned to what was known of the escape routes. How did the evader make contact and, if he did not, how was he picked up by the Resistance? What routes were known, and how did they operate? Kreis cut into the animated exchanges to tell us that, in due course, there would be detailed briefings on those very subjects.

At the end of a week of lectures and talks, Kreis informed us that our training programme was on schedule. He now wanted us to think about, and get used to, the particular rôle identities we might use if we were selected at the end of training. There was, of course, only one possible rôle for Albert Smith - that of rear gunner. His size alone recommended him for this duty, which Smith crudely referred to as that of a 'Arse-End Charlie'. Thomas Jones and I would carry on as pilots, while George Brown would become either a bombardier or a wireless operator. We were then told that we could look forward to a few days away from Spandau, at a place where we could study and use RAF equipment. Our lectures had been completed.

We were not very warm as we sat huddled in pairs, facing each other, in the back of a roaring, clattering, bumping Junkers 52. Our ancient aircraft had laboured away from Tempelhof, taking us to a special *Luftwaffe* unit which evaluated captured RAF aircraft and equipment. We were flying in cloud, and our newly-fledged rear-gunner was making it only too clear that he was no airman. He had been nervous and apprehensive from the start, and had vomited his breakfast into the aisle between us. We left him well alone, with the reminder that it was the custom in the *Luftwaffe,* if anyone was airsick, that he cleared up his own mess. After about an hour, we landed at Rechlin, where a special programme had been arranged for our benefit.

The unit *Kommandeur* himself met us in the Operations Room, and briefed us on the range of enemy aircraft under evaluation by his unit. Kreis had put me in charge of the group, and had evidently given the *Kommandeur* some idea of our special importance. We were then placed in the control of Rechlin's Chief Test Pilot, a well-known reserve officer with a brilliant operational record. He said that he was there to help us throughout our stay and that, if there was anything we particularly wished to see or know about, he would make the arrangements.

After a light meal in the small Officers' Mess, we made a start by first visiting the Parachute Section, where we were shown the various types of safety equipment used by the RAF. Their so-called 'Mae Wests', yellow inflatable life jackets with back-straps to pull a man out of the water, were laid out for us to inspect and try on. We were fitted with flying helmets and oxygen masks, and plugged into a system that allowed us to breathe oxygen and use the mask microphone. In answer to a question by Jones, we were told that the referee's whistle, attached to the lapel of the RAF battledress, was a means of summoning help when down in the water. There were dinghies arranged in a corner, small ones for fighter pilots and two larger versions for bomber crews. One of these had been inflated for our benefit and we sat in it, as a crew, and examined the contents of the various zipped pockets.

There were all manner of battledresses to be seen. One was shown complete in every detail: escape kit, rescue whistle, and hidden compasses in the waistband, shoulder strap, and left hand chest pocket. Jones and I were surprised to learn that bomber crews, with the exception of the rear-gunner, flew over Germany wearing only battledress and Mae Wests, since all bomber aircraft now had adequate heating systems, except in the gun turrets.

There were numerous types of parachutes, which had been recovered from crashed British aircraft or from dead aircrew. One 'chute had been pulled, and was laid out on the packing table. It was a chest type, such as worn by all members of a bomber crew other than the rear-gunner who, for operational reasons, had to use a seat-type 'chute so as to be able to lean forward to see into the gunsight. We were each fitted carefully with a parachute harness, the slack being taken up on the leg and chest straps until we were bowed into the trussed-chicken position. Each of us then had a parachute clipped into position, the only exception being Smith, who was rigged-up in the seat-type version. The test pilot showed us the D-ring, and how to pull it.

'These parachutes are first-class,' he said. 'They are the very best, designed by Irvin. The chances of them not opening are remote. The only problem to be found is with the chest-type. If you have your head down over the pack when you pull the D-ring, there is a good chance that, as the pack flies open, and the shroud straps spring out, you could get a nasty crack in the face. With the seat-type there is no such problem, as the harness straps are all at your back.'

We stood there in our uncomfortable bowed positions, which looked worse in the case of Smith, who had the parachute pack itself dangling under his rear.

'I believe you will better understand what I have been saying if we give you a practical demonstration,' said our smiling instructor. 'It is one that I am sure you will all enjoy ... just come along with me.' We had no idea what he meant, but followed him uncomfortably out of the building, with Smith waddling along in the rear, his 'chute slapping against the back of his bent legs. We were directed into a waiting Magirus, and told to sit on benches. I could see from the puzzled expressions around me that everyone was wondering what would happen next, although I was beginning to suspect it would be something a little out of the ordinary. Smith, in particular, was becoming agitated. As we were driven away, we could see outside only through the open end of the lorry. We travelled through the camp, and were soon bumping across the grass airfield. Then the lorry stopped, and we were told to get out: it was something of a shock to find ourselves alongside the winching engine of a captive balloon, fully inflated, its passenger basket resting on the ground in front of us.

'You fortunate fellows are going to have the pleasure of parachuting at no risk or expense whatsoever,' gloated our test pilot friend. 'I know there is no need to call for volunteers ... you heroes simply cannot wait for action!' He beamed at our mute astonishment. 'All right. Let's take you two at a time. This wonderful device has trouble in coping with a full load.

I had never made a parachute jump in my life nor, I suppose, had any of the others. I signalled Brown to join me, and we entered the basket, together with the test pilot. We were winched up to about 400 metres, a very pleasant process indeed, and then had our D-rings clipped on to a static line.

'All you have to do is jump,' said our instructor, as he opened the wicker basket door. 'But do keep your head up.' I went to the door and, for a split second, experienced vertigo as I looked straight down. Once away, the chest pack snapped open and, within seconds, my parachute was streaming out and I was happily on my way down, adjusting the shroud lines for a landing into a slight wind. I touched down softly, and was quickly out of my harness and gathering up the canopy by the time Brown landed close by. Together, we walked back to the winch, our arms full of parachute, while the balloon was being brought down to collect Smith and Jones.

We found Smith in a terrible state of funk. He was sitting on his seat-pack alongside the winch, rocking backwards and forwards, protesting that he was not feeling well. Jones was arguing with him. I did not hesitate, but ordered him into the basket with Jones, explaining that the whole thing was but a simple exercise, and that there was no risk. Tremulously, he continued to insist that he could not and would not go up in the balloon. As he absolutely refused to move, I indicated to Brown that I needed help and, together, we hauled Smith to his feet. He was shaking with fright as we first dragged and then propelled him into the basket. I clipped his D-ring to the static line. The test pilot, greatly amused by these antics, stood aside to allow me to take his place, merely asking if I could cope.

Together with Jones, who had remained silent throughout our tussle with Smith, we rose from the ground. Smith sat on the floor of the basket, moaning and trembling, head between his knees. When we got to the top of the ascent, I opened the basket door, and signalled to those below that we were ready. With the help of Jones, we literally threw Smith from the balloon, still in the sitting position, his eyes firmly shut. We watched him turn turtle, and heard his long departing scream. The parachute was late to open fully, and then oscillated badly, Smith hitting the ground heavily at the very end of a wide swing. Jones then unhurriedly jumped, and I was winched down. Despite his heavy landing, Smith seemed quite unshaken, and was already putting his disgraceful behaviour behind him. He had surprised himself, and was fast recovering his habitual bonhomie.

We returned to the parachute section with our bundles of white silk, and were then driven to our quarters, in an annexe to the Officers' Mess. We were told that security at Rechlin was all-important, and that under no circumstances were we to attempt to leave the camp. We were served a meal in our rooms. I was tired and, after a good bath, I turned in, hoping for a good night's sleep so as to be ready for whatever thrills awaited us on the morrow. But this was not to be, for, about three o'clock in the morning, I was aroused by a *Luftwaffe* policeman, who asked if I would go with him to the Guardroom. I dressed, wondering what new surprise was in store for me, and joined him in his *Kübelwagen*.

The mystery was soon revealed. I found Albert Smith, drunk and bleary-eyed, sitting in the guard commander's office, where he was giving a muted rendition of 'Eskimo Nell'. He had been apprehended trying to get through the barbed-wire perimeter into Rechlin and, despite his condition, had steadfastly refused to give his name or any other information, apart from the fact that I was his superior officer. He was glad to see me, and actually apologised for getting me out of bed. He saw nothing at all wrong with what he had done. He had just gone into town to celebrate his parachute jump. The beer had been good, but the girls unco-operative. He said that the powers-that-be should know that it was dead easy to escape from Rechlin, but a darned sight more difficult to break back in! We started early the next morning. I was surprised to find that Smith had no hangover, and was fully recovered from both the jump and his night out. Mercifully, he kept the sordid details of the latter to himself.

The captured Allied aircraft were housed in three large hangars.

We were taken first to look over Rechlin's prize exhibit, a four-engined Short Stirling bomber, standing there on its strange stalk-like undercarriage, but minus its front gun-turret. The whole nose of the machine had been covered by a strapped-down thick canvas, and we were told that, despite this unusual modification, the aircraft was in good condition and regularly flown. Our test pilot told us that he liked the Stirling.

'We hope soon to get another front end for it. This type is quite easy to shoot down, you know. The poor bastards who have to fly it can't get much above 4,000 metres with a full bomb load and, stuck at that altitude, they catch every bit of flak there is. The snag is, they usually come down in such small pieces that it is almost impossible to pick up what we want.'

We went thoroughly over the Stirling, exploring every nook and cranny, asking questions about the equipment as it was shown to us. Jones and I concentrated on the pilot's cockpit and navigator's cabin while Smith, his cocky self again, was shown how the four machin- guns in the rear turret were loaded and operated.

There was also a Wellington in the hangar, a Mark 1c which had once belonged to No. 9 Squadron. My thoughts flew back to my cousin, John Carey, who had been a member of that squadron at Mildenhall. This aircraft had been on a raid to Hanover about eighteen months previously and, on the way back, had got lost and landed by mistake in the Netherlands. The crew, all sergeants, had given themselves up to capture. Again, we were allowed to roam over the aircraft. The test pilot showed us how the machine had, in some respects, been brought up to date by the addition of superior captured equipment. This included a GEE navigation set, and the latest type of six-man rubber dinghy, which was actually released for us and inflated from the top of the port wing.

The second hangar was filled with French machines. These included a flyable Loire et Olivier bomber and quite a number of Dewoitine and Morane fighters, together with their ancillary equipment. There was little of particular interest, so we moved on to what must have been the 'spare parts' hangar. Spread out for our inspection were the remains of two Blenheims, two Fairey Battles and a Hampden. Off to one side were a Spitfire and a Hurricane, both of which had been restored to flying condition.

We were next taken across the airfield to the gunnery range, where two Frazer-Nash turrets had been set up, one with two and the other with four guns. We were shown how to load and traverse the turrets from side to side and up and down, and then took turns at firing the multiple machine-guns, using the standard British gunsight. This brought our visit to Rechlin to an end. We returned to our quarters to pack and, as leader of the party, I paid my respects to the *Kommandeur.* I thanked him, in particular, for the excellent services of the test pilot, and apologised for the trouble caused by Smith's drunken excursion into town, saying that he would, no doubt, be suitably dealt with. Again, our relatively privileged position was marked by the arrival of an aircraft, this time a Siebel, which flew us back to Berlin.

We had learned many things during the two days away from Berlin, not only about British machines and equipment, but about ourselves. There was little evidence to be seen of any comradeship developing within the group. The British were quite different from the Germans, both in manner and in spirit: I saw no common interest or enthusiasm in them, and in fact wondered what their value could be. The one most 'out-of-step' was Jones, the former British pilot, whose superior attitude and reticence annoyed the rest of us, and kept him apart. The German-American, Brown, was just the opposite. He knew his limitations, and wanted to learn, to participate, and to have a deliberate say in anything we were doing.

Albert Smith was perplexing. He had certainly made an impression, of sorts, at Rechlin. He was undoubtedly an opportunist, a low-bred type with the ability to take adversity in his stride, to bounce back, and settle matters to his own advantage. But would he have the intelligence, integrity and personal discipline to operate when on his own? That he was a quick learner was only too clear: he had now mastered control of his bowels, and was not the least bit queasy or air-sick during the return flight.

The next morning, Kreis called me to his office for a report on the Rechlin visit. He was anxious to know what benefits there had been, and whether I thought there were any other items of British equipment we should examine. I said that we had enjoyed ourselves, had learned much, and had not wasted a single minute. I told him about Smith's performance during the parachute instruction, and how he had reacted after being forced to jump. I had to speak up about his irresponsibility, and voiced my doubts about his integrity and motivation. Kreis simply replied that he, also, had reservations, about all of us. For the moment, we were all learning, and there was much still to be done before any decisions would be made.

CHAPTER THIRTEEN

Kreis then called a special briefing. We were sitting comfortably in his office, and had been allowed to smoke. He stood in front of us, very much like a schoolmaster about to start a lesson, and was obviously in a good humour

'Gentlemen, you have been with us for just over ten days. You seem to be learning well, and are behaving yourselves. So far, all you have been doing is reading and a little writing, dealing with books, instructions and lectures, examining equipment and asking questions of all kinds. Well... the time has come to get on with more practical things.'

He paused for a moment, scanning each of our faces in turn.

'I am only too well aware that my prime purpose is to convince you of the vital importance of our work, and that you will never be asked to undertake the impossible. The training which has been arranged for you must therefore be as complete as we can make it. We have to be sure that you have the skills which will easily enable you to outwit the enemy. So, with this very much in mind, you are about to begin the next, and probably the most important and vital stage of our work. We intend to see whether, without the slightest suspicion or danger of any sort, you can mix and pass yourselves off among the British. If the RAF accept you on equal terms, then there should be little problem when you meet the Resistance people, those who operate the escape routes.'

We looked askance at each other. I noticed that Jones was showing unusual interest. He was on the edge of his seat.

'I can see from your faces that you are going to like what has been planned for you. Yes, this will please you, without a doubt.' He paused for effect. 'You will soon be on your way to spend a week or so at *Dulag Luft.*'

We were dumbstruck. Kreis certainly had our full attention. He carefully lit a cigarette.

'This afternoon, you will each be given an RAF uniform which you will wear at all times from now on. There will have to be a little tailoring, so that it will appear that you have lived in the battledress for some time. Jones and Robert will wear pilots' brevets, and will have the rank of Flying Officer. Brown will be a Flight Sergeant in the Royal Canadian Air Force, and Smith... our Tail-End Charlie ... will be a Sergeant. You will be equipped as though you had just been shot down; in other words, wearing flying boots and carrying escape aids. We shall infiltrate you into the system immediately after the next terror raid.'

We looked at each other in amazement. This was an absolutely brilliant idea. We could certainly learn a lot and, at the same time, be as sure as possible that our disguises were perfect.

Jones, however, was worried: '*Herr Obersturmbannführer*, may I ask if this subterfuge has ever been tried before?'

'Why do you ask?', queried Kreis.

'Simply this. You know that I have been at *Dulag Luft* before. Is there not the chance that someone might recognise me? Don't forget that I have achieved some sort of notoriety, working on your behalf. Is it not perhaps better for all of us if I am left out of this part of the exercise?'

Kreis must have expected something like this from Jones. He replied at once, 'I think not. The standard practice, as you well know, is for aircrew to undergo detailed interrogation at *Dulag Luft* until we are satisfied that there is nothing more to be gained from them. This process seldom goes beyond three months; indeed, if anyone stays longer, then the British themselves know the man is suspect, a 'bad egg'. No... we usually have them on their way to the *Stalags* in a week or two. In any case, the "bad eggs" are generally worthless, and seldom of high intelligence.'

'Maybe so,' argued Jones, 'but we already know that the RAF are warned to beware of stool pigeons. Could it not be that they have been warned to look out for me in particular?'

'I really don't know, my dear Jones,' said Kreis. 'Bomber Command has been transformed since you left it, and I think your fears are unfounded. The old stagers are now either dead or locked up safely for a long time, far away from *Dulag Luft*. You have been away from the RAF for more than two years, and there is much for you to learn to bring yourself into step with the current generation of *Terrorflieger*. No... I want you to go.'

At this point, Smith cut in, 'What if we get rumbled, anyway? I'm a bloody pongo, and it's going to take me some time to get to know how the Brylcreem boys actually talk. All that *gen* business, you know.'

Kreis sought to calm his fears.

'There is nothing for you to worry about, Smith... and that goes for the rest of you. The *Kommandant* at *Dulag Luft* is fully aware of our plan, together with the chief interrogator, *Hauptmann* Eberhardt. If anything appears to be going wrong, we shall get you out of the place at once. I shall tell you more about this at your final briefing.'

That was a fair and pretty obvious answer, but I wanted to know more about the RAF at *Dulag Luft*.

'*Herr Obersturmbannführer*, you have emphasised that the RAF are actually trained to be escape conscious, and that they band together in the camps to form escape committees. Is there any chance of there being anything like that at *Dulag Luft?*'

Kreis was evidently pleased with my intervention. 'We cannot be absolutely sure, but our experience tells us that there would not be enough time for them to get organised. The population at *Dulag Luft* is always new and ever-changing. The hard-bitten escapers who get out time and again are all from the permanent camps, which certainly do have escape committees. There are, of course, those extroverts who start planning to escape as soon as we lock them up, but... no... I cannot believe that there could be an escape committee of any sort at *Dulag Luft.*'

We were given our RAF uniforms during the afternoon. Although the battledress was loose-fitting, to allow for thick underwear and pullovers, there was still a certain amount of tailoring to be done. I found it hard to believe that any fastidious Englishman would choose to go to war wearing the coarse, one-piece, long- legged underwear which was, so we were told, standard issue for aircrew. But, as there was nothing else suitable, or adaptable, I had to put it on.

Every item we were given was British and, in each case, it was carefully described to us. I did not know, for instance, that bomber crews did not fly wearing the detachable shirt collars and black ties, in case they ended up unconscious in the sea, being slowly strangled by the shrinking material around their necks. We had a few problems with the fitting of flying boots. They had to be loose enough to allow for walking reasonable distances, but not so large as to be jerked off by the sudden shock of an opening parachute. We were left to make our own choice from a range of sizes and styles. I was lucky enough to find a pair of the latest type, designed especially for evading. After removal of the leg-protection, held to the shoe portion by a zip, I had a fine pair of sturdy black shoes.

We collected smaller items, such as pullovers, socks, handkerchiefs, whistles, brevets and badges of rank and, finally, identity discs which Kreis described to us.

'These identity discs are bogus. They have not been taken from the dead. We have had them specially made. Just remember to wear them around your necks at all times. Memorise your serial number, rank and name, as you are expected to have that information ingrained in your soul.' He held them up. 'You will notice that one is green and the other brown. At the appropriate time, the green one goes for record purposes, while the brown is buried or goes into the flames with your body.'

All we had to do now was to wait. We knew that Kreis would unravel his plan only when he was ready, and thought fit to do so. I had already found my position as team leader involving me with loose ends and, at the same time, drawing me closer to Kreis and his thoughts. I was increasingly worried about the intended use of the Britishers, Smith and Jones. They were nothing but renegades, so how could they possibly become properly motivated, and loyal to the *Reich*? What was to stop them disappearing into a neutral country at the end of an escape route, and returning to England as heroes, with some cock and bull story to explain why they had been in Germany for so long, and how they had managed, at last, to escape? I put these doubts to Kreis one evening during dinner at his private quarters. He had a ready answer.

'My dear Wilhelm, you must remember that the *Gestapo* is perhaps the world's most efficient police force, and we take that credit seriously. We know all there is to know about these two turncoats. We expect them to have only a limited part in our plan, but we cannot be sure. Smith is nothing but a nasty little animal. He was in prison in England before the war and, when he joined the British *Freikorps,* we suspected that he had already been a double agent, working for or against ourselves, the British and the French. He betrayed British officers managing an escape route in Vichy France, after first helping them to set it up. He has even worked for the French *Milice* as an interrogator. One thing he does not know... and we do, is that British Intelligence had him marked for execution last year. We are well aware that there could be problems if we actually use these men. Until then, do you not think you derive some benefit from mixing with them? I am sure Brown does.'

'I suppose so,' I replied dubiously. 'They have been away from England for quite a time. They are both odd characters, and difficult to get on with.'

'That may be so, but remember, there are so many things that could happen and, in any case, you will all be operating on your own. Smith could, of course, be picked up by a group which will recognise him and, no doubt, deal with him. If, on the other hand, he gets to the end of a route, we can expect this crook to bargain with us. No matter what he does, however, we lose nothing and could possibly even gain something. And here is our trump card. In the cases of both Smith and Jones ... and our friend Jones is also in the British *Freikorps*... we have detailed accounts of what they have been doing for the past two years, plus a few imaginative embellishments, lodged at our Embassies in Madrid, Stockholm and Berne. If these two default, then the British authorities will be given this information, which amounts to a clear case of treason. I am sure you know that is a hanging offence in England. When the time does come, and we make a start with *"Aktion Kondor"*... yes, that is the intended code-name - "Operation *Kondor*" - I shall personally tell both Smith and Jones what awaits them, if they ever let us down.'

We did not have long to wait before the next stage began. What the British have since called the Battle of the Ruhr had reached a climax. The terror raids were taking place almost nightly, and both Dusseldorf and Bochum were struggling to recover from particularly damaging attacks. The British were still taking very heavy losses, and scores of their downed aircrew were wandering about, either trying to evade capture or waiting to be picked up and taken into captivity. We were warned to stand by to join this crowd.

We moved secretly from Berlin to Wildenrath, a night-fighter base on the edge of the Ruhr valley. There we made our final preparations. The intention was to drop us from vehicles, in pairs, somewhere in the area of the Belgo-Dutch frontier, where the British suffered frequent casualties from our night-fighters on their way back to England. Kreis had decided that the British renegades should be split. I was to go with Jones, and Smith with Brown. Our cover stories were to be that we had taken part in either the Dusseldorf or Bochum raids. We were given details of the locations and composition of the squadrons in which we had supposedly served.

The final briefing was held in a small guarded building on the edge of the airfield. We were dressed in our RAF uniforms, and wearing flying boots. We did not wear Mae Wests, since we were to pretend that we had started to evade capture and had therefore buried our parachutes and life jackets. Kreis explained that it was important for us to arrive at *Dulag Luft* exactly as though we had been captured after a terror raid. There would be nothing to fear if we kept our wits about us. It mattered little what we said to the German interrogators, but we would have to be very much on our guard if we were interrogated in the company of other Britishers. Standard retorts to any inquisitive Britisher should be '... remember what we were told at briefing... we must keep our mouths shut... we cannot trust anyone... there could be stool pigeons everywhere.'

After the briefing, Kreis gave us what he called the Last Supper. It was a good meal, not too heavy, washed down with *Stein* after *Stein* of good Rheinish beer. That old feeling of mounting tension and apprehension came back strongly, just the same as that which I had always experienced before a bombing raid. It heightened my awareness, but I knew that it would go, once we were on our way. At around eleven o'clock, Jones and I were called forward, and taken outside to clamber into a completely closed Magirus truck. It was raining hard, and pitch-dark. By all accounts we were in for a realistically miserable time, wandering around without any protection, in absolutely foul weather.

We drove off, with the two of us sitting on benches, facing each other, and an armed *SS Scharführer* somewhere in the semi-darkness at the end of the lorry. Not a word was spoken as we sped along what seemed to be well-surfaced main roads for the best part of an hour. We then began to bump and sway as we turned off into what must have been country lanes, and carried on in this way for twenty-five minutes, which I timed on the British navigator's watch I was wearing. At a signal from the driver, we were told to get ready to leave the vehicle. The Magirus began to slow down. The tailboard was lowered, and we had to stand up and move to the end. Then, while we were still moving at a good speed, we were thrown out by the *SS* man on to a hard, wet, dirt road, myself being the first to go, while Jones was ejected about fifty metres further on.

I landed badly, and hurt my shoulder. I walked on up the road, to find Jones sitting in a ditch, bleeding from a nasty gash in his left leg and a deep cut in his face. Once again Kreis had made sure that the line between reality and make-believe was as blurred as possible. Our arrival could not have been harder had we landed by parachute. We had little time to bemoan our injuries. A smaller lorry came along as we were sitting on the edge of the road, now thoroughly soaked with the heavy rain. Out jumped two *Kettenhunde* who quickly bundled us on board, delighted that they could lay their hands on a couple of *Terrorflieger*. We had to keep our hands on our heads while we were thoroughly searched. My watch was taken and, when I protested, I was struck in the face so hard that my nose bled. A similar protest from Jones, who had been told to drop his trousers for a rear-body search, resulted in a rifle-butt blow in the groin. There was certainly no play-acting in what was happening to us. We had been picked up as *Terrorflieger* and, from now on, could expect to be treated as such.

The next stage of our journey was almost unbearable. We had been injured, knocked about, and were soaking wet. Yet we had to sit on bare boards with our hands tied together with coarse rope, bumping across what felt like open country until we reached a made-up road and settled down to a steady speed. I wondered if our guards knew anything at all about this exercise. It might have been so, but I doubted it, because they took such sadistic delight in our discomfort. I deliberately kept my mind on other things, such as how to conduct myself in the days ahead. I kept forcing myself to remember that I was English, that my name was Flying Officer James Paterson, that my number was 102845 and that my religion was Other Denominational. I recalled how I had felt when shot down during the *Blitzkrieg,* and how my appetite had disappeared for days. This time, I was simply ravenous.

Jones said nothing as he sat opposite with a guard at his side. He seemed deep in thought, although he did provide some light relief when he leaned over to say that he was bursting, and had to 'ease springs', or else. His agitation and contortions amused the guards, who laughingly ignored his pained requests that we should stop for a moment. I sympathised with this unnecessary torture so, together, we began to stamp our feet and yell 'Stop, stop, stop' and, after a minute or so, the vehicle did indeed come to a halt. Jones was allowed to get down, and I joined him;

we managed, eventually, to relieve ourselves, albeit with some difficulty, as our hands were still bound together.

We realised that we had arrived in Germany when we stopped at a police post in the village of Neiderkruchten, which I knew was a few miles inside the border. We were pulled down from the lorry, our hands were unbound, and we were thrown into a cell, which was then locked and bolted. Jones collapsed onto the only wooden bench, moaning to himself, while I made myself as comfortable as possible on the stone floor. Eventually, exhaustion overtook us and we both slept. It was light when we were noisily awakened and taken from the cell to be handcuffed and handed over to a couple of soldiers. Papers had to be signed and exchanged, and then we were taken out to a small open lorry. We were settled in the back with the two soldiers guarding us, and then driven off, eastwards.

After about half an hour, we joined a main road, and soon found ourselves in the midst of traffic moving into the town of Moenchen Gladbach. As we passed through the western suburbs, we could see the results of random bombing as salvage teams worked among ruined dwellings. The streets were filling with people on their way to work, and we began to feel uncomfortably conspicuous, sitting there in full view of everyone. As we got nearer to the town centre, we could hear hostile abuse and threats, and clearly see the naked hate and revulsion in people's faces. Our journey finished outside the town *Kommandanteur's* office, directly opposite the main railway station.

We were quickly man-handled from the lorry and, in a nasty scuffle, dragged into the building through a shouting and vengeful mob. Little effort was made to protect us. People spat on us and hit us. Jones collected a nasty crack on the head from a woman's heavy walking stick.

'It's bloody difficult not to blame them,' he said, when we had reached the comparative safety of the foyer. 'When you think of what they go through, night after night, we are damned fortunate not to be lynched.'

I had to agree with him, while at the same time feeling pleased that I had been able to get through this difficult interlude, thinking and acting all the time as would a genuine Britisher. Once again there were papers to be signed and exchanged. Our handcuffs were removed, and we were hustled through the building and downstairs into a large cell in which, to our surprise, were three more RAF aircrew, sitting on the floor. They were very much at ease, and smoking what I instantly recognised by their smell to be English cigarettes.

'Come in, cobbers,' called an Australian voice, 'come and join the club. There's plenty of room for more.'

A fresh-faced navigator in a dark blue battledress looked up at our distress. 'Ye Gods. You look as though you've only just made it, chums.'

The cell door was locked and bolted. The trio got to their feet, shook hands with us, and introduced themselves as survivors of a Halifax crew which had been bombing the nearby town of Rheydt. They had been very quickly rounded up during the night. I spoke for Jones and myself.

'I'm James Paterson and this is John Cameron. We were shot down last week, and have been trying to get out of this bloody country ever since ... but they got both of us before we could get across the Maas.'

We sat with them on the floor and talked away about all manner of things. I was perfectly at ease with them, and even noticed that I was establishing some sort of authority as they began, instinctively, to defer to my superior rank. The Australian, the most vocal of the three, seemed worried.

'Any idea what they're going to do with us now?'

'Difficult to say,' I replied. 'These are bad times, and the Germans hate our guts. We've been smashing their country to bits and killing an awful lot of them... it's not impossible that we could find ourselves dangling from a lamp-post.'

I saw their open-mouthed astonishment. Remembering what I had seen myself in Dortmund, I went on.

'Sorry, but it does happen, you know. The *Krauts* call us terror flyers, and regard us as war criminals. It's tough titty if you come down anywhere near the target area. The Geneva Convention goes out of the window. No, I suppose we're the lucky ones. We are at least in the hands of the military, and more use to them than dead bodies. I reckon the worst that can happen will be at their blasted interrogation centre, which we have to go through before getting to a POW camp. Just remember what we were told at briefing about the place; then I'm sure it'll be all right.'

Before I could say more, the cell door was unlocked and thrown open, and in came armed soldiers, who noisily set about getting us ready to leave. With our hands clasped over our heads, we were pushed and prodded upstairs into the building's foyer, to be handcuffed and made to stand in line while an Army *Gefreiter* dealt with our departure documents. When everything was ready, we were marched across the street and into the railway station, struggling through a crowd which was, if anything, larger than before, and just as hostile. This time, thank goodness, our guards kept everyone at a distance.

A train was waiting in the station. We were placed in one end of an open compartment which had been set aside for us. The blinds were pulled down and we were made to sit at attention, each facing a guard, and told emphatically, in German, not to move or speak. The train pulled out after a few minutes, on its scheduled run to Frankfurt. We were uncomfortable, to say the least. Little was done at first to ease the tension between ourselves and the guards. Soon, however, our handcuffs were removed and, with this, our Australian friend responded by offering cigarettes to the soldiers. His single packet of Craven A was immediately confiscated, and the contents shared out amongst the soldiers.

It was clear that none of the soldiers understood English. Their conversation was strangely friendly, and had little to do with the war. Both Jones and I understood them well, but played our part in shrugging shoulders to indicate that we did not. They were particularly interested in Jones, because of the damage to his face, and the blood which had seeped through the leg of his trousers from a wound which should have been attended to hours earlier. However, apart from looking at the ugly gash, they did nothing, but left us to talk among ourselves. Soon, our only topic of conversation was food. We wondered when, if ever, we would be fed.

Later in the morning, the guards fed themselves from pre-packed cardboard cartons, letting us sit there, mouths watering, watching them devour sausage, sauerkraut and biscuit, washed down with strong-smelling beer. Happily, not long after this torture, the train stopped at a main railway station. Our handcuffs were replaced, and we were taken to the station waiting-room, where we spent the best part of an hour, again the subjects of abuse and hostility from curious onlookers. At last, to our great relief, we were escorted out of the station and taken to a closed lorry, parked at the station entrance. Once aboard, and completely shut in, we were driven off to make the long journey to *Dulag Luft* without a single stop.

CHAPTER FOURTEEN

What I remember best about our arrival at *Dulag Luft* was that, at last, we ate. I had slept for most of the journey, sitting jammed tight against Jones, both of us stinking of body odours and drying serge battledress. On arrival, we went through the necessary reception procedure and were then taken to a hut, set up as some sort of field kitchen. Like starving animals, we bolted a thick turnip and swede soup, in which floated bits of some sort of meat, with chunks of rye bread, and drank a beverage which tasted vaguely like coffee. We were watched all the time and, when the meal was finished, were taken away and locked into cells for the night.

Although we slept on a concrete floor, we passed a reasonably comfortable night, and were awakened by guards stamping along the corridor outside, bellowing: ' *'raus! 'raus!*' Our door was unlocked, and we were rooted out and hurried away to make our ablutions. Then we went directly to a mess hall for another meal of soup, bread and *Ersatzkaffee.* Afterwards, and to my great delight, I was able to have a tepid shower and a good scrub with carbolic soap. My clothes were taken away for cleansing and, wrapped in a blanket, I was led away to be examined by a doctor. In passable English, he asked questions about my general health, and then moved on to personal queries about my place of birth, where I was stationed and how things were going in England. There was little doubt that the interrogation process was beginning and, no doubt, the next thing would be the bogus Red Cross form.

And so it was, presented in a most natural way during my first interview with a middle-aged *Oberleutnant,* who spoke perfect English in a soft, charming and cultured voice. He went carefully through the preliminaries up to the actual presentation of the form for me to sign. This was a master at work, and I knew full well that, to avoid the disclosure of any information, I had to keep quiet. I had already told him that I was 102845 Flying Officer James Paterson OD, and this was the only information I wrote on the Red Cross form. I handed it over and waited for his reaction.

'You are being very foolish, young man,' he said quietly. 'All I have been trying to do is to help you... you must know full well that your loved ones have already been told you are 'Missing In Action' and, most likely by now, you have been posted as 'Missing Believed Killed.' This form merely tells the International Red Cross of your whereabouts, and your people will know, in a matter of a few days, that eventually you will return safely from this wretched war. If you do not complete the form, it will be many months before any word gets through officially to England ... if indeed, it does at all.'

I said nothing, and simply stared at him. He rang a bell, a guard appeared, and I was taken away. Next, I was locked in a cell already occupied by two aircrew. They introduced themselves. One, who said he was a Flight Lieutenant, drew us together and, in a low voice, warned that we should be on our guard because the cell could well have hidden microphones, and it would be best if we made a thorough search of the place. The other, a Warrant Officer pilot, wearing the ribbon of the Distinguished Flying Medal and what I recognised as a pre-war campaign medal for service on the North-West Frontier, nodded his agreement. Our search of the cell, which included the checking of the lights, the wood stripping and the wainscoting, disclosed nothing.

'I'm pretty sure this place is clean,' said the Flight Lieutenant. 'Even so, we should keep our voices down. Better still, let's sit together in the middle of the room away from the door and window, and have a good old natter.'

It was clear that this would be the first test of my credibility. I thought it best to take the initiative.

'How long have you been here?' I asked.

The Warrant Officer looked at me and miserably shook his head, but the Flight Lieutenant answered, 'Not too long. This is my second week.'

'Does this interrogation, or whatever it is, go on the whole time?'

'No, not at all. Only a couple of days, from what I can gather. They soon get fed up, and leave us alone. Then, like me, it is just a case of waiting around until they find a suitable prison camp. By the way, when were you shot down?'

I told them my cover story and then, each in turn, we gave some idea of how we had arrived at *Dulag Luft*. The conversation then broadened into general and personal views of how the war was going, family matters and reminiscences of life in our particular parts of Britain. I found myself resenting the Flight Lieutenant's somewhat irritating and patronising manner. He kept dwelling on details, often repeating a question, and asking about such things as morale at Feltwell, my supposed station. Other questions followed: could I confirm the climbing power ratings for the Lancaster B1; was Bob Carter still commanding 150 at Pocklington?; was it just a rumour that crews were no longer volunteering for the Pathfinders?'

This man was dominating the discussion and, for some reason, directing all his questions at me, probably because the Warrant Officer clearly did not want to join in. This was certainly not merely a cross-examination of me and my background, but an obvious attempt to glean intelligence information, and it was not difficult to deduce that I had been put together with the Warrant Officer and a 'stool pigeon'. I found it hard not to smile. I could, of course, have carried on and led him a merry dance, with highly imaginative answers to his particular questions, but there was the Warrant Officer to consider. So, from then on, I did not answer a single direct question, and did my best to steer the Flight Lieutenant's interest towards the Warrant Officer. Then, thankfully, the other two were taken away, and I was left alone for the rest of the day.

The next morning, after my usual wash and scrub in the communal ablutions, I was taken under guard, and left in a larger cell together with five aircrew. The *Oberleutnant* this time interrogated us as a group, putting us at ease with his charming manner, wheaten biscuits and more *Ersatzkaffee*. The general drift of conversation, sparked by the interrogator, was towards simple generalities. There was some response from the others to his gentle urging, particularly from a very young and nervous rear-gunner who, as an only child, desperately wanted his mother to know that he was safe and well. I kept quiet the whole time and, after a while, except for the rear-gunner, we were taken back to my cell. There we spent the rest of the morning swapping stories, which gave me the opportunity to learn even more RAF slang.

We were released from the cell for lunch and a welcome change of routine. This time we ate in what must have been a permanent mess hall, in which were packed about thirty or forty aircrew, mostly British. There were also some Canadians, a few Australians in their dark blue battledress, and even a New Zealander. I saw Brown in this crowd, arguing across a table with a Canadian, and evidently getting the better of the exchange. There was no sign of either Smith or Jones.

I sensed that the interrogation had come to an end after the third day. No longer did I spend my time in the cells, or being taken somewhere to be interviewed. I was moved into a barrack block and given a bunk, together with scores of exasperated aircrew. We spent most of our time penned in this block, where we bided our time playing games with makeshift cards, talking about everything under the sun, or just lounging and sleeping on our bunks. The weather had become settled and warm, and we eagerly awaited our daily release from the hut to exercise outside. Fortunately, we were reasonably well-fed, taking our meals in a large mess, twice a day.

I was certainly learning a lot from the British. I knew that I fitted in easily, and felt there were no doubts about me. On the other hand, as a German, I found it difficult to accept or understand most of what I had to listen to. I was annoyed and baffled by the strange superior attitude shown to the guards, and to *Dulag Luft* itself, as well as by the ridicule of the German people in general and what had been achieved by the Third *Reich*. At times it was difficult for me to keep my mouth shut, especially when someone was confidently predicting the inevitability of the British winning the war. Where did this cocksure arrogance come from? I had always thought there was much in common between our two nations. At school, I had heard much about our German cousins; and had there not been a German family on the British throne for more than two hundred years?

I had to conclude that much of the difference came from the peculiarities of British life, from their rigid social system with its various types of schooling. I had to smile at references to 'playing the game' and 'being a good sport', when their soldiers could turn tail and run as they had at Dunkirk, in Norway, in Greece and now in North Africa. And then there was so much talk about a decisive Battle of Britain. If there had been such a battle, then who had lost it? Certainly not the *Luftwaffe*. I damned well knew; I had been there.

I was, of course, circumspect at all times, especially when caught up in conversation, and usually listened more than I spoke. I made contact with Jones, who was housed in the next barrack block, and he confided that all was well; in fact even his bruises and cuts were being treated. Smith and Brown, as Sergeants, had been segregated from us, but I did see them once in the distance, playing a game of football with a bundle of rags being used as the ball.

Then, during our sixth night of captivity, a disturbing incident occurred. I had been trying to get to sleep when two RAF officers came to my bunk, and asked me to follow them. I asked why, and was told that they needed my advice. My immediate inclination was to remain where I was. However, there was authority and deadly seriousness in their manner, so I accompanied them to the end of the block, where there was a small storeroom. We squeezed in, and seated ourselves around a small table placed against the wooden wall. A candle was lit, and I saw facing me a somewhat elderly, bald-headed Squadron Leader with a worried expression on his face. He whispered to me, 'I'm sorry to surprise you like this, Paterson, but we need your help. You don't know who we are, but we are probably the oldest inhabitants in this wretched place. Why, we don't know but, in my case, it may be because I'm the most senior officer to come through here for some time. In the case of John Rogers, it is probably because he speaks such excellent German. I suppose the Krauts find us useful in helping them run the place.'

He pointed to a Flight Lieutenant in the half-light, whom I recognised as someone who had had much to say in a heated discussion about the *Gestapo,* and what the British thought was happening in the so-called concentration camps.

'John and I are kept very much in the centre of things. We have a good idea of German routine and intentions and, now and then, we are called in to intercede or try to explain why certain types refuse to conform, particularly those who will not accept captivity, and are always trying to escape. But, to get to the point, I'm sure you were told, back at the squadron, about the various tricks the Germans use to get information from us.'

He leant towards me and, in doing so, accidentally knocked over the candle, which fell to the floor and went out. Rogers fumbled around, retrieved it and relit it. The Squadron Leader collected his thoughts and carried on.

'Yes ... dirty tricks there are, and here they're using them all the time, so it is my duty to warn you about them. We have been told... loquacious Eberhardt let it slip when we had a drink with him... that their most successful trick is the use of stool pigeons. We had always thought these characters were German nationals, or Quislings who had taken up the German cause, but now we have good reason to suspect they may be using our own people. Dirty traitors, if that's the case.'

Both must have surely noticed my shocked expression in the semi-darkness. I instinctively gasped, yet tried hard not to show the fear I felt at apparently having been found out. My mind tried to tackle the problem of getting away from the two of them, and making contact with the *Kommandant*. But, luckily, the Squadron Leader just went on talking.

'You came here with a Flying Officer Cameron, did you not?' He held my eyes as I nodded. 'Well ... can you tell us anything about him? We have noticed that you often talk with him.'

Thank God, I thought. It's not me they suspect, but that poor fool Jones. I had difficulty in not showing my utter sense of relief. I composed myself and replied quietly.

'The first time I ever saw Cameron was when we found ourselves together in the back of a lorry on our way here. Like me, he had been trying to evade for a few days, and get across the Maas. I can tell you that he must have been knocked about by someone. He had a nasty gash in his leg, and his face was bruised. Apart from that, I don't know where he came down or what he had been flying. He was already in the lorry when they picked me up.'

The Squadron Leader was puzzled. He stroked his chin, 'Did you ever get the idea he wasn't a bomber type? Was he on his guard with you? Was he worried, anxious? Did he say anything which seemed out of place?'

I thought hard: I had to be careful with my reply. I now knew that all was not well and that I had to make sure I was not suspected of having had any contact with him.

'No ... he seemed as normal as anyone could be after being shot down. He was a bit concerned about his injuries but, otherwise, all seemed well. But then, Sir, how do you define a Bomber Command man? We come in all shapes and sizes, and from all walks of life. You have the regulars, like yourself, and then you have the sprogs - those just out of OTU. I even had a passenger from Group with me when I was shot down. He had only come along to see how the war was going.'

The two whispered together. I got the impression that the Flight Lieutenant was the dominant character making the decisions. He appeared to have heard enough, and wanted to go, but was held back by the Squadron Leader, who had something more to say.

'What if we were to confide in you something which worries us greatly, something which you must keep to yourself for the moment, until we decide what has to be done?'

I replied at once. 'Naturally, I would respect your confidence. Of course I would say nothing.'

The Squadron Leader lowered his voice still further. 'Well, we have reason to believe that our Flying Officer Cameron is bogus. One of the latest arrivals, a second-tour man, has told us that he is positive Cameron is the same man he served with back in 1940, when they were together on 142 in France, flying Battles. Apparently, during the retreat, when 142 was wiped out, our friend Cameron disappeared. But they heard, when the squadron reformed, that he was a prisoner in Germany. British Intelligence later discovered, believe it or not, that he had gone over to the Germans, and was actually working with Haw Haw. And then, to make things worse, he was even suspected of working here for a while as a stool pigeon. If all this is true, then what on earth is he doing back here again? What have the Germans in mind this time? From what we can see from his present behaviour, a second tour as a stool pigeon seems most unlikely.'

I had to say something. 'This is absolutely unbelievable. How could anyone do this?' But I had to know more. 'Why do you think he is not working as a stool pigeon again?'

They conversed again. This time it was the Flight Lieutenant who spoke.

'Everyone who comes in here is carefully watched. Cameron has been with us for almost a week, and it has been noticeable that he seldom speaks to anyone, nor does he take part in any of the contrived discussions arranged by the Germans. That is not the way they would use a stool pigeon - they have to make contact with people. Cameron does exactly the opposite. He shuns company. No, if this man is a traitor, as he seems to be, then there must be some damned good reason for him to come back here. It is our duty to find out what it is, and this is why we want you to help. We want you carefully to question Cameron, to speak to him about his Bomber Command background, and try to catch him out. We will contact you, like this, every night from now on.'

Nothing more was said. The candle was snuffed out, and we left the little room and quietly crept back between the two-tier bunks with their snoring occupants. After checking that all was clear outside, the two left, locking the door behind them, no doubt using a stolen key.

I returned to my bunk in a very worried state. I had to do something, and quickly, or there could be trouble in getting Jones safely away from the place. Somehow, I had to make contact with the *Kommandant* as soon as possible, but it had to be done circumspectly, making sure I gave the British no idea that I was involved with Jones. Kreis had told us that our stay at *Dulag Luft* would not last for more than a week, and we were already into our sixth night. I therefore decided that there was no need to take immediate action, and risk a commotion by being caught outside, trying to reach the *Kommandant*. What I had to do would be better left until morning when, in any case, we might well be on our way back to Berlin. I finally fell asleep, after reasoning that the British would themselves do nothing about the bogus Flying Officer Cameron until they had received the awaited report from me.

The usual explosion of noise made by the thumping of jackboots and rifle butts on the wooden floor and the harsh shouts of, ''*raus! 'raus!*'', woke me from a deep sleep. After a hurried wash and shave, we were paraded outside for the daily roll call. It was an altogether miserable morning, and we stood huddled in rows, without any protection whatsoever against the steady rain being blown into our faces by a strong westerly wind. We were impatient to get the process over and done with, so that we could get back to our meagre breakfast, when at least we would be able to dry out.

Our well-protected guards seemed to enjoy our discomfort, and took their time with the head-count. After two attempts, it was accepted as being correct. We stamped our feet, and made ribald remarks about the delay in our dismissal. Then the guard commander was handed a piece of paper and, calling us to attention, read from it the names of those who were to leave that morning to go to a *Stalag Luft*. Ten names were on the list, and mine was one of them. The parade was dismissed, but the ten of us were ordered to remain where we were. We were then marched to the administration office where, to my surprise, we were told that we would be on our way within the hour. We were documented, given a cursory medical check which amounted to little more than a look at our teeth and down our throats, issued with a blanket for use as a topcoat, and given a packet of food to be eaten on the journey.

There were other small groups waiting outside to be dealt with. I tried to see whether Smith, Jones and Roberts were in this exodus, but there was no sign of them. I was, however, immensely relieved to know that Kreis had kept his promise, that the make-believe of our stay at *Dulag Luft* was coming to an end, and that, very soon, the four of us would be reunited back in Berlin. Our group was the first to leave, packed into a lorry with armed guards at either side of the tailboard. The end tarpaulin was mercifully strapped up, so that we were able to see something of the world outside as we moved off in the pouring rain.

I had expected that we would be going to the railway station at Frankfurt but, instead, we were driven steadily for the best part of an hour, until we came to an Army camp. To our relief, we were herded into a mess hall and reasonably well fed on hot sausage, sauerkraut and a heavy suet pudding smothered in custard. Then, wonder of wonders, we were each offered a cigarette. We had been the subjects of much curiosity while eating our breakfast. Soldiers were coming and going around us, very interested in a first sight of their enemies. Every now and then, one or more would voice his real feelings, and have to be cautioned and sometimes restrained by our guards, who were sitting with us. It was after one such outburst about *verdammte Terrorflieger* that I noticed the arrival of a junior *SS* officer, who looked vaguely familiar. I then remembered that he was one of Kreis's staff.

It was time for us to move on. We were shepherded from the mess hall to a small convoy of *Kübelwagen*, drawn up with hoods in place against the driving rain. Our group of ten was split into singles and pairs, and I was not surprised when I found my *SS* friend alongside me as driver. Ours was the last vehicle in the convoy as we left the Army base and, when we reached an *Autobahn*, we turned onto it, heading north, while the remainder went southwards, presumably back to Frankfurt.

I appreciated the lengths which Kreis had gone to with this deception. Presumably, the same pantomime was being played with the other three, neatly removing any suspicion that four play-actors had been performing at *Dulag Luft* for the past week. The journey northwards eventually finished at Wildenrath, where I was much relieved to be able to get out of my filthy, damp battledress, scrub myself clean, and then wallow in a hot bath. My RAF uniform and everything else British was taken away to be cleaned. I dressed myself once again in *SS* uniform, and that evening was driven back to Berlin.

CHAPTER FIFTEEN

Smith and Brown were already waiting in Kreis's outer office when I arrived for the debriefing of our experiences at *Dulag Luft*. Kreis arrived soon afterwards, nodded a greeting and, without saying a word, went into his office, closing the door behind him. We waited for about twenty minutes before we were summoned. We went in, paid our respects, and took our usual seats in front of the desk. But, this time, there was something amiss. Normally, there would have been at least a greeting of some sort but, today, Kreis just stood silent before us, his face wearing a solemn look. He regarded each of us in turn, and it was then I realised Thomas Jones was not with us.

'Gentlemen, I was careful to point out at the very start that, when your training was finished, only then would you be asked to face any danger. I said that you would be able to learn much about our intended project at no risk whatsoever to yourselves and that, at the end, you would be free to decide whether you wanted to join us.'

For a moment or two he seemed lost for words.

'What I did not realise at the time was that, even during your training, you could be subjected to danger. Sadly, it is now only too clear that, despite all my experience, I have miscalculated and made a regrettable mistake. I sincerely regret what I have to tell you, something for which I am entirely responsible. Whilst you have been in *Dulag Luft,* we have kept you under constant and careful surveillance the whole time. This was done by experts of whom you had no knowledge. Everything you did was monitored, and daily reports were sent back to me. This procedure was maintained to the very end, and I am sure you noticed the discreet way in which you were each brought back.'

'Gentlemen, I am truly sorry, but it is my painful duty to tell you that last night, Jones was found hanged in a storeroom in his barrack block. The British tell us that he committed suicide, but we have reason to think otherwise.'

Our gasps of astonishment were audible. The news had stunned us. I felt a sense of guilt which almost overpowered me. Jones' fate had been in my hands, and I had done nothing to prevent it. I looked up at

Kreis, who saw my distress and said, 'I think it is only fair to tell you that Jones had already disappeared by the time his name was called for him to leave with you. What had happened to him, and where he had been, was a mystery to us. We made an extensive search for him at once and then, almost as if it were stage-managed, the Senior British Officer told us that they had found Jones, dead. We do not believe it was a case of suicide. We think he was killed by his fellow countrymen.'

Smith jumped to his feet with a terrified expression on his face.

'Jesus Christ, that's going to happen to me as well, isn't it,' he whined. 'They'll rumble me for sure.' His voice rose. 'I can't go on with this caper... it's too bloody dangerous!'

'Sit down, you fool,' snapped Kreis. 'Calm yourself. We shall deal fully with what concerns us in due course, when we have more information. In the meantime, I want you to spend the rest of the day preparing your reports and letting me know what you have learned from this experience.'

In a private discussion with Kreis that evening, I confessed to my part in Jones' death. I told him of the alarming meeting with the two RAF officers, and why I had decided to wait before I tried to contact the *Kommandant*, just long enough for Jones to be killed. Kreis assured me that if he had been faced with the same problem, he would have done exactly as I had. Had I acted prematurely, I might well have jeopardised my own position. As far as Kreis was concerned, the exercise had been a success for Brown and myself, and had also helped to confirm the weakness and unsuitability of Smith.

The next day, Smith reported to Kreis, formally expressing grave doubts about the feasibility of the operation. He was not going to put his life at risk for something he did not understand. He said bluntly that he could not cope, and asked to be returned to the British *Freikorps*. Kreis cautioned him on his oath not to reveal a word about his recent activities, and then agreed that he could leave. Kreis later told me that a most serious view would be taken of Smith's future - if he had one at all. He was certainly not to be returned to the safety of the British *Freikorps,* which was nothing more than a small propaganda unit. More likely, he would find himself on the Eastern Front or, perhaps better still, he would be imprisoned until our operation was completed, and then handed over to the British, who could no doubt hang him for treason.

I had never understood why the *Gestapo* had tried to employ the Englishmen in their plan. As far as I was concerned, their departure had tidied up a potentially dangerous situation. We had to use properly motivated and absolutely committed people, and these could only be found among steadfast Germans, prepared to do their very best to serve the Fatherland. For my part, I had already decided to work with the *Gestapo*. If I was unable to fight the RAF in the air then, surely, I could do no better than to oppose them by destroying the means whereby they could return to kill our women and children.

Every night, the British relentlessly dropped their bombs somewhere in Germany. A truly brilliant raid on the Ruhr dams resulted in more than a thousand workers being drowned as they slept. In an horrific attack on Wuppertal, more than three thousand hapless civilians had been turned into cinders, in a fire-storm fed by a rain of heavy phosphorous bombs. The promised 'whirlwind of retribution' was blowing all around us but, thank God, our people were bearing up well, and doing their very best to survive and carry on working. The British bombing had strengthened their resolve to win through, and nothing was going to break their spirit.

When we met Kreis at our first meeting after the break-up of the team, he was ill at ease, and by no means his usual composed self. He spoke scathingly about the British renegades, and admitted that he had made a mistake by trying to use them, if for no other reason than to Anglicise us. He had always known of Smith's criminal record, yet there had seemed some merit in using him. Now he had the unwelcome job of disposing of him. He was genuinely sorry about Jones, who had been a complex, well educated man, honestly believing in the future of National Socialism. He had had a gentle nature and should have been left to work at the Foreign Office rather than being compelled to undertake something beyond his capabilities. After these revelations, Kreis seemed to pull himself together. He brightened, and changed the subject.

'So, my friends, the time has come for me to tell you that your training is finished. I know that you have both benefited from your stay at *Dulag Luft,* and that you were accepted by the British and the Canadians. In your case, Wilhelm, the British thought so much of you that they wanted you to take a hand in running their affairs, and... by the way... those officers you met, who probably killed Jones, have been sent to our special camp at Sachsenhausen, with all the time in the world to reflect on what they have done.'

He offered us each one of his cherished cheroots. Relaxed and more his usual self, went to the drinks cabinet. 'I think it is now time for us to make a start on what really matters,' he said as he took out the usual Calvados and primed three glasses.

'First, I want properly to introduce you both. There is no need for the masquerade to continue any longer. *Oberleutnant* Wilhelm Rath, may I present *Unteroffizier* Conrad Weindl.' We shook hands warmly. 'As you will both remember, you are not bound to us, either by regulation or by oath, but now is the time for me to ask whether you have decided to help us.' He looked intently at us, smiling all the while. 'I somehow have the feeling that my words are unnecessary. You have already given me enough evidence of your intentions. Is that not so?'

I spoke at once. 'Indeed so Herr *Obersturmbannführer*. We have no doubts. We both wish to serve... and to make a start as soon as possible.'

Kreis was delighted. 'And so you shall,' he said. 'Excellent, my friends, excellent. Now, let us join in wishing every success to Kondor.' We raised our glasses and drained them.

There was nothing more to be usefully done in Berlin which, in any case, was far removed from where we could be expected to make a start with Kondor. The next day, we travelled by road to Butzweilerhof, a small grass airfield on the edge of the Ruhr valley, not far from Köln. It was there that Kreis thought we would be in the best position to move quickly, when the right opportunities presented themselves, and to adopt the identities of our intended British counterparts before, as Kreis jokingly put it - 'the bodies were cold.'

Weindl and I were comfortably housed in a small farmhouse on the edge of the airfield, and looked after by a farmer's wife who managed a smallholding with the help of her twelve-year-old son. Her husband was somewhere in Russia, a prisoner with the rest of the 6th Army, and she had not heard from him for many months. She felt that she had every reason to fear the worst. We waited. Kreis arranged for us to receive regular information on bomber operations, and went carefully over the many possibilities of what could happen at the start of Kondor. It would begin as though we had been shot down in a British aircraft. We would go through the procedures just as the enemy aircrew would have been briefed to do by their own intelligence officers.

Our arrival on the scene was to be as authentic as possible, in case we were spotted immediately by the Resistance people. We would parachute from one of our own machines, flying under the home-going bomber stream. After landing, we would bury our parachutes and Mae Wests, and move away as quickly as possible. No matter how unrealistic it might seem at times, we would keep resolutely on the move, and develop a plan to get well into the Netherlands, Belgium or France. On the way, we might be lucky and meet someone actually on the lookout for us, although it was more likely that we would take a chance by making a careful contact ourselves. Once on the escape route, we would allow ourselves to be controlled at all times by the enemy. We would obey their orders implicitly, all the way down the route, until we reached our destination in a neutral country. Then, and only then, would we make contact with the German authorities.

Kreis saw difficulties in our being able to retain the information which we would gather en route. Somehow, we had to remember names, addresses and locations. There would be no means of contact with the *Gestapo*, and such facts would best be committed to memory. It would be extremely dangerous to write anything down. However, once we were in a neutral country, the *Gestapo* could act at once and, together, we would retrace our steps from safe house to safe house, picking up the enemy as we went along.

We waited for days for something to happen, while the bad weather forced a lull in the British raids. We did not leave the farmhouse, preferring to spend our time reading, studying, and questioning each other about details of the RAF. Our disguises were more or less complete. I had chosen keep the pair of flying boots I had worn at *Dulag Luft,* while Weindl now had a pair of the earlier jackboot type, made for comfortable walking. Our escape kits were in place in the top left hand pockets of our battledress, and we both had fly-button and other miniature compasses sewn into the uniform. All that remained was the addition of rank and aircrew badges, which would come from the bodies of the two Britishers we were expecting to impersonate.

There was a false start during our fourth night at Butzweilerhof, when Kreis got us out of bed to go with him to the scene of a crash not far away. It was daylight when we arrived at a farm on the outskirts of Leutzen, where parts of a large aircraft had come down among the out buildings, killing a cow and a number of pigs. People were combing through the wreckage, and the *Luftwaffe* police had already taken charge. The badly smashed body of a pilot was found, mixed with the remains of the cow, and the legless body of a navigator lay stretched out in the farmyard. The rest of what appeared to have once been a Lancaster was spread as far as the eye could see.

As we walked around, we were surprised to be shown the body of another navigator and, in the end, the remains or mutilated bodies of no less than nine enemy aircrew. The bits and pieces of what could only have been a second four-engined aircraft came to light, suggesting a mid-air collision between the two, not a rare occurrence among the vast number of machines now being used by Bomber Command. Although it was quite impossible to know from which aircraft or squadron the victims had come, we pointed out to Kreis that, at least, we were sure of the identities of a pilot and a navigator, as confirmed by their identity discs. Surely, this was enough to enable us to make a start. Kreis, however, was adamant. There was too much confusion and doubt surrounding this crash. He would not allow unnecessary risks to be taken. Our assumed identities had to be as convincing as possible. So we returned to Butzweilerhof to await a better opportunity.

While we fretted at the farmhouse, the RAF raids continued apace. Kreis kept us informed of these happenings with exhaustive digests from *Luftwaffe Hauptquartier*. From one of these, we were able to deduce that the Halifax and Lancaster which had collided near Leutzen had been on a raid to Dusseldorf in which 800 bombers had killed more than 1,000 people, and made tens of thousands homeless. Bochum had been the next target, followed by heavy blows against Oberhausen, Köln and Freidrichshafen. Then they had struck at Krefeld, and had lost a large number of aircraft when our night-fighters had made the most of the excellent visibility provided by the full moon period.

The following morning we were eating breakfast when, through the kitchen window, we saw Kreis's staff car speeding up to the house. He rushed in, and addressed us excitedly. 'This is it. I am sure we have the right candidates this time. They are in a Wellington down somewhere in the Eiffel, between Duren and Monschau. Apparently, this lot lost their way home and, from what I am told, they can provide everything we want.'

We left as quickly as possible, and drove hard southwards into the wooded Eiffel, calling first at the *Gau* office in the picturesque town of Monschau. There we were told of the exact position of the crash, which was marked for us on our maps. Five bodies had already been recovered and, if we wished, these could be seen in the town's mortuary. Kreis thought that such a pleasure could wait until after we had examined the crashed aircraft. It had become a lovely summer's day, with cloudless blue skies and a light breeze. The drive up into the forests towards the crash site was quite enjoyable. After about thirty minutes we were stopped by a forest keeper, who told us the wreckage was about a kilometre from the mountain road, and that he could take us there. We left our car and made our way on foot up through the trees, to find the Wellington had crash-landed on the slope of a hill, cutting a swathe through a newly planted stand of pines.

The aircraft was, surprisingly, still in one piece. We searched for anti-aircraft, machine gun or cannon strikes, but found nothing. I then noticed that the wooden starboard propeller, two blades of which had snapped off in the landing, had been feathered. This, no doubt, had had something to do with the cause of the crash. The crew must have been in dire trouble, trying to get home on the one remaining underpowered engine.

Kreis just stood smoking and watching us as we examined the wreck. I was able to get into the crushed pilot's cockpit, where I worked the controls and memorised the instruments. I could see that the propeller had indeed been deliberately feathered, and that the Graviner system had been operated to deal with an engine fire. Weindl spent some time in the wireless operator's compartment and found, and took away, the navigator's log. I could not decide if the Wellington was a Mark 3 or 10, but noted its tail number, HF 589, and the squadron code, AS-M. It took about thirty minutes to complete our examination. We left, walking back down to the road, carrying two undamaged chest-type parachutes, which had been found still strapped into their racks. The journey back to Monschau was downhill most of the way, and we made good time.

I was not at all prepared for what I saw when we reached the mortuary. No doubt Kreis had left some instructions, but surely not that the corpses should be lined up as though ready for inspection. Each had been stripped of clothes, and was laid out on a stretcher with the bloody, blue-toned face staring at the ceiling, arms folded over the pale, naked body which, for some strange reason, had its legs splayed. There was a pervasive smell of carbolic, which just failed to hide the stronger smell of death. The clothes and equipment of each corpse had been arranged at the head of each stretcher; leather helmet, Mae West, parachute harness, flying boots and neatly folded battledress. At the foot were arranged the shirt, underclothes, escape kit and, here and there, a few personal possessions. The green and brown identity discs had been placed, faces up, on the bare chest of each body.

Kreis was as taken aback as we were at the sight of this grotesque parade. Holding his handkerchief to his face, he ordered the mortuary attendant and two fascinated onlookers to leave. When they had gone, and the door was closed, he tried to apologise.

'I am sorry for this awful display but, at least, it makes it easier for us to make a start on what we must do... and as quickly as possible. Honestly, my friends, I had no idea they would look so dreadful and stink so badly.'

Still with his handkerchief to his nose, he went to the first stretcher, on which lay the body of the pilot. He picked up the identity discs, and examined them.

'Just what we want. This is ready-made for you, Wilhelm, 144827 G.H.Harrison... and he was a Roman Catholic, just as you are.'

He moved on down the line, studying each set of identity discs in turn. At the end, he held one set up and called to Weindl, 'What a stroke of luck. There is even a Canadian here.' He bent down to examine the battledress. 'Well, well ... not bad,' he said. 'You are still a Flight Sergeant, Conrad, but you can forget about being a wireless-operator. This one was a bomb-aimer, and so shall you be. Good. You are now a Scottish Canadian. MacDonald is your name and you, too, are a Roman Catholic.'

The decisions that mattered had been made by Kreis, as usual. He had come prepared. He produced a small pair of scissors, and carefully removed the whistles, badges of rank, brevets and the 'Canada' flashes from MacDonald's battledress. He then began to cut into a battledress waistband. 'I have a surprise for you both', he said. 'Yes, here it is'. He extracted a small envelope, opened it and held up what looked like two passport photographs. 'You have to admire the British. These photographs of this particular hero were taken in civilian clothes to enable the escape organisation more easily to forge the necessary *laissez-passer* papers. They are stitched into the uniform of every airman who flies over here.'

He got up, his work finished. He collected all the identity discs and escape kits, and some of the underclothing. He told us to follow him, and we left, ignoring the mortuary officials and a couple of *Luftwaffe* policemen who had been waiting outside.

On the way back to Butzweilerhof we talked about every possible aspect of the crash. Our prime need, of course, was to learn as much as we could about the two airmen we were about to impersonate. Harrison, the pilot, had been a Pilot Officer, which typed him as probably being inexperienced, most likely at the start of his first tour of operations. Had he had been well into the tour, he would have been at least a Flying Officer, unless on a second tour after having been commissioned from the ranks. However, with the possible exception of the Canadian, the other three crew members had been sergeants, which seemed to suggest what the British called a 'sprog' crew. A quick telephone call by Kreis on our return to Butzweilerhof confirmed that the squadron using the code letters we had noted was the newly-formed No. 166, based at Kirmington in Lincolnshire. It had been operational only for the past five months.

Everything known about No. 166 Squadron was sent to us by teleprinter from *Luftwaffe Hauptquartier*, including details of the airfield at Kirmington, and that at Snaith, from which many of the aircrew had come to form the new squadron. The last known Commanding Officer was a Wing Commander E.J. Carter, who seemed to be something of an extrovert, a very experienced bomber pilot who did little 'by the book'. The squadron had been continually in action since January, and had suffered heavy losses. The turnover of crews must have been very high and, probably, morale on the squadron was correspondingly low. The Wellington was a Mark 10, the latest version, but by present Bomber Command standards, second rate and vulnerable.

Our battledresses were brought up-to-date. Mine now bore the thin blue stripe of a Pilot Officer, and Harrison's pilot's brevet. Weindl's bore the crown and stripes of a Canadian Flight Sergeant and a bombardier's half-wing brevet. Rescue whistles had been sewn on, escape kits buttoned down in pockets, and our two passport photographs set in place. Everything about us was British, even our underclothes, which Kreis had taken from the dead at Monschau. We were now as ready as we ever could be.

We did not have long to wait. Early in the morning of 24th June 1943, we were told to stand by. The weather over the Ruhr was expected to be good enough for the British to bomb that night and, if they did, then we would be on our way.

I now began to feel tense for the first time since leaving Venlo. At last I was beginning to realise the enormity of the task I had so willingly accepted. Within an hour or so, I would submit myself to the unknown, in an adventure involving great risk and which, if I was honest with myself, could well bring about my death in a most dishonourable way. I supposed there was still time to back out but then, I reasoned, the task I was about to tackle was no more dangerous to life and limb than flying as a bomber or night-fighter pilot. More importantly, if we were successful, a great blow would have been struck for the Fatherland.

Early in the evening, we were told that the British were actually preparing for a raid, and that we should make ready to go. Fully accoutered, we sat down to a magnificent meal, personally organised by Kreis. I remember to this day the main course of venison, marinated in bay and basil, garnished with cherries, flamed in cognac, and served with a delightful claret. We ate, in fact we gorged ourselves, almost in silence. At the end, Kreis rose to wish us well. 'My dear friends,' he said, 'You have prepared yourselves in the best way possible. You are indeed well trained and properly equipped. Above all, you are infinitely superior to the British in your dedication to destroy something so harmful to our beloved Fatherland. There is nothing more I can do or say to help you, except to wish you every success and a safe return. As I know you airmen always say - *'Hals- und Beinbruck.'*

CHAPTER SIXTEEN

We were told at about 22.00 hours that the British were on their way, and that the target was most likely to be somewhere in the Ruhr. We put on our Mae Wests and parachute harnesses, and were driven out to a Junkers 52 which had flown in during the afternoon. Kreis went with us, arranging a link with Operations by field telephone. Just before 23.00 hours, he told us that the target was, once again, the unfortunate town of Wuppertal, and that it was already being marked by the British Pathfinders. He shook hands, and wished us 'Good Luck and God Speed'. We took our seats in the Junkers, and a dispatcher checked that our parachutes were properly clipped on and attached to the static line. The engines were started, and we taxied across the airfield to turn into wind and take off. As we climbed away on a northerly course, we could see the ever-brightening glow of the Ruhr barrage, the searchlights, and the fires.

The raid must have been at its climax when we settled down to cruise, at a height of about 1,000 metres, on a course parallel with the Rhine and more or less under the expected path of the returning bombers. After a while, the pilot began to orbit over an area which I guessed to be about twenty kilometres or so from the river. Suddenly, about 2,000 metres above us, it looked as though one of our night-fighters had made a kill. We could see the results of an explosion from which burning pieces of wreckage were descending. As we stared at the scene through the open exit door, the dispatcher drew our attention to the red warning light which had been switched on.

We struggled to our feet, and the dispatcher again checked harnesses, parachutes and static line connections before moving us towards the exit. The red light went out and a green one came on. Weindl was led to the jump position; as soon as he was given a pat on the shoulder, he jumped. I took his place, and was held there while the dispatcher checked his watch, counted off a full minute, then patted me on the shoulder, and

I too leaped into the darkness.

I landed in a small tree, and slithered slowly down its trunk to find myself actually standing on my feet, hands above my head, still holding the parachute shroud lines. Everything had happened so quickly. I had not jumped cleanly from the Junkers and, in my tumbling, the opening parachute pack had struck me hard in the face. I had been unable to see the approaching ground, and there had only been enough time for me to begin to control the wild oscillations I was making. Nonetheless, I was relieved that my first ever jump from an aircraft was over, and that I was down in one piece. I fumbled for the quick release buckle, which I turned to unlock before giving it a firm thump with the ball of my hand. As the parachute harness slid off, I sank to my knees and, for a while, knelt there, collecting my thoughts, as I recovered from the shock of the last few minutes.

I stayed motionless under the tree for some time, trying to come to grips with my situation. It was a beautiful starlit night. The air was fresh, and the only sounds were the rustling of the leaves above me. I checked my body for damage. There was sharp pain in the cheekbone under my left eye, and I found a small bleeding wound on the back of my right hand, which I wrapped with my handkerchief. I got up, stamped my feet, and walked around the tree, surveying the parachute canopy which completely covered it, making it appear like a giant mushroom.

The silence was suddenly broken by a dog barking, not far away. I had apparently landed near some sort of habitation, and immediately wondered it anyone had seen the Junkers and watched me descending. I could not take a chance of meeting the wrong person at this stage, and knew that I had to move away at once. Looking up at the parachute, it was clear that it would take an age to get it down to be hidden. No amount of tugging or pulling on the shroud lines would untangle it from the branches. There was no alternative but to leave it where it was, an ideal starting point for a search for me to be made, either by my own people or the enemy. As there was no point now in trying to hide my yellow Mae West, I took it off, threw it under the tree and set off, at a fair pace, away from the noise of the still barking dog. I hoped to cover some distance before dawn, when I knew that I would have to find somewhere to hide.

I travelled quietly and surprisingly easily through uncultivated countryside, dotted with clumps of bushes and brush, copses and small woods. After a while there were no further signs of habitation, and it took more than an hour before I came upon a road, narrow and badly maintained, yet lining up roughly with the course I was taking to the north west. I had no need to resort to the compass, as the way ahead could easily be determined by reference to Polaris, standing out clearly in the night sky.

I felt progressively better as I moved on. My mind had cleared, and I was now fully alert. The game was on, and Pilot Officer George Harrison was about to do his duty. He would do his best to return to his unit, just as ordered. At first light, I began to search for somewhere to hide. The RAF Intelligence officers suggested remote, impenetrable areas and, particularly if there was any sort of following search, lonely places such as would make it difficult even for dogs to track and enter. With this in mind, I left the road and headed for a small copse of pine with thick uncleared undergrowth between the young trees. I made sure that I was not leaving any sort of trail behind me as I got on my hands and knees and painfully burrowed my way into the copse under and through the tangle of brush and brambles. When well inside, I made myself as comfortable as possible, curled up, dozed for a while and then fell asleep.

I woke in absolute terror as I heard the ever-increasing roar of engines coming towards me. I shot up, the brambles tearing at my skin, utterly confused because I did not know where I was or what was happening. The noise rose to a thundering crescendo and, when I looked up in amazement, I could see the huge black underbelly of an aircraft with wheels and flaps down, obviously making an approach to land. I was now wide awake. I had evidently made my hiding place near the perimeter of an airfield, placing myself in a very difficult position: it would be impossible to emerge from the spot in broad daylight, as it was overlooked by the nearby road which led to the airfield.

Carefully and quietly, I set about improving my hide by burrowing down into the spongy leaf mould to make a shallow pit, over which I pulled the branches and tendrils of bushes and brambles. As I had hoped, no one had reason to approach the copse, even though, as I peered through my camouflage, I could see people and the occasional vehicle coming to and from the airfield. From the sounds of activity at the place, particularly when engines were run up, I estimated that I was about 500 metres away.

I was kept on the alert for most of the day. Reasonably confident that no one was likely to enter the copse because of its overgrown state, I moved out of my pit and went further in, towards its centre. There I found a small clearing between the trees, and established my headquarters. It was now early afternoon on a fine, warm summer's day. The sky was gloriously blue, fringed at high altitude with cirrus cloud, the herald, perhaps, of an approaching warm front. I had no idea of my exact location, although it seemed likely, from the types of aircraft I had seen flying overhead and into the airfield, that I could be somewhere among the night-fighter stations which I knew were strung along the Maas.

My hand had stopped bleeding, but I still had pain in my cheekbone, and my left eye was swollen. The problem now was that I was feeling decidedly unwell. I was being subjected to waves of pain and nausea, which came and went, but steadily increased in intensity. As the afternoon wore on, it became clear that I was badly constipated. This was certainly confirmed when I began to have griping stomach pains, which became so severe that I doubled up, and was forced to lie squirming on the ground. I feared that, if I did not soon void my bowels, I would burst. I had completely forgotten to plan for this basic daily duty, and was quite unprepared for what had to happen. After straining for what seemed an age, the distasteful problem was at last resolved in the bushes on the edge of the clearing, where I had no alternative but to clean myself with some broad sorrel leaves, found growing nearby. It had indeed been a salutary lesson, well and truly learned. Stuffing myself with Kreis's Venison à la Greque and good Black Forest cheese had not been a very sensible idea.

Thus relieved, and more or less myself again, I returned to the centre of the clearing, where I started to make an inventory of my possessions, laying them out, one by one, on the ground. Apart from my RAF navigator's watch, a penknife, and blood-stained handkerchief, everything else came from the escape kit. I had mixed feelings of exasperation and disgust when, upon opening the tin box, I found, neatly folded on top of the contents, six pieces of toilet paper. I had seen and examined quite a few escape kits during my training, and the contents of this one were complete. The two silk maps, between them, covered the Netherlands, Belgium and Northern France. I took out the water bottle, which I would fill as soon as I found water, and put the Halazone, Benzedrine and Horlicks tablets into my right top pocket. I did not think it necessary to take a stimulant, nor did I feel in the least hungry.

The inventory finished, I took off the top of my battledress, which I rolled and used as a pillow on a makeshift bed of leaves and small twigs, and settled down to relax in the sun. For a while, I pondered on what I should do when nightfall allowed me to leave my lair but, with little else to distract me, I began to doze and then slept. I awoke in the late afternoon, feeling well, and impatient to be on my way. I left the hide as soon as dusk fell, first heading away from the airfield for some distance, and then resuming my north westerly course. I had set myself a target to walk during the six or seven hours of darkness, and hoped to push on about 25 kilometres, which ought take me into Belgium, or perhaps the eastern end of the Netherlands. From the nature of the countryside around me, I knew I was clear of the Ardennes, and that was a point in my favour, because it would be rough going through that wooded paradise at night, and the chances of meeting anyone trying to help me would be remote indeed.

I soon had the airfield well behind me, although I heard the noise of aircraft taking off for quite some time. I walked on paths and lanes whenever possible, reasoning that, if anyone was looking for me, they would not be doing so in the open country. I also knew that I would very soon be in an area where those out at night, and defying the curfew, were either Belgians or Dutch up to no good, or our own people going about the business of getting to crash sites and rounding up shot-down aircrew.

After an hour or so of steady walking, the character of the countryside began to change, and I sensed a familiar look about the flat cultivated area of small farms and holdings. I filled my water bottle from a ditch, added a water-purifying tablet, and took a drink. As I was at last feeling hungry, I ate the four useless Horlicks tablets. From now on, it would be a case of having to live off the land or, in other words, steal my food.

Just after midnight, I lost the benefit of the stars for my navigation. The skies had clouded over, and I had to resort to using one of the miniature compasses from the escape kit. Not long afterwards, I heard the drone of many aircraft flying high overhead on the same course I was taking. I was once more under the bomber stream, which was no doubt returning to England from a raid on the Ruhr. It then began to rain; light drizzle at first, increasing as the hours went by into a steady, drenching downpour which made me consider taking shelter. I chose, however, to stick to my plan and, finding a well-made road, pressed on faster, now heading westwards. Only once did I have to leave the road to take cover, when a small military convoy drove past. It had been easy to spot its approach through the rain by the reflected glare of the hooded headlights.

At first light, I started my search for somewhere to hide during the coming day but, by now, the whole countryside had awakened. Lights were on in the farms and houses, and people were already on the move on the roads. In the bad light caused by the falling rain, I noticed a gap into a field, leading onto a path which disappeared into the gloom. I splashed through a ditch up onto the path, and made off across the field, which I noticed was planted with root crops. Before I had reached the far side, I had gathered three small turnips and a few carrots.

The field was bordered by a narrow lane. I followed it for a while until, to my delight, I came upon the ruin of a small cottage, standing alone in its garden, well back from the lane. This was where I would take shelter. I had done more than enough for one night, in the most atrocious conditions. I was wet through, the pain in my feet was excruciating and, furthermore, it would soon be broad daylight. I therefore went quickly into the disused and overgrown garden, and through the open doorway of the cottage, where I collapsed on the floor, amidst dust and rubbish, in front of a gaping empty fireplace.

The night had been a contest of mind over matter. The bad weather had obviously affected me and, for a time, I had been very depressed. Now, at last, I could take a rest. It was getting light quickly, and I had to make preparations to hide. But first, I had to do something about the state I was in. My major concern was that I was soaked to the skin, and I had to get dry if I was to avoid catching a chill, or worse. I carefully removed my boots from my aching feet, and stripped off my battledress blouse and trousers, and my shirt. These I spread out on the floor to dry. I was now clad in only a damp singlet and cotton shorts but, thankfully, they soon began to dry from the heat of my body. Despite the early hour, it was, in fact, not the least cold.

My chief concern now was the condition of my feet. During the night I had experienced sharp, piercing, pains, but was not prepared for what I saw when I removed my blood-soaked socks. My feet looked as though they had been boiled. They were badly swollen, and covered with blisters and blood - on the heels, between the toes and, most painfully of all, on the pads of the feet. Whoever had designed the RAF escape kit had been a genius, a true Boy Scout, for, among the comforts it contained, I found not only a needle and thread, but a small roll of sticking-plaster. With this, I set about repairing the damage, systematically dealing with blister after blister, pricking each one, to force out the clear liquid inside, and drying them with a piece of my precious toilet paper. Then, on feet trembling with pain, I explored the room, keeping low to avoid being seen from the lane.

The cottage was really a shell. The one large room had alcoves at both ends, which might have been used as places in which to sleep or even to cook or, much more likely, to shelter animals at night. If I kept out of sight, it would be a reasonable place to spend the day, but, if anyone found me there, I would have no alternative but to throw myself on their mercy. I was in no condition to make a run for it.

I made my headquarters in one of the alcoves, and there I rested, dozed, and eventually fell asleep. When I awoke, the rain had stopped, the sun was bright overhead, and it was getting warm. My spirits rose, and I set about what had to be done. My battledress, shirt and boots were not yet dry, so, on hands and knees, I crawled out of the gap which had once been a back door, and spread them out in the hot sun on the ground outside. I then thought of lighting a smokeless fire from the bits of wood littering the place, and making a turnip and carrot stew, but abandoned the idea as too risky, particularly as I was unable to move quickly or defend myself.

I appeased my hunger a little during the afternoon by carefully peeling the turnips, cutting them into small pieces, and eating them raw, together with the carrots. My stomach had settled down, but I made sure that I chewed every piece thoroughly. My clothes were now dry, and I dressed. My only problem was getting the stiffened boots back onto my tortured feet.

As I waited for darkness, I decided that I would march for only one more night, in the hope that contact would be made with someone disposed to help. I knew I was somewhere inside Belgium, because I had noticed farm workers in the distance during the day, dressed in overalls and wearing the distinctive beret, so different from the dress of their Dutch neighbours, whom I had frequently seen around Venlo. I felt it was unwise to continue walking indefinitely. Somehow, at the right time, I would have to chance my arm, and try to make contact myself.

No one came near the cottage during the day. I had been left untroubled to dry myself and fully regain my composure. My only visitor had been a stray dog, which had wandered in looking for food, and been quickly sent on its way.

It was really dark when I set out again. It was a very painful start because of my blistered feet, but I forced myself to stamp them down hard in a measured marching rhythm, until the pain had gone. Everything now seemed reasonably straightforward, and I settled down to a walk which I intended should be of no more than about fifteen kilometres. I would not hurry. I would keep my eyes open for food, and carry on towards the north west.

It is surprising how an undisturbed walk can concentrate thought. My mind became disassociated from my body as I swung along, now blissfully unaware of pain or fatigue, yet thinking, reasoning, and evolving solutions to all manner of possible eventualities. I pondered on Kreis's explicit instructions as to how we would make contact with an escape route. I remembered that he expected people to be out at night looking for us. I also recalled that there was a background of local intelligence on passing strangers, which enabled the Resistance to intercept individuals such as myself. But, in my case, I felt no one could possibly have seen me, hiding or walking during the past two days, and I was convinced that I would have to adopt what Kreis considered to be the last resort: I had to make the first move myself, to take the initiative and try to make contact, which I would do at first light.

I had little idea how this should be done, but I recalled some of the advice we had been given during our training, back in Berlin. British Intelligence officers advised aircrew that it was best to make contact with poorer people, the middle-aged and elderly who could remember the occupation during the Great War, and, possibly, the clergy. Young people should be avoided and, in particular, so should civil servants, although, how a tired and harassed evader would be able to recognise, at first sight, a foreign civil servant, was beyond me. I then remembered the comical final piece of advice, to be used *in extremis*. If all else had failed, then someone should be found who was poor, aged, and feeble enough to be knocked down and left, if not disposed to help!

I also knew that I would have to tell any possible helper what objective I had in mind. This, I decided, would have to be a forlorn hope of reaching the North Sea coast, where I would try to find some way of sailing back to England. Above all, I would say that I was looking for patriots who would help me get home by means of an escape route. It was too good a night for the RAF to stay on the ground and, true to form, at about two o'clock in the morning, I again heard the bomber armada on its way back to England. This time, I saw searchlights in the far distance ahead of me, and once, but only once, I heard the exchange of cannon and machine gun fire, high overhead.

I was taking my time, resting at regular intervals, and drinking frequently from the water bottle. I was not very hungry, certainly not hungry enough to go looking for another meal of raw vegetables. Once again, I remembered advice we had been given; that a man was so physically and mentally shaken after being shot down, that he would not want to eat for at least the first two days. At about four o'clock, the countryside began to awaken. Lights could be seen coming on all around me, and people were stirring. As I walked past a small farm I could see, in the outbuildings, that milking had already begun. I felt quite certain, in fact positive, that I was nowhere near a town or a military base and, if ever I was to make contact, then it had best be done very soon.

CHAPTER SEVENTEEN

I had turned into a narrow, straight lane, bordered on both sides with water filled ditches, when I saw, ahead of me, a faint light approaching. It was a man on a bicycle, coming straight at me, too fast for me to get out of the way and down into a ditch. He saw me, put on his brakes, and came to a stop, right in front of me. We stood looking hard at each other. I was the first to speak, just the word *'Morgen'*. *'Guten Morgen,'* came the reply. The cyclist had dismounted, and walked towards me to stand almost at attention, as though awaiting an order. In the half-light, he must have thought, by the nature of my uniform, that I was a German. He then ventured a step nearer and peered at my RAF pilot's wings. He looked up at me, excited, rapidly nodding his head. He whispered the question, 'RAF? RAF? *Ja? Ja?'*

I could not have been more surprised. By an incredible stroke of luck, my chief concern, ever since the start of the journey, could be about to be resolved. This was my first contact with the enemy. I kept my composure, looked him straight in the face, and replied in English, 'Yes, I am RAF; I am English.' I pointed to my breast, 'I am a British pilot. Can you help me? *Aidez-moi? Hilfe?'*

The man let the bicycle fall to the ground, grabbing my arm and shaking my hand. He put his arms around me and embraced me, with kisses on both cheeks. He seemed overjoyed, and made it quite clear that he wanted me to go with him. I did my best to react naturally, so as not to give him any idea that I understood the *norddeutsch* he was speaking. He picked up the bicycle, turned it around, and indicated that I should join him by sitting sideways on the bar. We then cycled off back down the lane, my new-found friend talking excitedly all the time.

Within less than a kilometre we were in the outskirts of a village, and then stopped at a large official-looking house, just short of the village centre. I was hustled inside, and found myself in a large room, next to what must have been a kitchen, to judge from the wonderful smell of cooking bread. Very soon, the room began to fill with people who jostled to shake my hand, slap my back, and try to assure me that all was well. For a time, there was no sign of anyone in charge. From the language being spoken, I knew I was somewhere in Flanders, surrounded by a happy group of Flemish villagers, expressing their friendliness and comradeship. Repeatedly, I heard of the deep hatred of my country, of how the cursed *Boche* had to be driven out, and of how the RAF would destroy Germany and so regain freedom for them.

Some sort of order was restored when I was taken to the kitchen where, to my intense delight, a splendid meal of eggs, ham and bread was laid out for me. I ate ravenously at first, and then more slowly, the better to digest and relish the food. I had almost cleared my plate, when a smartly dressed middle-aged woman drew up a chair opposite me.

'*Parlez-vous Français?*', she asked. '*Comprenez-vous la langue?*'

I replied at once in French, 'Yes, I do. I speak French, but not well, although, if you speak slowly, I will understand everything you say.'

She measured her words. 'Good. Good. That is most unusual for an Englishman. I am *Madame* Giraud. I am Walloon, not Flemish. You can obviously see you are among friends, although I suppose you have no idea where you are?'

I shook my head.

'You are fortunate to be in Balen, in the Flemish part of Belgium, so all those you have met so far speak Flemish. I know that is a language which means nothing to you, as I well remember the Tommies from the last war. The English cannot be bothered to learn other people's languages! I know this because I am the school teacher here. Now, what are your plans, and where were you going, my friend?'

'*Madame,* I am a British pilot, Pilot Officer George Harrison. I was shot down three nights ago, after we had bombed Wuppertal. I have been walking ever since, trying to reach the coast, where I hope to find some way of getting back to England. Now, thank goodness, I am with friends who might be able to assist me, just as we were told back in

England. Are you, in fact, someone who can help me find an escape route?'

This entreaty took her aback. She was obviously surprised. I must have said something wrong. She looked quizzically at me, turned to some men grouped behind her, got up and, together with them, left the room. I finished my meal in silence. When *Madame* Giraud returned she was accompanied by three men. I rose from my chair but was motioned to sit again, and we all grouped around the table. *Madame* was clearly in charge of the proceedings.

'We have decided to do what we can to help you, for that is our chosen duty. There are not many of us here in Balen, but we are all patriots, and we shall do our very best. First, however, we must have a look at you, and get you well again.'

She spoke to one of the men, who went back into the main room and asked the many curious spectators to leave. I was then taken upstairs to a small bathroom and left to clean myself. I stripped completely, got into a lukewarm bath and scrubbed myself from top to toe with a strongly scented antiseptic soap. While I was doing this, someone came into the room and took away all my clothes: battledress, shirt, underclothes and boots, leaving me with a white dressing gown. I finished my bath as quickly as possible and, wearing nothing but the dressing gown, returned downstairs to the kitchen, where *Madame*, the three men, and a newcomer, were waiting for me.

The fourth man was the village doctor. He asked me in French whether I had any ailments. Using a hand-held mirror, he showed me that the swelling of my eye was going down, but that the bruise was now an odd yellow-greenish colour. He took my temperature, and put tape on my damaged hand. Then he went to work on my feet, deflating some of the many blisters, treating them with antiseptic, and taping them firmly. He told *Madame* Giraud that all was well, and left. We sat at the table. I was beginning to feel physically tired, and very relaxed. I needed a good sleep, but this would have to wait: I had to know how I was to make contact with the escape routes. *Madame* spoke.

'We are part of what we call the village council. I will not tell you the names of my friends here, although we are all resolved to help, but I regret we have no idea of the whereabouts of these escape routes, as you call them. We believe there are some south of here, and we think the important ones are managed by Walloons, but we do not know how to contact such people. It must be difficult and dangerous. There are so many collaborators these days.'

My disappointment must have shown clearly in my face.

'You are only the second flyer we have ever seen here in Balen,' she explained. 'Last winter, we tried to help... what is the word... a navigator? Such a young man. But he did not understand us, and would not do as he was told. He put us at great risk when the Germans took him from the *estaminet*, where he just sat until they made their daily patrol through the village.'

She told the others what she had just said about the poor *'petit navigateur'*. They shook their heads knowingly, and I heard one say... 'but then he was such a young boy, an innocent.' *Madame* Giraud went on. 'Whatever we do, my friend, must be done quickly, because the German patrol will be here this afternoon. As I have already said, we know little about the Resistance, except that these routes you are looking for are to the south, and that is where you should go.'

She turned to her compatriots for reassurance.

'In any case, what you are doing is all wrong. If you carry on walking through the night towards the coast, dressed in uniform, you will surely be captured. The Germans learned a lesson when the Canadians tried to land at Dieppe. Since then they have been building their West Wall, all along the coast. You could never get into that area and find help or a boat. No, you are going in the wrong direction, and in the wrong manner. You must go south, and you must travel during the day and, to help you, we will see that you are properly dressed.'

What could I say? What could I to do but comply with this unexpected advice? I had not foreseen the dramatic change that would have to be made to my plans as a result. However, I had little alternative; any objection or disagreement would only arouse suspicion.

'While you were bathing,' said *Madame*, 'we took the precaution of getting rid of the evidence of your arrival. We have destroyed all your belongings. The only remaining evidence that you are English is around your neck. May I have those, please.'

I put my hands protectively over my identity discs.

'No. You cannot have these,' I protested. 'These are all I have to prove that I am English. I must keep them, to protect myself.'

'Rather the opposite, I think, *Monsieur*. If you keep them, and the Germans catch you in the clothes we are about to give you, then they will shoot you as a spy. If you are not carrying those discs, the Germans will have no way of knowing that you are a British flyer.'

She turned and spoke to her compatriots, while my mind raced, searching for the right reply.

'Yes, *Madame*, I understand what you say, but what is to happen when I find an escape route? How will I identify myself? No, I must keep my identity. It is the only passport I have.'

There was another hurried discussion, and I could see that I had made my point.

'You are quite right,' said *Madame*, 'You must, of course, be able to prove your identity, even though it could be dangerous ... but now we must hurry. We have to prepare you for your journey.'

One of the men took me back to the bathroom, where a pile of clothing had been placed on a chair. My escape kit was on top. I began to dress with deep misgivings, having always thought that, when the time came for me to change into plain clothes, I would do so in the comparative security of a safe house somewhere on an escape route. Now, I was about to venture forth without any civilian identity or documents to show if anyone were to challenge me along the way.

I had been given a motley collection of clothes. There was a dirty grey shirt without a collar, and striped trousers, far too short in the leg and too wide in the waist. These I tied with a length of cord. I put on a threadbare jacket, again too big, and donned a workman's cap. The shoes were *Ersatz,* made of some poor apology for leather, and of little use for prolonged walking, but they fitted well, and were comfortable over my blisters. I discarded the escape kit box, and secreted the contents around my person. The map of the Netherlands I left on the chair, while the other, of Belgium, I stuffed into a trouser pocket. I took a look at myself in the mirror, and had to admit that the disguise was good. In need of a shave and sporting, as I did, a discoloured eye, I looked like someone down on his luck, some sort of tramp, certainly not likely to draw attention.

I went downstairs into the main room, to be greeted by a dozen or more villagers who had come to wish me *bon voyage*. There was some laughter at my appearance, as *Madame* Giraud walked around me making her inspection.

'I believe *Monsieur* Harrison has disappeared,' she joked. 'Surely, no self respecting German will be interested in you dressed like this. It is perfect.'

A woman came shyly forward, mumbled a few self-conscious words in Flemish and, to my great surprise, handed me a bundle of Belgian bank notes.

'Practically everyone in Balen has made a contribution,' said *Madame* Giraud. 'We all wish you well,' she chuckled, before adding, 'you have enough money now to travel first class, if you wish, to the far south of France.'

For a moment, I forgot my rôle and purpose: I was genuinely moved by this unselfish generosity, and blurted out my thanks. Just as quickly, I checked myself, remembering that they were *not* my friends and that, one day, they would learn just how wrong they had been to help me. Nonetheless, I had to say something.

'*Madame*, please tell everyone how grateful I am. How I appreciate the wonderful help I have been given. I shall never forget any of you.'

It was then all hustle and bustle, as I shook hands with everyone in the room. I was told they would all be walking with me to the railway halt, where the train was expected within twenty minutes. Once outside, there were other villagers waiting to join us and, together, we set off noisily along the road. As we walked, *Madame* Giraud gave me a ticket for Namur in the Ardennes, and told me that I should arrive there in the afternoon, changing trains at Tienen. There were about ten minutes to wait until the arrival of the train. The villagers packed themselves into the small waiting room, intent on giving me a good send-off. Everyone wanted to say farewell and then, to my consternation, an elderly man produced a concertina, and began to pick out a well-known tune, at first softly, then louder, until all joined in the rousing chorus of 'It's a long way to Tipperary'. I was obliged to join in, and did so with gusto, remembering this favourite from my OTC days back in Yorkshire.

This bizarre scene was brought to a close when the train pulled into the small single platform. I was hustled out by the crowd, and pushed into an empty compartment. To my relief, there was no delay, and I was soon on the move, leaning out of the window for almost a minute, waving goodbye to the poor, misguided people of Balen. The train travelled slowly southwards. For the first half an hour or so, I was alone in the compartment, worried by the situation in which I now found myself, and searching for some positive idea of what I should do next. One thing was clear. No longer could I hope that someone would find me; I now had to search out the enemy myself.

I settled down to take stock. I took my navigator's watch from my wrist and hid it in a trouser pocket. I opened out the silk evasion map of Belgium, and tried to find Balen, and the small halts at which we were stopping. This proved impossible, as the scale was far too small, and the few place names were in French, not Flemish. I could not even find Tienen. When we stopped at a small halt named Beringen, a middle-aged couple joined me in the compartment. From then on, at each successive stop, more and more people joined the train, until the compartment was absolutely crammed, at least half a dozen having to stand. The crush was made all the worse by the baskets of farm produce which, I supposed, were being taken to market. We arrived at Diest, where everyone else got out.

Alone in the compartment, I wondered what I should do as the train was eventually shunted to another platform. To my relief, it began to fill again with passengers and, after ten minutes or so, pulled slowly out of the station. The compartment was once more full of people and, for the first time since leaving Balen, I began to feel ill at ease. I was sitting in a corner window seat, where I had taken the fancy of a plump young woman seated directly in front of me, a grubby youngster on her knee. She had been staring hard at me for some time and, when I finally met her eyes, she smiled, then pursed her lips, and blew me a kiss. I flushed, and hung my head. Thankfully, she gave up this torment, and busied herself with feeding the youngster, while I kept my eyes fixed steadily on the passing countryside until we began to enter the outskirts of Tienen.

There I had to change trains. They had told me in Balen that I would have to wait for about two hours to make the connection to Namur. This I was able to check on the station timetable, which was flanked by *Abwehr* notices warning that the penalty for helping *Terrorflieger* was death. I had no difficulty in leaving the station, merely showing my ticket at the barrier and mumbling 'Namur'. With so much time to waste, I decided the best thing to do would be to walk around the town, where I could test my disguise while looking at the shops, houses and people. As I went, I noticed that I attracted no undue attention. I began to feel quite at ease and, when I saw my first fellow countrymen - a couple of *Luftwaffe* cooks, dressed in their white working smocks - I could not resist the challenge they presented. As they were passing, I asked them the time of day, in French. Neither knew the language, but one produced a fine hunter watch and held it out for me to read.

I spent about an hour wandering around Tienen, or Tirlemont as it seemed to be called in French. I then waited on a bench in the town square, in front of the *Kommandeur's* office, where I could watch the comings and goings of various officials and many ordinary people. Ten minutes before the Namur train was due to leave, I got up and walked across the square into the station, presented my ticket at the barrier, and went onto the platform where the train was waiting. I found a seat in an empty compartment. The train pulled out, exactly on time. Again, it was to be a slow journey but, this time, there were very few passengers to distract me. I settled back to enjoy the trip, now totally relaxed, but beginning to feel hungry. Like a fool, I had overlooked the possibility of buying food in Tienen, where I had been far too preoccupied to think about eating.

The train made frequent stops, and was twice held up, for no apparent reason as far as I could see, for long periods. It was not until early evening that we reached Namur. I joined the crowd queuing at the exit, noticing, ahead of me, *Feldgendarmerie* checking documents alongside the Belgian ticket collector. As I got nearer, I was relieved to see that the police were only concerned with a group of *Wehrmacht* soldiers, who must have joined the train at one of the many stops. I kept my place in the queue, handed in my ticket, and left the station as quickly as possible.

I knew that I had to be away from the town before curfew was imposed. I walked along the riverbank road, crossed the bridge over the Meuse, and set off briskly up the hill on the road to Dinant. As I hurried on, I decided, if the ideal opportunity arose, to try to contact help before nightfall. The weather was fine and warm and, if I did not succeed in finding anyone, then I could spend the night reasonably comfortably in the open. At first light, probably the best time, I would try again.

I pressed on, appraising various houses on the way. By the time I reached open country, I had seen nowhere likely to be worth the risk of trying to make a contact. Dusk was falling, and I turned my attention to finding a place to spend the night. I left the main road and, for a while, walked along a lane which I thought might lead either to a hamlet or a large farm. Then, ahead of me in the failing light, I saw someone at work in a small plot on the edge of the lane. As I drew nearer, I could see that it was an elderly man in working clothes, clearing weeds from between rows of vegetables. Without doubt, this was the text-book situation for taking a chance.

I walked up to him. He looked up at me, but carried on with his work. Choosing my words carefully, I spoke to him quietly, being ready to run if things went wrong.

'Monsieur, je suis un aviator Anglais. S'il vous plaît, aidez-moi. Avez- vous quelque place ou je peus passer la nuit?'

The man said not a word, but carried on with his digging. I stood there like a fool, wondering what to do. Then he looked up at me, and pointed to a small bank a few metres away.

'*Pour le moment, mon ami, restez là.*'

He returned to his work. I went over to the bank and sat down. The old man worked on until it was dark, then placed his tools in a wheel-barrow, and beckoned me to follow him. We walked down the lane and turned onto a path which led to a small farm. He took me by the arm and led me into the farmhouse. I found myself in a living room, in the centre of which, seated at a table, was a family waiting to start a meal. They were, understandably, startled to see such a dishevelled stranger. The old man introduced me to his wife, his son and his son's wife, but both women became distressed when he explained who I was. His wife remonstrated loudly with him, saying that the *Boche* would kill them all, and wanting me out of the house, there and then. However, the farmer exerted his authority as head of the family, and the women grew quiet when he said something about the '*brave anglais*', who would be leav-ing very early in the morning. With that, his wife grudgingly set a place for me at the table.

The farmer said grace, and added a prayer for my safety. I was offered first choice from a tureen of delicious beef stew, to which was added a pile of roast potatoes and cabbage. We ate in silence. I cleared every last morsel from my plate with a large piece of homemade bread: I then ate a chunk of cheese, and some boar pâté, and drank a glass of rough red wine. I was thoroughly satisfied, feeling warm and relaxed in their company. Then everyone, including the farmer's wife, began to ask me questions, in a dialect which I found a little hard to follow. I told them I had been shot down a few days ago, while dropping bombs on Germany. This news was received rapturously. I told them how I had got to Balen, and why I had chosen to set out on the long journey to *Vichy* France, in the hope of contacting an escape route which would take me to Spain, and thence to England.

Most of what I said was accepted with open-mouthed amazement by these simple people. Even so, I had to keep my wits about me, as I was being plied with more red wine, and then the cognac was brought out to

toast the Kings of Belgium and Britain. I became immersed in this friendliness and concern for me. They were so likeable and sincere that I felt
genuine regret that I would have to report them to the *Gestapo* when all
was over and done with. The meal over, the son made his excuses, shook
hands with me, and said he had to leave: he had work to do. The farmer's
wife arranged for me to wash, and I borrowed her husband's open razor
to shave. I was told that I would be welcome to spend the night with
them, but that I would have to leave early in the morning. I expressed my
thanks and wished them goodnight. The farmer led me by lantern light to
a barn, where I was offered a bed of fresh straw. I lay down and soon fell
asleep.

The slight creaking of the barn door awakened me. A sixth sense
warned me to be on my guard, and I just lay there, eyes closed, waiting
for the unexpected. A torch was flashed in my eyes. I was grabbed by the
shoulders and violently shaken by someone yelling: *'Wach' auf Du
deutscher Scheissker! Was in Gottes Namen machst Du?'*

So someone thought I was German. I bit my tongue to stop
myself replying instinctively. Instead, I blurted out my concern in
English. 'Good God. What's the matter. What's going on? What are you
saying?'

From the darkness, someone spoke in English, 'It is all right, my
friend. We are here to help you, but first we had to be sure of you. We are
taking you to a place where you will be safe.'

A lantern was lit, and in its light I could see two men, both
dressed in town suits, one carrying a brief case. I got to my feet and followed them outside, where the farmer's son was waiting to shake my
hand and wish me well. We left the farm at once, walking in single file,
one man leading and the other behind me. It was very dark, and we had
to go carefully and slowly across the fields until we reached a small road
leading towards Namur, whose dim lights could be seen in the distance.
We hurried on, and finally stopped at a barred window, strangely set in a
long wall skirting the road. A bell was rung, and after a few minutes, a
whispered conversation was held with someone inside. I was told to
climb over the wall and, as I dropped to the ground on the other side, a

cowled monk appeared at my side and took me by the hand.

'You will be safe with us, my son,' he said.

CHAPTER EIGHTEEN

I awoke with a start as the Angelus began to toll loudly, almost directly overhead. It took me a moment or two to realise where I was - that last night I had been brought to a monastery. I had slept the sleep of the dead in a small whitewashed room, which had a narrow cell-like window at one end and a door, with a grille set in it, at the other. Opposite my bed, placed along a wall, were a wash basin, a mirror, and a shelf with a towel, safety razor, soap, toothbrush and tooth powder. My clothes had been taken away but, on the back of a chair, was a brown robe. The room was spotless, and smelt fresh and clean. The only adornment was a crucifix on the wall above the bed.

I got up, and washed and shaved in cold water. I donned the robe which, by its colour, I recognised as Carmelite, the same as worn by those who had tutored me at school in Yorkshire. My ablutions finished, I sat on the edge of the bed and, almost at once, the door was opened and a short, tubby, bespectacled monk entered, bearing a tray of food: bread, sliced cheese and ham, and a glass of milk.

'Eat, my son,' he said, in English. 'I will return when you have finished.' I smiled my thanks, and he left.

Whilst eating slowly, relishing each morsel, I congratulated myself on my good fortune. I felt sure that I was now very close to an escape route, possibly in a safe house whence I would soon be on my way: *Kondor* would then be able to achieve its objective, as planned by Kreis. There seemed little doubt that the first link in the chain was the farmer's son, who had left the house after our meal and reappeared with the two men who had brought me here. It occurred to me that I knew neither his name nor that of his family; nor did I know his address. No matter: my memory was good and, when the time came, I would find them.

The monk had been waiting outside for me to finish my meal: I put the tray on the bed, and he came in, sat down, and introduced himself.

'Welcome to the *Monastère des Carmes,* my son. I am Father Pierre. It was I who met you last night at the wall. I have been asked by our Father Prior to look after you, because I am the only one here who speaks some English. I am not fluent, but I hope you will understand. What really matters is that you should be safe with us.'

He made the sign of the Cross and I, instinctively, did the same. He looked at me in surprise.

'Are you also of the Faith?'

'Yes, Father,' I replied. 'My family is Catholic. I was educated as a Roman Catholic, and I have kept the Faith ever since.'

I took my identity discs from around my neck and showed them to him.

'Look, you can see that my name is Harrison. The initial G is for George, and the "RC" means that my religion is Roman Catholic. And I think that your knowledge of my language is good, better than mine of yours. *Je parle Français, un petit peu.*'

He was pleased. He put his hand on my shoulder and blessed me.

'We shall be able to praise the Lord and give thanks together in due time. Meanwhile, I must ask you to stay in this room until I see you again later this morning, after my devotions and duties have been completed. I will then be able to tell you a little more. Until then, perhaps you would care to read.' He produced, from under his robe, an English version of the Holy Bible.

Father Pierre came back just before midday. He was worried, and told me that my arrival at the monastery had unfortunately been observed by others. The whole place was in ferment. Nothing like this had ever happened before, and a serious situation had arisen because, although most of the monks were Belgian, and in favour of helping me, there were also Dutchmen, a Frenchman, two Spaniards, an Irishman and some Germans, who thought otherwise. All were now aware that a British pilot was being hidden in one of the cells, and the Father Prior had been petitioned either to have me leave the monastery at once, or to hand me over to the Belgian Police. The penalties for hiding or helping a British flyer were ruthless. If it were known that the brethren were helping me, everyone in the monastery would be put to death.

The Father Prior had been firm. He had admonished the reluctant brothers, reminding them that it was their bounden Christian duty to help those in distress, no matter who they might be, and certainly those fighting to rid the country of the Anti-Christ. In his wisdom, he had decided to make the decision easy for them, and had ordered the eleven dissidents out of the monastery for an indefinite period. They were to go to the much stricter monastery at Liège, whose brethren were bound by a vow of silence. They would leave that afternoon, and be taken to Liège "by secure means," whatever that meant.

I spent six days at the monastery, learning much about the Belgians and the Church militant, but nothing at all about escape routes. After the departure of the dissident monks, the Father Prior confirmed through Father Pierre, acting as interpreter, that I was a welcome guest, and that everything possible would be done to help me. When and how this would be done, and by whom, was not his concern, but all would be made clear in the Lord's good time. I would be allowed to leave my cell, and would be given a conducted tour of the buildings. I was invited to join the brethren at their prayers, and responded by saying I would like to do so at Vespers.

The central figure in all this was Father Pierre who, despite his mild appearance, was a man of integrity and purpose, holding a bitter hatred for the *Boche,* as he called us. His father, mother and grandfather had been shot in the massacre of hundreds of Belgian civilians during our looting of Dinant in August 1914. He had grown up with a revulsion of all things German. He had joined the Belgian Army at an early age, and had fought against us during the *Blitzkrieg,* when he had been wounded and captured whilst defending the Albert Canal. Although taken to Germany as a prisoner of war, he had been released after a few months to study Holy Orders, and so devote the rest of his life to Christ and humanity. Paradoxically, however, he had remained a soldier at heart, and had drawn around him others of like mind, who vowed that, when the day came, as they prayed it would, they would do their best to help in the liberation of Belgium.

My doubts about the Christian morality of the monastery were confirmed one day, when Father Pierre took me to a small room in the belfry tower, and proudly showed me a cache of arms, including a heavy

Hotchkiss machine gun complete with boxes of ammunition clips. This clearly indicated a doctrine not of 'love thy neighbour' or 'blessed are the peacemakers', but rather, 'an eye for an eye, a tooth for a tooth'. I happily joined in the mutual hypocrisy by eating and praying with them, and took the Sacrament every day. For most of the time, I was left to myself to read from a small collection of English books found for me by Father Pierre. One, on the life and death of Sir Thomas More, had its particular appeal, as I pondered on the paradox of the beliefs and myths of the Church amid the needs and practicalities of National Socialism. In all this, I could not forget my duty. I longed for the moment when I would again be on my way, even though it would mean, one day, retribution for these likeable but misguided men of God.

During the warm, sunny afternoon of the sixth day, as I was sitting alone in the monastery orchard, dozing after repeated attempts to digest the dull account of John Wesley's travels through the Midlands of England, Father Pierre gently woke me with a hand on my shoulder.

'Wake up, my son. It is time for you to leave us. I have a friend for you to meet.'

At last, something was about to happen. We went quickly back to my cell, where I discarded my monk's habit and dressed in a reasonably well-fitting suit of plain clothes, which I found laid out on the bed. I could sense Father Pierre's emotion as we neared the point of saying farewell.

'My duty is done,' he said. 'You will now go with others who will help you to return to England. You will be able to rejoin your comrades, and come back to defeat the *Boche.*' He held out something in his hand. 'I want you to wear this for your protection.' He handed me a small golden crucifix and chain. 'The Father Prior knows that you are leaving, and gives you God's blessing. We shall all pray for you and look forward to the time when we shall see you again.'

I was at a loss for something to say. I took my RAF watch from my wrist and handed it to him.

'Please keep this as a small measure of my thanks, and a memento of my stay with you. Be assured that I will return one day. I shall never forget you or your brothers.'

We shook hands warmly, and said goodbye at the monastery gate. As Father Pierre embraced me, I felt like Judas.

I was then introduced to a thin, middle-aged man who spoke to me in French, explaining that I was to follow him at a distance of about twenty paces, and that I would be led to my next destination. He refused to answer questions, telling me only that he had a job to do, and that was all. We set off without a backward glance. I was feeling in good form, at last being decently dressed and looking forward to the next development in this intriguing adventure. There were few people to be seen as we walked at a good pace down into the suburbs of Namur. After about twenty minutes, the guide stopped outside a large house, set back from the road and standing in its own grounds. A nod told me that I was to follow him inside. We went through the front garden and around to the back of the house, which we entered through a back door: the place was absolutely deserted - empty of all furniture, fittings and coverings. This was certainly not a safe house: I had been brought here for some sinister reason, I suspected.

This was confirmed when the guide led me upstairs into a room in which, sitting like magistrates, behind a trestle table, were two men and a woman. I stood before them for a moment or two while the guide left us, and then the silence was broken by the man in the centre. He spoke in perfect English. 'You say that you are Pilot Officer George Harrison. I would like to see what evidence you have.'

I took the identity discs from around my neck, and handed them to him. He studied them and showed them to the other two.

'We shall now ask you some questions, each of which you must answer completely and correctly. If all goes well, and we are convinced by your answers, then you will be in safe hands. If not, then your short journey will end here in Namur.'

With that, he dramatically produced a Luger pistol and placed it on the table with the barrel pointing towards me. I had recovered from my initial surprise, and did not like the idea of being threatened. My stay at the monastery had convinced me that I was in the safe hands of those at least on the fringe of an escape route, yet here were three people treating me as an impostor. Either they were playing a game with me, as they probably did with all evaders, or I had been handed over to a bogus escape route, and was looking at collaborators working for the *Gestapo*. I had nothing to lose, apart from precious time, if they were not genuine. I therefore went straight to the point.

'Are you about to question my credentials? If so, then how can I be sure of yours? We are warned, back in England, to be careful about how we contact help. We know we could fall into the hands of traitors masquerading as the patriots who operate escape routes, people who would take us in, interrogate us as you are about to do... and then, when we have divulged as much as we know... hand us over for disposal by the Germans. Until I am sure of you, all I will tell you is that I am 144827 Pilot Officer George Harrison.'

All three had listened intently, and now conversed among themselves in French. The men seemed to defer to the woman, who, I now noticed for the first time, was remarkably attractive. She caught my appreciative eye, and spoke carefully to me in English with a Dutch or, more likely, Flemish accent.

'You are quite correct, *Monsieur* Harrison, to doubt anyone and everyone at this stage, but you must remember that it is we who have the greater responsibility. We must be absolutely sure of your identity. It is indeed true that collaborators help the Germans, but they also work to destroy us. Many of them, to their regret, have already tried to infiltrate our escape routes. You have good cause to doubt us, but we have equal reason to be careful of you. Imagine what would happen if we accepted a collaborator, and sent him back to England. Therefore, we must ask you to answer a few simple questions. I can say no more.'

She indicated to the man who had first spoken that he should continue, I forestalled him.

'You're English, are you not? You should have no difficulty in vouching for me.'

He was not at all pleased with my bravado, and snapped back at me. 'Never mind who I am, old boy; I'm here to do a job, and it's I who will be making absolutely sure you are the real thing. Just answer the questions. Now let's get on with it. First, which is your squadron, and where were you stationed?'

'166 and we are at Kirmington.'

'Which operation were you on?'

'Wuppertal.'

'When and how were you shot down?'

'About ten days ago, and it was flak that got us. We were coned.'

'What aircraft were you flying, and who were your crew?'

My flow of quick answers stopped, but I was ready for this one. 'We were flying a Wellington Mark 10. But I'm afraid I know little about the crew. You see, I had only just arrived and was actually about to start my second tour. I hadn't even unpacked when they asked me to take the place of a pilot who had gone sick. All I know is that they were a bunch of sprogs. There was a bomb-aimer who had done a few trips. I am pretty sure of this because he was a Canadian, and the only Flight Sergeant in the crew. The others were all Sergeants.'

The woman whispered something to the Englishman. He asked me if I knew anything about the others, whether they could also be evading capture.

'I've no idea. I don't even know whether everyone got out,' I replied. 'There was very little time, but it is likely they did. The bomb-aimer probably made it, because he clipped on my 'chute before he went out. But I can't be sure.'

'OK,' said the Englishman, 'just a few more questions. Who is the Foreign Secretary?'

'I think it's Lord Halifax, or maybe Anthony Eden.'

'Who is your A.O.C.?'

I wrinkled my brow. 'You've got me there. On a squadron we have little contact with the high and mighty, you know. I'm not sure... but I think it's Cochrane.'

There was nothing subtle about this questioning. I could have done a much better job myself, more on the lines of the techniques used by the experts. This man was not trying to lead me anywhere. His questions had no particular aim; in fact he seemed to be reciting them almost parrot-fashion.

'Where did you go to school?'

Another carefully prepared answer. I would be found out if I gave the name of my school in Yorkshire, so I replied self-deprecatingly: 'I wasn't particularly bright. I went to a secondary school in Dorchester.'

'I wouldn't worry about that, old boy. You seem to have done well enough anyway. You learned to fly, and you've even got a commission.'

He looked down at the notes he had been making. He had come to the end of his questions. Then, with a broad grin on his face, he asked me.

'Which is your favourite pub?'

I tried to give the impression of deep thought. 'I suppose it has to be Betty's Bar in York. That's where my old squadron used to hang out. If Ops. were scrubbed, you could always find us there... and there were some damned fine popsies.'

He turned to the others, and I heard them discussing what I had said. The Englishman picked up the Luger, and put it away in his waistband. The young woman laughed as she spoke.

'You must forgive my friend's dramatics. He loves playing with guns, but then, he is English, and we have to put up with all that.'

The Englishman got up, came around the table to me, and held out his hand, which I took.

'Yes, I'm Flight Lieutenant Ian Cartwright. I'm duty dog around this place for the moment, but I used to be with 57 Squadron, until I got knocked down on a raid on Essen about four months ago. I smashed up my leg, but these wonderful people have been looking after me ever since. I try to help them by running an eye over any new arrivals, but I'm hoping to be on my way home very soon as well.'

A discreet tapping on the table by the woman stopped his flow of talk. He looked at his watch.

'Good grief! You must excuse me. I must be off now. I have other things to do. Just in case I don't see you again, best of luck and, as they say over here, *bon voyage.*'

Cartwright left, together with the other man, and I was alone with the woman. She certainly was attractive. Of medium height, she was dressed smartly in a tailored coat and matching skirt, and was using a fine though discreet perfume, which added to her decidedly fresh and womanly appeal. There was an air of authority and determination about her, most unusual for someone who could have been no more than twenty-one years old.

She told me that she would now take me to a place where I would be hidden until arrangements could be made to get me out of Namur. She reminded me of the rules of the game which applied when anyone was being taken from place to place; that I would walk behind her at a given distance, or on the other side of the road. From now on, no matter where I went, I would be in the hands of a guide. If there was any trouble, then it was my duty to keep away from the guide. Guides were valuable people, with important work to do. In any case, the organisation would find me again.

'You are surrounded by friends in my country,' she added. 'Whatever you have to do in the future, you will be under observation most of the time.'

Without further ado, we left the deserted house, the girl going first, and I followed about twenty paces behind. We set off into Namur and, religiously, I obeyed her instructions, keeping a steady distance behind her and, whenever possible, watching her as I walked on the other side of the road. We were soon in the narrow streets leading to the Meuse bridge, which we crossed before entering the centre of the town. It must have been market day, because the place was crammed with people, including quite a number of German soldiers. For a while, I had drawn closer to my charming escort for fear of losing her but, once clear of the market place, I dropped back again as we left the town centre and walked on towards its northern suburbs.

In a tree-lined avenue of imposing houses, she turned into a short driveway. There, out of sight of the road, she beckoned me forward and, together, we approached the front door of a house whose well-polished nameplate proclaimed that a Doctor Klermans practised there. I had already noted that I was in the *Avenue Adolf Duret*, and that we were standing at the door of Number 10. A young girl answered the door, and we were taken to an empty waiting room. We sat there for a while, until a tall, distinguished man came in and warmly greeted my guide. She introduced me to Dr. Klermans and, after some whispered conversation with him, she left us, bidding me *'au revoir'* with a fetching smile.

'It is now my turn to help you,' said Klermans, who spoke good English. 'I welcome you to my house. You will be safe with me until arrangements are made for you to travel on. I know where you have been, and how you have managed to get this far. Later, you might like to tell me something of your adventures. But first, I want to check that you have not suffered in any way from your experiences. You will have a long way to go, and we must be sure that you are fit to travel.' He took me by the shoulder. 'Come into the surgery, where I can have a look at you.'

His examination was thorough. Eyes, nose and throat, heart and lungs, a check on muscular response in arms and legs, and then he had a good look at my feet. He trimmed away scar tissue on the heels and pads, and even between the toes. He then washed them in surgical spirit. He found evidence of a chipped or broken small bone in my right hand which, because it gave no pain, he thought best to leave alone.

'There is nothing very much wrong with you, young man. You appear to be very fit. In fact, apart from the punishment your feet have taken, I would classify you as extremely fit. Also, I have been told that you are not an excitable person, someone who might break down under pressure... that's true, is it not?'

'Probably,' I answered with a shrug.

'Now and then, my family and I have to handle a parcel... that is what we call an evader... who is temperamentally unsuited to cope with the boredom of being held in a safe house or, on the other hand, to deal with the excitement and danger of travelling an escape route. Such a person is a menace to us all.'

'What happens to someone like that?' I asked.

Klermans looked puzzled for a moment. 'Oh, I see what you mean,' he said. 'I do not know. That's not my business but, obviously, such a person cannot stay with us for long.'

I met the rest of the Klermans family at dinner that night. *Madame* Klermans, a tall, handsome woman of about fifty, spoke no English, and was delighted when I responded to her welcome in French. She said she was surprised, because I was the first of *'les braves Anglais'* she had met who had any idea of the language. Also at the table were the two daughters, both of whom had been away from the house all day. The older, Clothilde, was tall and angular, but with some of the handsomeness of her mother. She told me in, good English, that she was a schoolteacher. The other, Madeleine, was smaller, pert, and pretty. She also spoke English, and worked as a secretary at a local engineering firm.

The Klermans were Jewish, by no means of the strictly orthodox type but, nonetheless, staunch in their faith. The second day of my stay with them was the Sabbath, and Klermans seemed somewhat embarrassed when he invited me to celebrate the holy day with his family at the evening meal. He said that thanks would be offered for my salvation from the Germans. As it would have been foolish to protest, even to demur by saying I was a Roman Catholic, I decided to accept. I always had something to learn, and never before had I attended a Jewish ceremony of any sort.

I was surprised to find the curtains drawn when we assembled for the meal. The Menorah had been lit and placed on the table. I was politely asked if I would care to wear a prayer cap. If I did not wish to, it would not matter but, if I did, it would draw us further together in faith. I accepted the black cap from Klermans, and put it on the back of my head. After a short incantation and prayers in Hebrew, we sat down to eat a simple, yet wholesome, meal. We did so almost in silence until, at the end, Klermans held up a hand. He looked distraught as he addressed me.

'My friend, although we give thanks for your safe return, we also have to pray for the lives and safety of some of those very dear to us. This afternoon, we received the terrible news that the whole of my cousin's family have been taken from their home at Boxtel in the Netherlands and transported, with many others, to Germany. We do not know what will happen to them, but we fear for them.'

I bowed my head, not knowing what to say. I was shocked, to say the least. Of course I knew there was strong antipathy to the Jews in Germany, but not that there was such a widespread programme. I could scarcely believe what I had heard.

'I know that it is hard for you to understand, my dear Harrison. In fact, it surprises me that every one of you English we have had here with us seems unaware of the bestiality of the Germans. We, ourselves, can accept why they adopt such savage counter-measures against our Resistance work, but it is beyond us to understand why they are set on this terrible programme of genocide. It is going on, not only in their own country, but everywhere they have taken control.'

I remembered the *'Arbeit Macht Frei'* slogan which appeared over the gates of camps in many parts of Germany, where criminals, undesirables and others were put to work. It seemed likely that Klerman's relatives could be destined for such a fate.

'It is true that we hear little about this in England, Doctor Klermans. Could it not be that the Germans are recruiting workers from the occupied countries to help them with the war work?'

'I hardly think so. In a normal society, men have freedom of choice concerning such matters. No, these people are being rounded up and transported somewhere, and why only the Jews? This crime is going on everywhere: in France and the Netherlands in particular, and even in my own country, often helped by people who want to settle old scores against us. Why do you think we have the curtains drawn? We have to be on our guard all the time, even here in Namur.'

That night, it was hard to get to sleep. My mind went back to the perplexity of the *Kristallnacht*, not so long ago. Then I remembered some of the happenings in Poland, where an immense ghetto had been formed in Warsaw, and only dispersed when the Jews had been taken to labour camps. I also recalled that my own father was somehow involved with this in the Baltic States, and even within Russia, but was this not all a necessary means of dealing with the problems hindering the creation of the Greater German *Reich*? Before I eventually slept, I had to admit that there were now doubts in my mind. I could not understand how all this had been kept from us, leaving us so much in the dark.

I spent most of my time with the Klermans in my room on the second floor, overlooking a large well-kept garden, fringed on all sides with trees and shrubs. Klermans kept a good library, and provided me with an abundance of reading material, all in French. He left me well alone, and I saw little of him during the day as he was constantly dealing with patients in his surgery or out on calls, using a bicycle fitted with a pannier to hold his medical bag. He did find time, now and then, usually in the evening, for us to chat, and for me to learn a little more.

It was clear that Klermans was but a small cog in the escape organisation. His responsibilities were limited to the care of whoever had to be hidden in his house. This was partly confirmed when he told me that he had been asked to forward the two passport photographs which I should have been carrying in my battledress. I had to tell him, of course, that they must have gone up in flames when the good folk of Balen had destroyed my uniform, whilst making preparations for me to journey to Namur. I said that it had been careless of me not to retrieve them but, in any case, who would want them now? It was then that he explained his singular responsibility. Each safe house was a refuge in itself, deliberately concealed from the next. It was the organisation's policy that those in charge of a safe house were given no information of the bigger picture or, indeed, of what would be the evader's next step. There was a constant need for the best possible security.

Nevertheless, I found his naïvety truly surprising. This was no better illustrated than when, after an evening meal, he invited me to join him in his study for a cognac, and then produced evidence of what he had been doing to help the Resistance. He had set down, in a small leather-bound book, the details of all the airmen he and his family had sheltered. It was hard to believe that, in his innocence, he had been so stupid, and I solicitously berated him for compiling evidence which, if found by the Germans, would mean certain death for him and his family. I well remember his foolishly complacent reply: 'Do not concern yourself so, my friend. I defy any German to find my hiding place. I keep my records so safely that even my wife does not know where they are hidden. These entries are personal, and have nothing to do with anyone else.'

He pushed the book across his desk towards me. 'I would very much like you to tell me if there is anyone there that you know.'

I glanced through pages of names, addresses, anecdotes and thank-you notes. None of the names meant anything to me, but I did mutter, here and there, that I thought I knew this chap, or perhaps that one. From the dates which appeared against each entry, numbered almost like a battle score, I estimated that Klermans had been operating his safe house for about ten months, and that eighteen evaders had been passed on. I handed the book back to him, but he pushed it back towards me.

'My dear friend, I would appreciate it if you would add something. You can make it as personal as you wish.'

Indeed I will, I thought. Something very much to the point, which will take care of you and yours when the day of reckoning comes. 'Of course,' I said, with a smile. 'I will do so with pleasure, and with heartfelt thanks.' Klermans offered me his fountain pen, and I wrote a terse account of all that had happened from Balen to his house, and finished with a flamboyant flourish about the friendship between Belgium and England. I signed the damning statement, adding my name, rank and the number of my supposed squadron.

The next morning, after breakfast, Madeleine came to my room, with the suggestion that I might like to take a walk. She was not required at school that day, and her father thought it would be a good idea for me to practice walking in the company of a guide. I was pleased at the idea. It was a beautiful day, and the prospect of getting away from the confines of my room greatly appealed to me.

Madeleine assured me that there was nothing for me to do but relax and enjoy my walk. There was no danger, and nothing unusual about a couple out for a stroll. I was, in any case, well-dressed and unlikely to attract attention. We set off, walking side by side. I felt completely at ease. My new brown brogue shoes were a little tight, but a kilometre or two of walking would ease them. I had no documents, but Madeleine assured me that we would not be going near any checkpoints, or other places where I could be challenged. At the end of the road, we did not turn away into the woodlands as I had expected, but back down the road towards Namur. The reason for this was soon apparent, when we stopped at a small shop on the outskirts, and my photograph was taken, as Madeleine explained, so that her cousin could obtain a new *Laissez-passer*. That done, we wandered on into the town, Madeleine constantly pointing out this and that until, at last, she suggested it was time for a coffee.

We found a delightful little café, full of the warm smells of fresh bread and cakes, and brewing coffee. We sat outside in the sun, and ate croissants. Madeleine sipped her coffee while I sat back and relished a tankard of Stella Artois. It struck me how easy it was to merge into the scene around us. No one took the slightest notice and, even when a young, self-conscious, *Wehrmacht* soldier sat at the next table, it seemed to me that the only serious risk for a properly dressed and briefed RAF evader would be during a specific search, when there would be checks and demands to see papers. Even then, if his papers were good, the risk should be slight. Problems would only arise if evaders were foolish enough to take unnecessary chances. Our meal finished, we returned to collect my photographs and then retraced our steps, taking our time as we trudged up the long hill. I had enjoyed my excursion, and hoped that it could be repeated.

I was not prepared for the surprise of finding Ian Cartwright waiting in my room when we got back. He was speaking heatedly with Klermans, who broke off when he saw me, and left to attend to the patients waiting downstairs. Cartwright was in an animated mood.

'It's good to see you, old chap. I'm cutting this fine, I know, but the powers-that-be thought I should see you before I push off. There are a few loose ends to be tied up.'

I nodded my agreement, for the moment being on my guard and unable to think of anything to say.

'Come on, Harrison, show a little interest! Ye Gods, I've been over here for more than four months, and now I'm on my way home at last.'

So that was it. I was very relieved to know that his presence had nothing to do with the interview in the deserted house.

'You say you are on the way home?' I queried, 'but how on earth will you manage with that game leg of yours?'

'No problem at all,' he replied excitedly. 'These people take care of everything. I'm not walking, old boy... not a single bloody step... no, I'm going home in style. By Lysander! Can you imagine my luck?'

He was beside himself with excitement. His face was flushed, and the words came tumbling out.

'And, to cap it all, if there is room in the back seat for you as well, you are coming with me! How about that, old chap?'

It was as though I had been hit with a rock. I just gaped at

Cartwright, trying to grapple with the ridiculous prospect of being land-ed at some RAF airfield in the south of England.

'What's wrong, old boy? You look as though I've shaken you rigid.'

He certainly had. This revelation was a disaster. 'No, it's all right,' I said, finding words at last. 'I just can't take it in. I had no idea they were using aircraft to get us home.'

'Oh, no. It's not that,' he said. 'It's just that there is one coming in tonight... full moon, old chap... or haven't you noticed? It's bringing in someone special, I think, and some equipment and money. I'm dead lucky. The Lysanders usually have much more important work to do but, as the back seat will be empty when they return, they've decided to evac-uate me as walking wounded. It was my idea that you should come along, if the load was right and there was room.'

At that moment, Madeleine came in, all smiles, carrying a large tray on which were two large bowls of soup, hunks of cheese, and slices of rye bread.

'I thought you would like your meal served here while you talk busi-ness,' she said, setting the try down on the writing-desk. *'Bon appétit.'*

As we ate, my mind raced. What could I do to avoid the *Kondor* operation coming to an abrupt end? Obviously, I could not allow myself to be taken anywhere with Cartwright in close attendance: thankfully, time was on my side, since a decision still had to be made as to whether the Lysander could take two of us in the rear cockpit, and so I decided to delay any action until the last moment. *Kondor* would be safe if there was no room for me. If it proved otherwise, I would have to make a bolt for it on the way to the landing strip.

It was difficult to see anything but disaster ahead for my rôle in *Kondor* but, in any event, there was nothing to be lost by trying to gain some last-minute information. I therefore began to pump Cartwright for details of the escape organisation with which he had been working. He was surprisingly forthcoming, although he did stress that, because of tight security, those involved only told him what he needed to know. I asked him about the lovely young woman who had brought me to Klermans' house. He replied jokingly that she appealed to him as well.

In fact, she was considered 'the belle of the ball' by almost everyone. But, unfortunately, she was something of a Puritan: utterly dedicated to her work, with no time at all for frivolity or romance. She was held in great respect by an escape line known as Phoenix: she was called Emilie, but that was probably a code name. The Phoenix route was very important, perhaps the best in Belgium or anywhere else. From his minor position in the organisation, he knew nothing of the people really in control. He had been working in only a sector of the route. Overall control was located elsewhere; maybe in Brussels or Antwerp, or even in Paris.

The time soon came for Cartwright to leave. We shook hands, and wished each other good luck. He gave me my final instructions.

'Just sit tight for the time being, old boy. Get your things together, and be ready to leave at once. We ought to be on our way just before midnight, which means there should be a standby call to Klermans first, and then they will come for you at around nine o'clock. If there is no call by then you will know there has been a delay or that something has gone wrong... or, more probably, that we have a full load on board.'

Waiting for the call was sheer agony. I had no idea what would happen, or what I might have to do to save my skin. I had dinner with Klermans and his family in an atmosphere of great excitement. Never before had the family dealt with a 'parcel' in this way. They all knew I was about to escape by air, and did their best to put my fears at rest by wishing me all kinds of good luck. When the meal was over, Klermans came with me to my room, and watched as I put my few possessions together. He stopped me from filling the briefcase I had been given, because he had been told by Cartwright that there would be no room for it in the aircraft, and that it would be a hindrance in the rush to get away quickly.

By now, I was myself again. I had made my decision and, if they did come to collect me, then I would make a dash for it somewhere on the way to the landing strip, before I was handed over to those organising the departure of the Lysander. My part in *Kondor* would then be over. It would be pointless to do more than find my way back to Kreis with the information I had already gathered, and let the *Gestapo* do their best by interrogating those I could already list as helpers. At one point, I noticed

Klermans looking curiously at me because I was smiling to myself - a careless mistake on my part. I had been wondering what Kreis would do if his prodigy had indeed been flown to England in an enemy aircraft, and been taken to London to meet the very same intelligence organisation as that working with Phoenix in Belgium.

Klermans and I spent the time playing chess, and I won two games. We were into the third when the clock struck nine. We played on, but it was clear that Klermans could not concentrate. I deliberately delayed my moves as he grew more agitated and preoccupied while, at the same time, my spirits began to rise. By ten o'clock, it began to look as though I had been reprieved. Klermans had now lost all interest in the game, and sat at his desk with his head in a book. Just after midnight, the telephone rang. Klermans grabbed the receiver, listened but said nothing. He hung up, turned to me and said, almost apologetically:

'Your friend had to leave without you. Someone else had to take your place. He is on his way home. I am really sorry, my dear friend.'

I slept like a log. In fact, I was allowed to oversleep, and rose late. Nothing was said about the night's happenings and then, almost as a portent of my change of fortune, the weather broke. It blew a gale and rained heavily all day. I returned to my reading, and considered what next would need to be done to get closer to the nerve-centre of Phoenix. Klermans gave me a hint, the next day. In his study, he handed me my *Laissez-passer*, a passport which had been expertly forged, with my photograph impressed with the mark of the city of Antwerp. It declared that I was Flemish, one called André de Vougelaar, born in Hasselt, but living in Diest. My occupation was that of a commercial traveller, dealing in agricultural machinery and fertilisers, and I had a work permit which enabled me to travel in the Low Countries and France. The passport even had a special visa for a journey to Biarritz, of all places.

He gave me other things: a small commercial diary, and food and clothing coupons. He then took me through the rare occasions when I would be asked to show my identity documents, and we practised the responses I would need to make to challenges in both French and German. He began to address me as André, and I had to ask him why it had been decided I was to be Flemish when, at least, I did know some reasonable French, and could perhaps better pass as a Walloon. He said that it hardly mattered what identity I was given. Most routine examinations would be made by Germans who, in any case, knew very little French, or by Frenchmen with no idea of Flanders or the Flemish. He foresaw little trouble in my case, because I was far more knowledgeable than the usual Britisher he had helped in the past. In fact, he said, he often found it hard to believe I was British, because I appeared so cosmopolitan.

The following afternoon, Klermans brought a rather tired-looking, middle-aged woman to my room, and introduced her simply as Elvire. Her appearance belied an inner strength, which was soon apparent when she began to brief me on the next stage of my journey. She spoke rather poor English, sometimes lapsing into a kind of Anglicised French. In the style of a schoolmistress teaching a backward pupil, she went through every detail of what I would have to do on the way to my next hiding place.

She emphasised the rules that applied when an escaper was being guided, and warned me that, if anything went wrong, I would be left on my own. I had to follow her to Namur railway station, where I would present the ticket she gave me, and then board the train to Brussels, making sure I got into the same carriage, but to sit nowhere near her. On arrival in Brussels, there would be a change of guide, made in the entrance to the station. Another woman would take me to a large church, where I was to sit in the third row of chairs on the right of the aisle. Then, after a little while, I would be contacted by a man wearing a Belgian red, black and yellow *boutonniére*, who would lead me to the next safe house.

She repeated these instructions, and tested me with a few questions. She asked if I knew how to conduct myself in a church, and was pleased when I told her I was a Roman Catholic. She expected no trouble during the journey. Anyone wanting to see my ticket would just say *'Billet'*, and I should always keep it ready for inspection. The train was a fast one, stopping only at Ottignes and Gembloux. Did I have any questions?

There was one which had remained uppermost in my mind throughout her briefing: 'Madame, what am I to do if something does go wrong? Where should I go?'

'My dear man, I have told you this journey is just routine and quite straightforward. If anything untoward should happen, then I will have nothing to do with you. Surely it would not be beyond your capability to find your way back to Namur?'

I said goodbye to the Klermans family at breakfast the next morning. I had to admit I had grown to like them, particularly the ladies. I was touched when *Madame* gave me a small gold Star of David brooch, which she said would protect me against the evil Germans; but I was to be sure to keep it out of sight.

CHAPTER NINETEEN

I was packed and ready when Elvire arrived, just before nine o'clock. I took her somewhat aback by greeting her in the Belgian fashion, with three kisses on the cheeks, but she was pleased with this gallantry - realising it was an attempt by a Britisher to play his part properly. She checked that I had the single ticket from Namur to Brussels which she had given me, and handed me newspapers to read on the train. She then bade farewell to the Klermans, and I followed her out of the house, walking briskly about twenty metres behind her, down into Namur. At the railway station barrier, I presented my ticket to a uninterested collector and went in, carefully watching Elvire as she boarded the train. I followed, and sat at the end of a third class compartment from where I could keep her in sight. The train left on time. The journey to Brussels was uneventful but interesting, and just as Elvire had predicted. My ticket was inspected twice, and then retained by the collector. No one spoke to me or bothered me and, just before eleven thirty, we arrived at Brussels Midi.

I followed Elvire through the crowds leaving the station. Being on the tall side, she was easy to keep in sight. In the forecourt to the station she appeared to meet a friend. Together, they walked on for a while, and then parted company on a street corner. I switched my attention to the other guide. I did not know Brussels, as I had only been to the city twice before, and then only for a day or two. I soon gave up trying to establish my whereabouts as the new guide led me off, taking no chances on being followed, and constantly changing direction. At one stage, I could have sworn that we even completed a rectangular circuit through the narrow streets. However, after about twenty minutes or so, we arrived at a place I remembered - *La Place des Princes* - the truly beautiful medieval square set more or less in the centre of Brussels.

We wandered around the square for a while, mingling with the sightseers, who included many Germans. Now and then, we stopped to admire the beautiful displays of flowers for sale, but then set off into the old part of the city. After about a kilometre, we came out into a market place, at the top of which stood a fine old church. I watched carefully as my guide went in, after looking back at me to check that I was following. I went up to the foot of the steps at the main entrance, from where I could see, on the church notice board, that this was *L'Église de Notre Dame au Sablon*. I paused for a while, then entered the church, taking up the Water and paying my respects. I then passed through a heavy wooden screen and walked slowly up the aisle towards the altar, on the way passing my guide, who was sitting at prayer, head covered and bowed. I stopped in front of the altar, genuflected, and then withdrew to sit in the third row of chairs on the right of the aisle. As I did so, I noticed that the guide was already on her way out of the church.

As I sat there waiting, I offered a selfish prayer for the protection of my precious hide. Almost as an answer from above, a portly, well-dressed man came to sit near me, and I noticed at once that he was wearing the Belgian *boutonniére*. We sat alongside each other in silence for a minute or so; then he got up and left and, after a while, I followed him outside into the broad daylight. I stopped at the top of the steps to watch him crossing to the other side of the road. When he got there, he turned and waved his hand in my direction, and walked off, crossing a busy main road into an ornamental garden shrouded by trees. I followed him, going into the garden and around a large stone pond, in which many goldfish were swimming, and up a semi-circular flight of steps at the back of which, in ivy covered alcoves, stood statues of ancient notables. It was easy to follow him, because he walked slowly and with some difficulty.

We left the garden, and I followed him along a narrow street, *l'Avenue des Petits Carmes*. Halfway along, we passed an extensive barracks area, thronged with soldiers of the *Wehrmacht*. It occurred to me that this was probably the military headquarters for our occupancy of Brussels. We turned right at the end of the street, and made our way up to the wide *Avenue de l'Oison d'Or,* which we crossed into another busy thoroughfare. After about a hundred metres, we crossed to the other side, dodging a double tramcar in the process, and stopped at the entrance to an apartment building. Inside, we found there was no concièrge on duty, and we could not open the door to the lift. We slowly plodded up the staircase to the very top of the building where, on the fifth floor, the guide knocked on a door numbered 5C, and beckoned me forward. The door was opened, and I was ushered in. Thus I arrived at my second safe house. This one was very different. As a large apartment, it had a central reception room from which there were entrances to two or three bedrooms, a kitchen and a bathroom. It was well-furnished, the home of a Belgian widow, clearly of some means, who introduced herself, in perfect English, as *Madame* Françoise Gervaert. She welcomed me as a guest, she said, for as long as proved necessary, but only, as she half-jokingly put it, if I behaved myself and did as I was told. She reminded me that I was a fugitive Englishman about to be hidden in a busy house, in the very heart of Brussels. The *Boche* were in and out of the building every day, visiting their friends, mostly women, and one always had to be on the lookout for them, and for the wretched collaborators they came to see. There were many Belgians who did not like the British, and who had, long since, accepted the fact of a second German occupation. Such people were perhaps more dangerous than the *Boche*.

After my escort had left, *Madame* Gervaert showed me around the apartment, in which she lived alone. I was taken through the various rooms, and cautioned never to go near the windows, which were overlooked from other tall buildings across the street. She explained that, if the apartment were raided, I should make my escape through the bathroom window, and then either down the fire escape or across the roofs of the adjacent houses. She showed me how to open the window, and then pointed to a trapdoor in the ceiling: her expression became more serious.

'We must always be prepared for the worst. Your arrival has only added to my problems. Let me show you what I mean.'

She picked up a long bamboo rod, reached up and rapped three times on the trapdoor. There was a sound from above the door, which was then opened: a ladder was let down and I found myself looking up at the smiling face of a young man.

'Strewth, not another one,' he muttered in a sharp Cockney accent. 'Sorry chum, we're full up. No more room on top.'

Prodded by *Madame*, I climbed the ladder into a scene of utter disorder. In a large, well-lit, but incredibly stuffy attic, crammed with chairs, mattresses, piles of papers and books, were three men. *Madame* called up that she would leave me for the moment, and that my friends would explain everything. Dinner would be ready very soon. The youngster made the introductions.

'I'm Bob Green, rear gunner, and that one over there is another gunner, a mid-upper. He's Jim Broadhurst. The other one is our good friend, Flight Sergeant Teddy Kawalski. He doesn't say much, but then he's a bloody Pole. All the same, he is one of the best.' Looking across the attic, I acknowledged a broad-faced, blue-eyed, blond-headed Slav, lounging in a collapsible chair. He nodded to me, but did not smile.

'I'm George Harrison,' I said. 'Sorry I can't join the air-gunners' club. I'm just a pilot.'

'Tough luck,' said Green. 'Teddy's a pilot as well.'

I had really been looking forward to the comfort of one of the bedrooms down below, but now space had to be found for me to stay in this make-shift room, with its pervading smell of overheated bodies - and something else. Green, the self-appointed spokesman, allocated me a place to sit, or to lie down and stretch out. The trio told me that life in the attic was sheer hell, with nothing to do but read, sleep, and wait. The whole day had to be spent in the roof, with a break only in the evenings when they went down for a meal in the kitchen, and a wash and shave in the bathroom. They never wore shoes, and had to keep very quiet. At least twice a day, they went through a silent keep-fit routine, encouraged by the very fit Kawalski. Green's particular grudge was that he was guardian of what they called the 'honey bucket'. *Madame* Gervaert insisted on this being used, because too much flushing of the toilet would draw attention to the fact that she was not alone in the apartment. The honey bucket was kept in the far corner of the attic and Green, apparently the most junior among us, emptied it, cleaned it, and added the necessary chemicals.

I had my first meal with them when, about an hour later, we carefully and quietly went down to the kitchen. We returned to the attic after our various ablutions, talked about ourselves, and guessed at what might lie ahead. They seemed a little crestfallen when they learned I was commissioned, although only as a lowly Pilot Officer. At bedtime, I was shown where I would sleep, sharing one of the two double mattresses placed on either side of the attic. My companion was Broadhurst, a restless, excitable character who took ages to fall asleep. No sooner had he done so, than he began to breathe heavily, mutter to himself and then, with a stifled scream, he would roll over, holding his arms over his chest, and thrust himself away from the mattress. In my alarm, I got up and fumbled my way around to him in the darkness. The light was switched on. The other two were sitting up resignedly, as though familiar with this performance. Rubbing his eyes as he got back on to the mattress, Broadhurst apologised: 'Sorry, sir. I suppose we should have warned you. I have this nightmare every night. It's the same every time. I'm baling out, just as I did a month ago, and the plane's on fire... on fire, you see. I'm all right now, it's all over. I shall sleep now.'

Surprisingly, at first, I found life in the attic fascinating. I had all the time I needed to brush up my knowledge of the RAF and Bomber Command by means of careful questions. I was older than the two Sergeants and roughly the same age as Kawalski. The two Englishmen deferred to my rank and, now and then, sought my advice. I encouraged them to talk about every subject on which they held an opinion. The Pole was a different proposition. He kept very much to himself but, nonetheless, together, they were a mixture of worthwhile talents, bonded by a common desire to escape from the Germans and return to England. The Cockney, Sergeant Green, was just eighteen years old, but had made twenty-nine trips over Germany: he held the Distinguished Flying Medal, awarded after shooting down his second night-fighter. This one had badly damaged his Stirling, knocked out one engine, and killed two members of the crew.

He had no memory of what had happened when he was shot down. They had been attacking Bochum, and there must have been a tremendous explosion of some sort on the way back, because the only thing he remembered was coming to his senses whilst dangling under his opened parachute. He had landed on the steep roof of a farmhouse, with his 'chute tangled around the chimney stack, and had been left hanging down the side of the building, unable to get out of his harness. He had been there for an hour or so, trussed-up like a chicken, until someone coming back to the farm in the early hours had seen him, and used a ladder to get him down. Safely inside the farmhouse, he was told that his rescuer had been out that night, looking for shot-down aircrew!

Sergeant Broadhurst was a pathetic introvert. He was still suffering from the shock of being shot down, but it was clear that the strain of operational flying had been affecting him for some time. His fears of flying over Germany were deep-rooted, and I sensed he was on the verge of a breakdown. He had baled out of a Halifax which had been attacked by a night-fighter, and he, too, had been lucky to find help just a day later, when he had been found asleep in a barn, somewhere near the Dutch border with Belgium. He had then been hidden in a nursing home and, after a month, had been taken under control by an escape group and brought to Brussels. His motivation to escape was half-hearted. If things had been otherwise, I believe he would have thankfully accepted captivity. I saw little threat from these two simple Englishmen. They accepted me as their superior, and I was sure that neither had the slightest suspicion of me.

The Pole, however, was a different matter. There was something about him that constantly kept me on guard: I felt his eyes on me at all times. Flight Sergeant Kawalski spoke poor English, and only slightly better French. He had difficulty in expressing himself, and volunteered little information except when the conversation turned to the subject of Germany and the Germans, whom he hated beyond all reason. He was thirty, and had been a fighter pilot in the Polish Air Force. During the unprovoked attack on his country, as he put it, he had been shot down while ground-strafing a German transport column. He had landed unhurt, and managed to stay ahead of the advancing troops, but had been unable to get back to his unit. He had travelled on foot and by train until reaching Odessa, where he had found a French ship about to return to Marseilles. He had then joined the French Air Force and flown the Potez light bomber until, during the *Blitzkrieg*, his squadron had been wiped out. Again, he had avoided capture, this time by getting to Bordeaux, where he had been picked up by a ship of the Royal Navy and taken to England. He had then joined the RAF as a bomber pilot. He had been given the rank of Flight Sergeant, and posted to No. 301 (Polish) Squadron, where he had flown Wellingtons until shot down.

I had to admire Kawalski. Here was a mature and determined man who would, I knew, fight to the bitter end for what he believed. Although I realised there was a danger in doing so, I found myself curiously drawn to him, and he gradually responded to my questioning, opened up, and told me more about himself. He had been born in Warsaw, where his mother and sister had been killed during our devastating bombing. He was obsessed with revenge; it seemed to dominate his existence, yet gave him the ability to succeed where any ordinary person would have given up. When shot down, just outside Wilhelmshaven, he had been badly wounded in the back by a fragment of flak - he showed me the large scarred hole to prove it - yet had survived for days without any medical attention. He had stolen a bicycle, clothes and food, and had got as far as the Dutch border before managing to get help. The shrapnel had been dug out of his festering wound, and he had carried on, still on his own, across the Netherlands until, somewhere in Flanders, he was picked up by the escape group.

He told me this story as a matter of fact, modestly, and without frills. He did, however, let slip that he had been awarded the *Virtuti Militari* by the exiled Polish Government in London, and that, after more than forty operations over Germany, he had been decorated with the Distinguished Flying Medal by the British. His constant worry was that the escape organisation doubted his story, and possibly questioned his identity. He was a Pole, but looked like a German. His English was poor, but he spoke good German and, from what he had been told, the escape route people had never before seen a Polish flyer. He was glad that I had arrived because now, as an RAF officer, I would be able to vouch for him.

My fascination with the attic scene soon ended when a heat wave set in, and the temperature and fetid atmosphere in the room became almost unbearable. *Madame* got us an electric fan, which was kept going at all times, but we had to sit and sleep in our underclothes. We kept movement to a minimum, and the trap door open all the time. Our tempers grew shorter, and we often snapped at each other over trivialities. Kawalski's exercise sessions were suspended, as we were physically beyond that degree of effort. In the end, we simply had to get out of the attic during the day, keeping out of sight by spending most of our time sitting in the kitchen, which had no windows.

We endured three days of this purgatory, wondering when and how we would ever leave and move on down the route. Then, at least for me, there was a dramatic respite. During the mid-morning, as I languished in the kitchen, *Madame* received a telephone call, as a result of which she asked me to get dressed. In guarded tones, she told me that I was to be taken somewhere, and that my guide, the same man who had brought me from the church, was downstairs waiting for me. None of us had the slightest idea what was happening. I reasoned that all must be well in my case because, if there were doubts about me, I would surely not be entrusted to the care of a fat, middle-aged guide. I dressed quickly and *Madame* checked me over, saying that I would pass inspection. She gave me some Belgian banknotes, and wished me luck.

CHAPTER TWENTY

I easily recognised my guide, who was standing outside on the pavement, leaning on a walking stick and looking impatient. This time, we shook hands and he wished me good morning. He handed me a tram ticket, and I followed him across the road to the *Arret* where, after a short wait, we boarded a double-tram. He sat in a seat at the front, while I chose to stand at the other end. We travelled to the end of the line, and got off at the Terveren terminus. There, we began to stroll out into the countryside. It was a truly lovely day, and my spirits were high as I followed my guide, who walked slowly and ponderously in the hot summer sunshine.

Fortunately, there was not far to go. He stopped at the entrance of what appeared to be a private estate and, passing between two imposing stone pillars, we walked up a long carriageway, lined with linden trees, to a small château. I followed the guide to the back of the building, through a large conservatory, and eventually to a back door, which was opened by a maidservant. She took us to a kitchen, where the guide stayed, while I was led into the spacious main hallway, to be greeted by a well-groomed, aristocratic looking man of about fifty. We shook hands.

'It was good of you to come, *Monsieur*,' he said in French. 'I must apologise for getting you to walk here, but it is fine weather, is it not? Please come with me.'

We crossed the hallway, and he opened a door for me to enter a reading room where two people were standing at the window, one of whom was Emilie.

'I know you have already had the pleasure of meeting our dear Emilie. This is Benedict, and all you need to know about me is that my name is Arthos.'

He motioned us to a highly polished table in the centre of the room.

'Let us sit. We have things to discuss but, first... we must have coffee.'

He went over to the fireplace, and pulled the tapestry cord of a bell. I felt ill at ease. I was certainly not in another safe house, but among important people who perhaps had something to do with the control of the escape route. I had not prepared myself for this and knew, full well, that I had to be careful. It could even be that I was under suspicion, and that the stage was being set to trap me. Real coffee and chocolate biscuits were brought in and left on the table for Emilie to serve. We sat quietly, savouring these luxuries, until Arthos began to speak, haltingly, in English.

'We know about you from our good friend, Cartwright. He is now safe in England. He left us because it was his duty to return. He helped us... he was a good officer.' Frowning, he put his hand to his brow and, lapsing into French, spoke briefly to Emilie, and then addressed me once again.

'It is not possible for me to speak well in the English. *Pardonnez-moi*. Emilie will speak for me.'

It had apparently been forgotten, that I could have understood them easily in French, but I thought it best to keep quiet, and Emilie took up the story.

'Ian told us that he had given you some information about our work. That was unwise but, fortunately, no harm has been done. We want to speak to you about the importance of the work we do, and about what is always our greatest concern. To be successful, it is essential that we keep the best security we can. Our lives, and those of the ones we help, are dependent upon our utmost vigilance. The Germans will do anything they can to destroy us. We are in constant danger, not only from our cursed collaborators, but now, it seems, from the *SD* - German Secret Police, and the *Gestapo*.'

She paused, looked to the others as if for confirmation of her words, and then, directly at me. I felt that my moment of judgement had come.

'Only a few months ago,' she continued, 'we had to deal with a serious problem in France, where the *Gestapo* had used French collaborators, posing as French flyers who had escaped from Germany, in an attempt to penetrate our escape routes.'

She pierced me with her look. Her voice was cold as steel. 'We dealt quickly with them... but now, we have good reason to believe that the Germans themselves have taken up this subterfuge, and are trying to do the same thing here in Belgium. This time, we believe their own people are disguised as RAF flyers.'

My God! She was toying with me, just as a cat would with a mouse. I had been found out! My consternation must have been apparent as I slumped in my chair.

'Yes, *Monsieur*, I can see how surprised you are. The matter is deadly serious and, unless we find them, it could perhaps mean the end of our work. We want you to help us... as Ian Cartwright did... but only for a while. Then we will make sure that you are speedily sent home. We need the help of someone who has detailed knowledge of the RAF and England, and who can work with us to eliminate this threat.'

I hoped that no one around the table could detect my immense relief. My heart was pounding. I had thought that the game was up, and that I would have to fight for my survival, and now it was all, unbelievably, too good to be true. They were actually inviting me to join them them in the search for those, like myself, who were set upon destroying them! I held my head down and kept my eyes averted whilst I quietly replied, 'Of course I will.' I then looked up, expectantly, at Emilie, who spoke again.

'We have good reason to believe that the Germans are expertly disguising their agents so that we will pick them up and take them into our organisation. We do not believe, however, that the enemy knows how well we check and double-check and even, sometimes, refer our problems to British Intelligence. But now, there seems little time for that. The position is serious. We actually have two men under suspicion. One, we are virtually certain, is German, while the other is actually being hidden with you by *Madame* Gervaert. I am sure you know who I mean - Flight Sergeant Kawalski.'

I could not contain my surprise; everyone could see it in my startled expression.

'Yes, *Monsieur*, we would like him to be your first assignment. Will you do whatever you can, and as quickly as possible, to find out if indeed he is a German implant. Be careful, because, if he is bogus, we will not want to lose him. We already have him under close observation, and you have only to alert us should you fail to detain him.'

I was now completely composed. This heaven-sent opportunity was too good to be true, but I knew I would have to use my wits to make the most of it. Surely, this sudden turn of events had brought me almost to the very heart of Phoenix or, at least, close to those who knew where it lay.

'I have already found Kawalski difficult to get to know,' I told them, 'He keeps very much to himself, and doesn't speak good English. He knows a little French, but I believe he understands and speaks German, yet makes no secret of the fact. I'm sure I can make progress, because he has already confided in me that he suspects you have doubts about him.'

'I hope you will be able to make your decision quickly,' said Emilie. 'There is great danger, and we can take no chances. Tomorrow morning, Benedict will come to you for your answer, and we shall then take action, one way or the other. And, by the way, you can tell your friends, including Kawalski if you are certain that he is genuine, that they will soon be on their way... but without you. In your case, we shall let London know that Pilot Officer Harrison will be returning a little later.'

'You mentioned another suspect?' I asked.

'Yes, there is another,' said Emilie. 'We will need your advice on him as well, although we have every reason to believe that we have, this time, trapped a German spy. He cannot get away and, at the right time, we shall want your help to learn the details of what seems to be a remarkable German plot. But that is for the future. First, please deal with Kawalski.'

With that, she stood up, and so did the others. The meeting seemed to be over.

'It so happens that I have to go into Brussels,' said Arthos. 'I can take you and your friend, who is waiting outside, and drop you somewhere near where you are living. It will then be only a short walk for you.'

We returned to Brussels in what seemed to be an official car, and were dropped off by the forecourt to the Royal Palace.

My return to the stifling attic was greeted with surprise and a clamouring for news. Where had I been and what had happened? *Madame*

Gervaert had said nothing to them after my departure: in fact, I was reasonably certain that she was quite unaware of the reason I had been taken to the château. I decided to hold back nothing. I told them that the Resistance people wanted to know more about us and, because I was the only one who spoke French, I had been asked questions which I had answered to the best of my ability. Above all, they were anxious to get us on our way, but first wanted to be absolutely certain of our identities.

Kawalski drew me aside, and asked if there had been any mention of him and whether, or why, the Resistance group seemed to have doubts about him. I had already decided that I would not prolong his agony. I told him that he had indeed been under suspicion, but that I had been instrumental in giving him a clean bill of health. I had convinced my questioners that he was a genuine member of the RAF, saying that, with his operational career, he was of more value to Bomber Command than the rest of us, and that in any case, the awful wound in his back had certainly not been self-inflicted. I added that all of us had been under suspicion, as was to be expected. Now, all was well, and our little group would very soon be on the escape route, but without me. For reasons I could not divulge, I had to stay behind and would be moved to another safe house in the morning.

Benedict arrived early the next day. Alone with him in the sitting room, I told him I was absolutely certain that Kawalski was genuine. I gave him a detailed account of Kawalski's background, which I had written down during the night, and assured him there would be no risk to Phoenix if he were returned to England. Benedict was pleased, and thanked me for clearing up a matter which he, all along, had thought was straightforward: the other man being held by Phoenix was his real problem. I then said goodbye to the other three, wished them well, and hoped that we would, one day, meet again. Kawalski, for once, put aside his usual reserve and, as we shook hands, hugged me to his chest and muttered a heartfelt, 'Thanks be to God.' I paid my respects to *Madame* Gervaert, and thanked her for all she was doing to help us, and then we left.

Benedict clearly had some connection with the Church, because my next abode was his house in the grounds of a theological college, very close to the *Luftwaffe* airfield at Évere, on the outskirts of Brussels. There

I was given the room used by Ian Cartwright during the latter part of his convalescence: spacious, well-furnished, with a wonderful double-bed, and overlooking the college grounds. I was left to myself until lunchtime, when Benedict returned from some duty in the college. Together we ate a good meal, which had been prepared by a housekeeper, a taciturn old woman whom I had seen only briefly on my arrival. During the meal, Benedict told me that he was a Doctor of Theology, and a tutor at the nearby College of Divinity. We talked of religion, and he said that he could easily and safely arrange for me to join him at devotion, if I so wished. His mood then changed: becoming very serious, and speaking slowly in French, he returned to the subject of Kawalski.

'I have readily accepted your opinion of Sergeant Kawalski, but I would like to know how you can be so certain he is not a renegade? If you are wrong about him, we could face great danger. If you have the slightest doubts, we can still, very easily, put matters right.'

'No, Doctor, I have no doubts about the man. I am certain that he is a valuable member of the RAF. There are many hundreds of Poles in both Fighter and Bomber Commands. Kawalski is with Number 301 Squadron, part of Number 1 Group, based mainly in Lincolnshire, to which my own squadron belongs. You should have seen the huge wound in his back, which he said was caused by anti-aircraft fire over Wilhelmshaven: that, incidentally, was a raid in which I took part myself. The wound must have been neglected for some time while he was evading capture, and had festered badly. Even the most fanatical German would hardly have gone to such extremes, simply to cover his tracks.'

Benedict was clearly reassured by this argument, but told me he still had very grave misgivings about the other suspect, whom I was soon to meet.

That afternoon, I had the pleasure of seeing Emilie again. She had come to hear more of my appraisal of Kawalski. Speaking in English, I gave her my candid opinion. She asked a few casual questions, and then said she agreed with me; in fact, her woman's intuition had always told her there was nothing of the renegade about him. Laughingly, she blamed the suspicion on Arthos and Benedict who, from their lofty and protected positions, had difficulty in understanding the ways of ordinary people. I began to appreciate her authority and position in Phoenix. She would ensure that Kawalski would stay with his group, and leave Brussels as soon as possible. She thanked me for my help, which had been particularly valuable when there was so much to worry about along the line. The German threat to break Phoenix was ever-present, at a time when there were literally hundreds of brave boys needing its help.

She then explained that I had been selected from a number of RAF officers being held in safe houses in and around Brussels, to help them during this difficult time. I had dealt quickly with the Kawalski problem, and that had pleased her. But there still remained the other suspect to be investigated, although the time was not yet right for me to interview him. I would stay with Benedict and, while awaiting this particular assignment, I could make myself useful by checking some of the other evaders being held in various safe houses in the Brussels area. One could never be too careful. Some of these boys were, understandably, still in a state of shock from their experiences, and it might well be dangerous to move them too soon. I would, however, only be detained for as long as it took to establish the true identity of the other suspect. With any luck, I should be on my way home in a matter of weeks.

Throughout this discussion, I had listened intently and concentrated on details which I would have to remember for the time when Operation *Kondor* was completed and we could set about destroying Phoenix. But I found it increasingly more difficult to accept that this lovely woman was indeed my enemy. I was being drawn towards her by her manner, her appearance and, above all, by her femininity. She was out of the ordinary, so different to the women I had known in Germany. She was someone for whom a man could have real affection; someone whom I could easily love and cherish. I began to realise that I might be creating yet another problem for myself, and that I had to control the feelings growing within me.

The first task I was given was to check on three evaders hiding in a farm just outside Brussels, near the village of Hoeilaart. I went there with Benedict, who watched everything I did. Two of the men were from the same crew, while the other was an American serving with the Royal Canadian Air Force. They were suitably surprised when I revealed that I was an RAF officer, also on my way back. All were forthcoming with information on their squadrons, and how they had been shot down. None seemed in the least nervous, excitable or apprehensive. I gave Benedict a case-history of each evader before we left the farm. I was naturally interested in getting to know as much as possible about this safe house, and the people who operated it. I had a fruitful talk with the farmer who owned the place. He was a veteran of the Great War, helped by his two sons, one of whom had lost a leg when serving in the Belgian Army during our *Blitzkrieg* in 1940.

Two days later, this time in the company of a good-looking blonde girl called Natalie, we went to a fine suburban house in the southern suburbs of Brussels to question two RAF officers, one of whom held the highest rank I had so far encountered: he was a Group Captain. I knew I had to be on my mettle this time, and avoid being questioned myself by someone who would have a comprehensive knowledge of his Service. I therefore held back my identity until almost the very end of the interrogation when, as I had expected, the Group Captain, who commanded a bomber station in Yorkshire, began to question me, first saying that, from the start, he had known I was English. Whilst deferring to his senior rank, I took pains to caution him that the less he knew about me the better. I was working on particular matters involving the escape organisation with the approval of British Intelligence. He seemed satisfied with this explanation, and wished me every success.

He was a remarkable man. He explained his immaculate appearance, being dressed, as he was, in a beautifully-cut lounge suit with matching shirt, tie and shoes. Although, as a Station Commander, he did not have to fly operationally, he chose to do so regularly, flying in turn with every crew on his Station. He did this to boost morale while, at the same time, being able to learn more about his men's capabilities, in the best way possible. He always flew prepared for emergencies. He wore an over-sized battledress over the very suit he was wearing now, and even carried a trilby hat, tucked inside his battledress blouse, to complete his travelling ensemble. He believed he had made a flying start to his evasion, and was determined to break the record for the fastest return to England.

CHAPTER TWENTY-ONE

I kept my spirits up by continually reminding myself that I would be moved out of Brussels as soon as I had interviewed the other suspect. He was being held somewhere under guard by Phoenix, but I was told nothing about this until one evening, after I had returned to Benedict's house. I had been out with Natalie, interrogating a Sergeant Pilot held in Ottignes, and the matter of the dubious second man was broached by Benedict at dinner. He asked my opinion on the curious nature of a certain man's capture. Almost a month ago, a woodcutter in the Ardennes had found this airman, unconscious and bleeding badly from a severed artery in his broken leg, lying under his parachute, deep in the forest.

He had managed to stop the bleeding with a tourniquet, and had then somehow carried him to a doctor in the village nearby. Because of the seriousness of the man's injuries, he had been taken to a private nursing home, where he underwent an emergency operation to save his life. It had been a case of 'touch and go'. The man had remained unconscious throughout, and had then developed a fever, so serious that he had had to be kept under constant observation. The fever had worsened and then, to everyone's amazement, the airman, now in delirium, had begun to babble in German. A German-speaker was brought in to listen to his ramblings about endless walking, *verdammte Engländers*, concealment, a bird of some sort, a Condor they thought.

I was dumbstruck. There was little doubt that my colleague Weindl was in the hands of Phoenix, and this meant that I was also in a serious position. Benedict continued with his story. The man was now kept under armed guard at all times. As he had started to regain consciousness, he had been challenged in German and had made a few responses until, when fully awake, he had realised where he was and that something was wrong. He had remained silent, even when addressed in English and French. The man was damning himself with silence, so drugs had been used to get him to speak. He had responded to questions in German by answering in both German and English, and to those in

English he fervently replied in German. He had shown a determined resistance to the truth drug, never revealing his identity until, at the very end, he had given the number and name on his identity discs.

'You can see how serious this is for us,' said Benedict. 'We have little doubt that this man is an implant, and that the Germans have a new and deadly plan to defeat us. We are convinced that he is German, although we have heard him speaking with an American accent. Is it possible that you have Germans serving in the RAF? Many Germans were forced to leave their country before the war.'

'Yes, he could be Jewish,' I said quickly, clutching at straws.

'No, he is not.' said Benedict. 'That thought had occurred to us, and we examined him. We must know everything possible about him. We have had trouble like this before with our own collaborators, but never with Germans. We want you to do your best to find out more about him, and whether there are any more of them.'

Once again, I had inadvertently been placed in a dangerous situation, perhaps, this time, one almost impossible to rectify. I could only fear the worst for Weindl, and wondered what should be my next move. It would be out of the question for me to go to his rescue, and any interview with him ran the risk of us both being exposed, which would bring an abrupt end to *Kondor*. I had to speak up, to say something to hide my growing apprehension.

'Do you have any idea who this man really is? How was he dressed?'

Without a word, Natalie opened her handbag and withdrew a pair of RAF identity discs, stamped with the rank, name and serial number of a Flight Sergeant MacDonald, the very discs Kreis had given Weindl at Monschau.

I was left with my mind in turmoil as to my immediate future. I tried to think what I could do to avert the possible end of *Kondor*. I wondered whether I should contact the *Gestapo* in Brussels and, thereby, at least attempt to save Weindl. That, however, would entail the risk of having to meet him under the close scrutiny of Phoenix; otherwise I would have no idea where he was being held or what information I could give the *Gestapo*. The timing of my actions would be critical. Even if I could manage to confuse the Belgians for a while, their security was so tight that Weindl would very probably be dead before the *Gestapo* could reach him. I would then have to abandon *Kondor,* since I, too, would have become suspect. I already knew enough about Phoenix to damage them considerably. However, they could no doubt recover from any losses resulting from my knowledge of their work, which was, after all, limited to the Brussels area. I would, I supposed, be able to bring Arthos, Benedict and Emilie to book, but the other leaders and the unknown extent of the escape organisation would remain. Phoenix would find new recruits, and carry on with its remarkable work.

I reasoned that, somehow, I had to protect myself and make the most of the incongruous position I had been given in Phoenix. If Weindl were in full possession of his senses, he would understand the golden opportunity I had to make *Kondor* a success, although realising that he, personally, was doomed. *Kondor* was all-important, and could still be a going concern.

At breakfast the next morning, Benedict said nothing about our conversation of the night before. He gave me my next assignment, which was to interview two Sergeants hidden, of all places, in *Madame* Gervaert's attic. They had taken the places of Green, Broadhurst and Kawalski, who were now in Paris. Benedict had arranged that I would conduct the interviews in the company of Natalie. The job would not take very long, and I should be back by early afternoon. Before leaving, I could not resist asking Benedict when I might see Emilie again. He looked at me with a smile, shook his head, and wagged his finger at me.

'My dear young fellow, the lovely Emilie is not with us for the moment. She is very busy, but she will be seeing you again, do not fear, long before you are on your way home.'

I had already become used to the various forms of public transport in Brussels, and how comparatively easy it was to get around the city, even though it meant that most transportation was always crowded. And so it was on this occasion. With thoughts of Weindl and his problems at the back of my mind, I walked to the tram terminus about a kilometre away, where I found Natalie waiting. Together we boarded a packed double-tram, and settled down for the journey into the centre of

Brussels. The weather was good. The sun was shining as we rattled away, with every seat taken and many people having to stand. I had found a seat at the back-end of the second car. Natalie was somewhere in the other. Throughout the journey, my mind was preoccupied with the plight of poor Weindl. Then, as we were slowing in the road alongside the *Gare du Nord*, I looked out and saw a *Kübelwagen,* with a *Wehrmacht* officer signalling to the tram driver to stop.

The tram pulled up abruptly and, within seconds, was surrounded by armed soldiers. The officer, a *Leutnant,* supervised the action. There was panic aboard the tram as various people did their best to get out, but the soldiers had taken control of the exits. Then, one by one, we were ordered to get out, and were passed through a screen of soldiers who counted out twenty of us, sixteen men, including myself, and four women, and lined us up on the pavement. The remaining passengers, including Natalie, were ordered back onto the tram, which then drove off.

Our protests were ignored. Those of us who tried to object by moving away were threatened, and then beaten with rifle butts. We were then each handcuffed, forced into the back of a waiting Magirus lorry, and driven off, standing jammed together in a terrified group, holding on to each other for support. We were taken to the German military headquarters in Brussels and grouped together, still handcuffed, in a room. We were told by an *SS Sturmführer*, who spoke excellent French, that, unless those who had killed a German soldier during the night were handed over to the German authorities within the next twenty-four hours, each of us would be executed.

Wails of protest were quickly stifled. We were told to keep quiet, or else. A few dissenters were savagely beaten. I kept my mouth shut, and just stood quietly by, marvelling at yet another incredible change of fortune. Then our handcuffs were removed, and we were taken downstairs where we were left, four to a cell, to await our fate. My three companions were utterly demoralised, but I found it hard to feign terror, because I knew I had little to fear. At the right time, I would make my identity known. No matter how things went, whether or not the Belgians produced the culprits, there would always be a time and a place for me to get away from this group of unfortunates. I therefore tried to give the impression, as I sat alone in a corner, that I had resigned myself to the inevitable, and to my Maker. And so, in this way, we passed the remainder of the day, without food or water, or any contact with those outside.

We spent a restless night, finding it almost impossible to sleep on the hard wooden floor. We were fed in the morning, but given no opportunity to wash. The twenty-four-hour deadline would expire at mid-day, and I began to prepare myself for the right opportunity to reveal my true identity. It would have to be done in such a way that only Germans could hear what I had to say. I thought the time had come when we were taken from our cell and upstairs to a large room, where we were assembled in a very sorry-looking group. An *SS Sturmbannführer* faced us, together with the *Sturmführer* we had seen the previous day, apparently present to act as interpreter. I also noticed, in the background, two civilians. The *Sturmführer* addressed us in a high-pitched voice.

'It has been decided to delay your punishment for another day. Your government has assured us that the culprits will be found, and we are prepared to believe them. However, if this has not been done by noon tomorrow, your sentence will be carried out, at once.'
I could feel the general release of emotion; in fact, instinctively, I found myself affected by it. The two civilians came forward and sat at a desk where, each in turn, we had to provide our names and addresses, and those of our next-of-kin. As we stood in line, patiently waiting, someone began softly to whistle *La Brabaçonne*, the Belgian national anthem, which was taken up by most of the group until soldiers forced them to stop with threats and blows. That afternoon we were allowed to wash and shave, and even to walk in the guarded quadrangle. We were given a reasonable meal later in the day, and then locked into our cells.

This sadistic performance was repeated on the second day when, again, we were told that the execution would take place at a given time, the next day. Most were still resigned to their fate, believing that the delays were merely a German perversion. The *Boche* were born with sadism deep in their hearts, so they said. I knew otherwise, and was convinced that everything possible was being done by the Belgians to avert these executions. The delays seemed to suggest to me that something had already been achieved, and that the German authorities were in the process of making a final decision.

I was proved right. Early in the morning of the third day we were released, without any warning. We had to go through a formal procedure with the same two Belgian clerks, and signed a prepared statement absolving the German authorities of any misconduct during the past three days. A most curious performance, I thought, and surely entirely pointless. News of our expected release must have been announced by someone in authority because, when we got outside, we were met by a crowd of relatives, friends and newspaper men. I was pleased to see Natalie among them, and we left quickly, this time walking all the way back to Benedict's house, separated by a discreet distance.

The taking of the hostages had been the major item of news in Brussels that week. Phoenix had, of course, been concerned, but their major worry had been what I might be forced to do or say; and what could happen if the Germans had discovered that I was British, and had then subjected me to expert interrogation by the *Gestapo*. They had reasoned that I would naturally claim the protection of the Geneva Convention but, if so, they might well have suffered as a consequence.

I was told that the work for our release had been co-ordinated by an operational Resistance organisation within the city, working with the Mayor and a government department directed by Arthos. Within the stipulated twenty four-hours, the dead bodies of two Belgians, with ropes suitably arranged around their necks, had been handed over to the *Gestapo*. Our release had been delayed because the Germans had known that revenge had been taken on two collaborators who had been working with the *Gestapo*. There had been protracted negotiations between the Belgian Police and the German authorities, who were only too well aware that they had been out-foxed, but wanted to discover whatever they could, which, according to Benedict, was nothing at all.

The episode had been a trial for all of us, and my friends were anxious to know how close I had come to death. I made up a plausible story and then, for some reason, was left to myself in my room, with nothing to do but read and ponder on the future. It was as though I had been ostracised. Uppermost in my mind was the inevitable meeting with Weindl. It had been almost a week since the subject had been raised, and it could well be that my isolation was due to something Phoenix had learned from him during one of their drug-assisted interrogations. Perhaps it was time for me to part company with Phoenix. I had learned much about their organisation, enough to arrest at least three or four of the principals, and so give the *Gestapo* experts a strong foundation for destroying the route. I decided, however, to wait and see, and to ignore the advice given to me by Kreis. I set to, and compiled a cryptic listing of all contacts I had made during my travels from Balen to Brussels, which I intended to keep hidden on my person. If the Belgians found it, I would explain that it was my natural attempt to make a diary of events, so that the right people could, in due course, be suitably rewarded.

Then, without any warning, I was taken to a house within the old city area of Brussels, where I was faced with Benedict, Arthos and Emilie. The girl surprised me with her news.

'The time has come for you to leave us. We have decided that we are inviting unnecessary risks by asking you to help us. You have indeed been of assistance to us, and have done well, but it is wrong to use you in this way, and to delay your return to the RAF.'

This was certainly not what I had expected. I had prepared myself for a meeting with Weindl, but now, to my intense relief, it looked as though I had been given a reprieve: I would be able to continue my journey along the route, hopefully to its very end, as planned. However, my curiosity got the upper hand.

'What about the second task you had for me?' I asked.

Emilie had somehow sensed my doubts. 'I knew you would not have forgotten that matter - how we would deal with that German traitor. Had you not been taken as a hostage, then, of course, you would have been with us at Bourg Leopold a few days ago, when we had to make our decision.' Emilie's expression hardened.

'We were left in no doubt that this man, who called himself MacDonald, was a German spy, and that he had been sent to penetrate our route by impersonating a Canadian airman. We think that he might originally have been a Canadian, but he had a strong German background. Also, he had been well prepared for his work. He was, in the end, well aware that we knew he was a spy. We had to give him full credit for his bravery; no matter what we did, he would not talk, nor were we able to discover if there were any others, like him, involved.'

'What happened to him?' I asked, hesitantly.

'That, my friend, is none of your business,' she replied icily. 'Let us just say that this unfortunate episode is over and done with. It is you English who have the expression... the only good Germans are dead ones...'

There was no doubt that I had been exceptionally lucky. Fortune had favoured me from the very start, and now I would soon be on my way again, moving nearer to the goal I had been set by my masters in Berlin. I no longer had doubts about the morality of what I was doing; everything was for the good of my country.

The next day, I was moved from my comfortable quarters with Benedict to a small house in Scaarbeck. This place was managed by a retired naval officer who had moved from Zeebrugge, where he had once been the harbourmaster. There I met up with two more evaders who could not have been more different in age, looks and mannerisms.

The first was a dour, taciturn New Zealander, a Flight Lieutenant of at least thirty-five. He had been a sheep farmer before becoming a member of No. 77 Squadron, and had been almost at the end of his second tour in Bomber Command when shot down by a night-fighter. The other was like so many I had already met during my stay at *Dulag Luft*: a very young, callow Sergeant. He had been a Halifax gunner and had gone down on his third trip, also the victim of a night-fighter. I told them a little about Phoenix, and that I had been in Brussels for some time. Also that they would be on the move very soon and, that because I spoke French well, I would probably lead the group. Neither questioned this, nor my identity, although the New Zealander, James Cook, wondered why I was still only a Pilot Officer despite being also on my second tour. I countered with a well-prepared explanation - all members of my course at flying school had been Volunteer Reservists who had graduated as Sergeant Pilots and been rushed into Bomber Command. No one had had the time or inclination to worry about rank. The youngster, Gerald Smithson, just listened to the conversation of two officers, nodding his head now and then, but not daring to speak.

As we settled down, both began to defer to me and to seek my advice. Neither understood nor spoke a word of French, and their knowledge of where they were, and what would have to be done, was abysmal. Cook was fully aware of his limitations and jokingly referred to himself as a 'bloody Colonial from the other side of the world.' But he was, nonetheless, astute, mature and composed. He had been fitted out with a well-cut lounge suit, and gave the impression of a successful and assured Dutch or Belgian businessman. His disguise was suitably completed when he donned a dark brown trilby hat, which matched the colour of the expensive-looking brief-case he would carry. This was the man I would have to watch. Smithson, on the other hand, was a misfit who, to say the least, looked like an errant youngster just out of school. He was basically shy but, put at ease, became full of boundless energy, curious about everything, and forever asking questions. He had been poorly educated, but was sharp and a quick learner, doing his best to catch up with the demands and complications of a man's world.

I took time to prepare them for their first journey along the route. I explained that although there would always be a guide with us, they should take their instructions from me, because I would be the only one who properly understood what the guide had in mind. Under no circumstances should either of them attempt to answer questions put to them in French or German and, if the situation became difficult, then I would step in to explain that they were both deaf and dumb, and would be expecting me to speak for them. I dealt with other matters touching on personal hygiene, care of the feet, and the obvious value of the guide, whose safety was far more important than ours. I could not, however, resist a word of warning about the comeliness of some of the guides I had already met. Although these ladies were extremely attractive, physical contact with them was out of the question. Romance, of any sort, was the last thing they should think about.

We were together in this safe house for three days. During the last evening, we were told to be ready to move early the next morning. To my delight, it was Natalie who arrived just after nine o'clock to be our guide, and it gave me great pleasure to greet her warmly in the customary way. She was dressed smartly in a fawn-coloured business suit, which perfectly set off her blue eyes and blonde hair.

'What was that you told us about the ladies?' Cook said, with a twinkle in his eye.

Natalie looked questioningly at me and then, mischievously, in French, asked what he meant. I told her I had said Phoenix was blessed with the best-looking guides to be found anywhere. She laughed, and then began her briefing.

CHAPTER TWENTY-TWO

Her duty was to take us to Paris. We would be travelling on a mainline train which, unfortunately, would stop in Lille, where we would have to wait for about three hours, before changing to a different train. During the wait, we would be able to eat at a restaurant near the railway station, where arrangements had already been made for us. The only possible complication she foresaw was the unavoidable Customs check which would be made at Bassieux, on the border with France. She handed me the railway tickets to Paris, and assured me that there was little to worry about, provided we watched her every step and behaved sensibly. In the event of an emergency, which might lead to us losing contact with her, we would be on our own again. However, Phoenix had a large network, and we should try to get back into Belgium, where the best would be done to find us again. I passed on these instructions to Cook and Smithson, checked that they had their documents ready and in order, and told them that Natalie had put me implicitly in charge of our group. We then said farewell to our host.

Natalie went ahead, and we followed her, the three of us walking in a loose group about twenty metres behind. We took the tram into the centre of Brussels, where we got out to walk the rest of the way to the Gare du Midi. I was feeling remarkably at ease, despite having to come to grips with the seriousness of this new stage in the operation. Acting as an Englishman was all too easy, and none of the Britishers I had met so far had shown even the slightest doubts about me. How very right Kreis had been to take so much time and care with our preparations. By contrast with my own relaxed state, I could sense the tension in the other two as we mixed with the crowds on their way to work in the shops and offices. Cook walked with measured steps, head down as though his mind were concentrated on important matters. Smithson was exactly the opposite. He looked at everything we passed, his head and eyes forever on the move as though anxious to miss nothing. He walked with a spring in his step, and was evidently reacting to the excitement of being on the move. I had to wonder whether he would create his own problems; his ignorance of the world around him was so clear. On one occasion, I had to glare at him and then nudge him to stop whistling what was very probably a popular British tune!

We walked through the flower market in the *Place des Princes*, and on into the old part of the city. There was no difficulty in keeping Natalie in sight and, now and then, I looked back to see if anyone was following us. It was a long walk to the *Gare du Midi,* and when we got there we had to wait in the station forecourt for a while as Natalie greeted another young woman who, by her good looks, could well have been a relative. They embraced, linked arms and went on into the station. We followed, each showing our tickets for inspection at the barrier, and then up the steps onto the platform, where the train to Lille was already indicated. While we waited, Natalie left her companion and signalled to me that she wanted to speak. I went over to her, and she repeated her earlier instructions. She reminded me to keep her in sight at all times, and particularly during the Customs inspection at the frontier. She added that she did not expect to speak to us again until we arrived at Lille.

The train was packed. Somehow, the three of us managed to keep together, and to get into the same carriage as Natalie and her friend. They were able to find room to sit in a compartment, thanks to the courtesy of two German soldiers. We had no alternative but to stand jammed together in the corridor. We were surrounded by all manner of people, many of them sailors with sea-bags and personal kit. It proved to be a most uncomfortable journey. We spoke not a word to each other, and even the effervescent Smithson kept quiet, his face pressed against the window, watching the countryside slowly passing by. The sailors around us were very noisy, and I quickly gathered that they were a replacement U-boat crew, on their way to Nieuport. It was a relief when they left us at one of the many stops; not only did the noise level drop, but at last we had room to stand comfortably.

Notice of the approaching frontier check was heralded by a conductor, forcing his way along the corridor and repeating loudly, in French: 'Attention, all passengers. We are approaching Bassieux. You must descend with your baggage ready for inspection at the control. Have your documents ready.'

I saw that Cook understood some of this , but noticed the alarm spreading on Smithson's face. I spoke quietly to them, and told them to get their documents ready and that, when the train stopped, they were to take no notice of anyone except myself - not even of Natalie. Smithson was now becoming agitated, and his face was flushing; I was worried that he might lose his head, and do something foolish. I therefore diverted his thoughts by speaking to him loudly in French, and then offered him a hard mint toffee for him to suck. That did the trick. He took the toffee, put it in his mouth, and visibly began to relax. The train stopped a full length short of the only platform in the little station at Bassieux, so that the passengers had to climb down from the carriages onto the gravel border of the track. This proved to be a noisy, confused process, with French police and German soldiers shepherding everyone into a long three-abreast column which stretched the length of the train, and headed towards a row of desks where French Customs officials awaited us, armed German soldiers standing behind them.

Natalie and her friend were a little ahead of us. I had deliberately taken in hand an old lady whom I had helped to get down from the train, while Cook and Smithson were right behind us. There must have been hundreds in the column, but I could see, that the officials were dealing with everyone fairly quickly. As we moved along, the train steamed past us, and pulled up at the platform inside the station. Just before it stopped, a commotion broke out ahead of us, near the inspection tables. A man in a raincoat broke away from the column and ran headlong down the railroad enbankment, and off towards a fringe of trees. There were shouts to stop, and then a shot was fired. A French policeman and one of our soldiers went after him, but he was well away, and had already disappeared into the trees which stretched back into the Belgian side of the border.

Perhaps this sort of thing happened often, because no one seemed unduly concerned. The policeman and the soldier returned, and the column continued moving forward. I saw Natalie and her friend having their handbags inspected, possibly only because they were the best-looking females on the train, and then it was our turn. I took care to escort the old lady forward, and helped her with her belongings, trying to give the impression that I was her relative. We passed through with only a cursory glance being given at our papers, and it was the same with Cook and Smithson.

Back on the train, we noticed there were now seats available, single ones, here and there. However, we chose to stay together, and again stood in the corridor, this time right outside the door of the compartment in which Natalie was seated. After about half an hour, we arrived in Lille. I led my party through the ticket barrier. We then strolled across to the main bookstall, where Natalie was saying goodbye to her friend who, to my amazement, sauntered across the forecourt and, with a cheery wave, greeted what could be nothing other than another group of three British evaders on the move down the line! They were mirror images of us, one even carrying a briefcase and wearing a trilby hat. They had obviously recognised us as well, and I had to restrain Smithson from giving them the 'thumbs-up'. Needless to say, they were as surprised as we were: I could see it in their smiling faces.

Natalie had been watching us closely.

'Yes,' she said, 'just a few more parcels being delivered... nothing to concern you.

Looking somewhat preoccupied, she turned away, saying, 'Are you ready, my friends? It is time for you to eat... after that we must be off to Paris, but there will be no need for you to hurry. The train does not leave until three o'clock.'

The restaurant which had been chosen for us was in a narrow street just outside the station. As we walked there, Natalie told me it was used regularly by her organisation. She gave me a generous amount of French francs to pay for our meal. She said she would not be eating with us, but would be somewhere near at hand. I was to be in charge of the other two, but that should present little problem. All I had to do was be sure we were outside the building, waiting for her to collect us, at half past two. Natalie then left us at the entrance to the restaurant, and I passed the word on to Cook and Smithson. They looked at me anxiously, clearly worried about being left alone for the first time, and having to take a meal in strange surroundings.

I had to admit that I was beginning to feel some concern myself.

I knew there was little risk involved, but I had to be sure that all went well; that nothing would prevent my getting to Paris and further along the route.

'Cheer up, chaps,' was all I could say, 'there's nothing to it. Just keep quiet and leave everything to me. I can cope. Let's enjoy a decent meal for a change.'

With that, we entered a passageway, and climbed the stairs to the restaurant on the first floor. We were greeted at the door by a man, probably the manager, who seemed to know that we were expected. He had us seated at a corner table at the far end of the room, conveniently close to a fire exit. I also noticed that the wall clock was showing 12.45, giving us all the time we needed to take our meal at leisure. The restaurant was about half-filled and, not far from us, were two *Wehrmacht* soldiers, already well into their meal.

I did the ordering, going through the motions of asking the other two what they wanted, and receiving their nods of approval to my description of the dishes, spoken clearly in French for anyone to hear. I ordered a bottle of house red wine and, little by little, we settled down and began to relax. The meal was a good one, served at a steady pace and without any fuss. Cook was true to his briefing and kept quiet. The wretched Smithson, however... no doubt warmed by the unaccustomed wine... tried time and again to mutter an aside, or make some stupid comment. This was always with his head down, and in whispers. He was a damned nuisance and, as the restaurant began to fill to its capacity, Cook told him bluntly to shut up.

Throughout the meal, I had been checking that no undue interest was being taken in our presence. The waiter was a great help with his matter-of-fact manner, which kept attention away from our table, and by the end of the meal, we were feeling both satisfied and relaxed: I also felt relieved that all had gone well.

It was nearly two o'clock when the coffee was served. Smithson, who had been looking uncomfortable for a while, leant across to me and desperately whispered: 'I'm bursting for a pee. I can't hold out much longer. Can I go to the lavatory?'

I did not give this natural request another thought.

'Of course. It's over there, next to the cashier's desk. Through the curtains. But, for heaven's sake, do remember to keep your mouth shut.'

Smithson was on his feet in a flash. He dashed across the room and pushed through the curtains. There was the slamming of a door, followed by a piercing female scream. The curtains were thrown back, and we could see the lavatory *Madame* struggling with Smithson in the entrance to the ladies' toilet. A hush descended on the restaurant as attention focussed on the embarrassing scene. It was then that Smithson showed his mettle. He drew back, screwed up his face, and tried to indicate that he did not understand what was happening. He pointed to his ears and mouth to indicate that he was both deaf and dumb.

Cook and I watched in dismay. This could well be the end of Smithson and, if we were not careful, of us as well. The Germans near us seemed fascinated, yet were laughing. Cook, for once, had something to say: 'I think we had better get out of here. There's no point in them getting us as well.'

He began to get up, but I pulled him back.

'No, we can't leave the silly fool here. We're in this together. Just sit tight. I'll see what I can do.'

I was very annoyed with this ridiculous situation, but knew that it had to be dealt with carefully. I walked over, pushing my way past a couple of curious on-lookers and took Smithson by the arm. He was no longer play-acting, but absolutely terrified. I quietly said to the woman.'

'My brother is an idiot. He is not well. Pray, permit me to apologise.'

'Indeed, he is an idiot.' she babbled, 'Why do you not keep the imbecile under control? Is he not dangerous?'

I shook my head, placed a franc on her plate and, although I could see it was no longer necessary, led Smithson along to the men's lavatory, where he made a poor attempt to clean and dry himself.

We were the focus of all eyes as I escorted the crestfallen lad back to our table. There was still time to kill before our rendezvous with Natalie, but I decided it would be best to get the soiled Smithson outside into the fresh air. I therefore asked for *l'addition,* and we quietly got up and made our way across to the cashier, Cook leading and Smithson between us. The others went ahead and I paid the bill, leaving something extra for service. Then, just as I was about to leave, a heavy hand fell on my shoulder, and someone behind me whispered in English.

'You were lucky that time. You really must try to do better or you will never get back to England, my dear fellow. Anyway, *bonne chance*, and give my regards to Piccadilly.'

Natalie had reacted as expected, and had left the building as soon as the commotion had begun. She was waiting for us across the road when we got out outside. Shamefaced, we crossed the road and, without a word, she turned away and we followed her back to the station. She was very angry and, once there, tersely admonished us for our foolishness, particularly berating me for letting it happen in the first place. I did feel responsible and, indeed, contrite, yet I was also surprised at myself. At first, I had not given a thought to the others, but now I had become to feel as one with them. In a strange way, it was as though I had changed sides, and really was a British evader, with a duty not only to my fellows, but also to the escape organisation. However, I put such odd thoughts to one side and, once again, began to concentrate on the seriousness of the job in hand.

'You have to admit that the deaf and dumb routine worked well, Natalie,' I said. 'You must give us some credit for that.' She merely looked at us, and despairingly shook her head.

She had regained some of her good humour by the time we boarded the train to Paris. This time we managed to find seats together in a third class compartment, and endured a silent and uneventful journey which ended late in the afternoon at the *Gare de L'Est*, when hundreds of people were making their various ways home. Again, I saw evidence of the expert organisation of Phoenix. Natalie said goodbye to us under the indicator board, and handed us over to a well-dressed, middle-aged man who appeared from out of the crowd. With his briefcase, rolled umbrella and black Homburg hat, he had all the trappings of a professional man on his way home.

'Goodbye, *mes braves'*, she said. 'I will not tell my friend Jean, here, just how naughty you have been. You are going to find many things different here in Paris, but... please, above all, do as you are told and take no more silly chances.'

She then introduced us to Jean, explaining that, as I was the only French-speaker, I was the leader of the party. She embraced each of us in turn, and walked away into the crowds. Our new guide greeted us.

'I am pleased to meet you,' he said. 'The first thing I should tell you is that there is no need to follow me as dogs follow cats. We will walk together. After all, you are welcome visitors to Paris. We are now going to take the *Metro*, and you shall come home with me.'

We went down into the crowded *Metro*, where Jean bought us each a book of tickets. I had been on the *Metro* many times before the war, and also during various short leaves during the *Kanalkampf*. I explained to the others, *sotto voce*, how the tickets should be used. As we travelled, I tried some underground map-reading, but this did not work as I soon lost myself in the many changes and stops along the way. We finally surfaced at Courçelles and then walked, in a roundabout route, until we came to a large modern block of apartments. We took a lift to the top floor, where Jean let us into a spacious suite of rooms.

'This will be your home for some time to come, my friends. You will be very comfortable here... and safe.'

The suite occupied the whole of the sixth floor. It had many well furnished rooms. We were taken to a large bedroom with one double and one single bed, which would be ours, and then around the rest of the suite. I was surprised to be shown a dental surgery and a waiting room, Jean explaining that dentistry was, indeed, his profession. He also explained that, in case of trouble, we could get away by using either the fire escapes, or a particular traverse across nearby roof-tops. He left us in our room to unpack our few possessions and to freshen up. Cook and I agreed that young Smithson should bath first, and that we should try to get his suit cleaned. Cook asserted his rank and commandeered the single bed, and, after Smithson, I took my turn and indulged in the luxury of a bath.

After some rather pointless conversation about what might have befallen us if we had been captured in the restaurant, Jean came to the room and asked us to follow him. It was time for dinner. In the dining room, a large table had been set for six. We were offered aperitifs, which we were slowly sipping when two men arrived, and were introduced by Jean. One was youngish, perhaps no more than twenty-five, of medium height, with a dark complexion, short black hair and deep brown eyes. The other was a short, balding individual of about fifty, obviously the more important, since I noticed that Jean and the younger man treated him with great respect. Both spoke good English, and their attitudes were businesslike and to the point.

We sat down to a meal served by a woman who must have prepared it, unseen, in the suite. Jean played host, and there was some guarded conversation at first until, after a glass or two of very good wine, we began to relax. The food was excellent, and we rounded off the meal with cognac, toasting ourselves and others. The table was cleared and our glasses were refilled. It was then that I began to notice the strength of character evident in the face of the balding man. He spoke to us with assurance.

'Despite what you have been told in England about not asking questions, not worrying and trusting us implicitly, it is necessary that I tell you something of what lies ahead; about certain things which require your careful consideration.'

He had our full attention. I had a feeling that, at last, I was close to someone of real importance in Phoenix.

'All you need to know at the moment is that I am Paul Vercours, and that my friend here is Claude Resin. We are both Belgian... which may surprise you... but we have a clear duty to get you, and hundreds more like you, from Paris to Spain, from where you will be able to return to England and resume your rôle in helping to bring an end to this war.'

He was now looking directly at me.

'We know all about what you have done, George Harrison, and we are grateful for your help. I am sure you will be pleased to know that there are no similar requirements for you here in Paris. You are now more than half-way home; the worst is over, but I would like you to continue as leader of the team until we can hand you over to the British in Spain.'

He paused to take a sip of cognac, looking quizzically at Cook and Smithson in turn. Both nodded their assent. Vercours continued.

'Paris happens to be the main assembly point for our route. It is something of a junction, crammed with evaders from all parts of the Netherlands, Belgium and France; even a few from Germany, when they manage to escape from the prisoner-of-war camps. Unfortunately, because of sheer numbers, we must hold you here in Paris until we have the means of taking you to the Pyrenees and guiding you across into Spain. This can be done only by trusted and expert operators. They are unfortunately few in number, and can only deal with so many of you at a time. We cannot move our assembly point from Paris nearer to the mountains, and this means that the guides who take you into Spain are constantly on the move between here and there. We are, in fact, operating what I believe you call a 'single-track railway', with all its drawbacks.'

As his glass was refilled, I congratulated myself on being briefed by someone who, if not the actual leader of Phoenix, was at least one of its chief operatives. This was a man to be remembered, one who had to be brought to book. Then, to my surprise, Cook, of all people, seemed to wake up, and asked the very question I had in mind.

'Surely the Germans are well aware that your main holding point is here in Paris? With such increasing numbers... not only of RAF, but soon of Americans... surely the Germans are doing everything possible to find you?'

'Yes, they are indeed. Our organisation is always under threat. It has been ever since we began. Not only do we have the *Gestapo* to contend with, but there are many wretched French collaborators, and there is also the hated *Milice*, the military police force working side by side with the Germans. We cannot trust anyone but ourselves; this is why we Belgians control the escape lines all the way, even through France.'

He paused to let this revelation sink in, and then continued.

'Paris is a very big place. We do have some good friends, and good places to hide you while you have to wait, but we go in daily dread of the *Gestapo*. They are at work against us all the time but, fortunately, we have means of knowing of many of their tricks in advance. We understand their capabilities, and how they operate. Sometime, my friends, we might show you their headquarters in the *Avenue Foch*, where we, in turn, keep a close watch on them.'

Much to my annoyance, Smithson interrupted at this point, unfortunately changing the subject.

'How long before we get out of Paris? Can you give us any idea?'

'Not exactly,' replied Vercours. 'Naturally we have some notion of when we might move the next batch of parcels, but we can never be absolutely sure, because so many difficulties can arise to delay our work... problems on the frontier, in the *Zone Interdite*, availability of guides, sickness, train delays, and so on. You three are just one of more than a dozen groups now being held in Paris, and you must take your turn, but, if all goes well, we should have you on your way in about three or four weeks' time. In the meantime, you will be able to relax and, now and then, I trust, enjoy yourselves.'

'How do we do that?' asked Smithson.

'My dear young man, it is not very difficult in Paris. It will not be necessary to keep you indoors all the time. We actually prefer to have you out of the apartment during the day, admiring this beautiful city. Paris is a wonderful place. There is so much you can do and see. In fact, we shall ask you to spend your days sightseeing, and visiting the many museums and libraries... and there is even the cinema and the theatre. You see, my friend, these are places where the Germans would least expect to find the ruthless young terror-flyers of the RAF. This place is so busy during the day that no one will notice your comings and goings, provided you are discreet. We shall guide you with advice, and give you papers and money. What could be better? It is best for you, and for us, that you go out and join with the hundreds of sightseers who enjoy this lovely city.'

For the best part of the next fortnight we did just that. The three of us spent the daylight hours doing nothing more than touring Paris and seeing the sights. We had our breakfast in the apartment, usually in the company of Jean, and then left around nine o'clock, before his first patients arrived. If we planned to go far, there was often a picnic of bread, cheese and vegetables but, usually, we did not bother to eat again until we returned in the early evening.

———————————————

CHAPTER TWENTY-THREE

Our sightseeing followed the pattern set for the many visitors who thronged the spectacular places of Paris. We began with the *Ile de la Cité, Notre Dame* and *Montmartre,* being taken there by a likeable middle-aged lady who confided that she missed her friends in Antwerp, and hoped soon to be back with them again after she had completed a rather extended 'duty holiday', as she put it. We had two more conducted tours, again with female guides; then it was decided that we could be trusted to go out on our own, with me expressly in charge, provided we said where we planned to go, and when we expected to be back.

We made a start with the time-honoured ritual of climbing every step to the top of the Eiffel Tower, actually doing so in the company of a party of *Hitler Jugend*. We then went further afield to the *Palais de Versailles*, and discreetly ate our picnic on a bench outside the grounds. The *Metro* whisked us, without restriction, to every part of Paris, and we were always provided with adequate money to spend. We began to feel very much at ease, even the ever-vigilant Cook. The unreality of our life had become hard to understand. Paris, and its inhabitants, seemed untouched by the war, and appeared to have accepted the presence of its conquerors without any reserve. Practically all the Germans we saw were doing the same as we were, just wandering around and sightseeing. They mixed easily with the French, whose attitude was so different to that which I had seen in such places as Amsterdam and Brussels.

This atmosphere of *laisser faire* began to affect us as well, although it took a while for me to realise just how easy it would be to make a fatal mistake. One afternoon, when returning on the *Metro*, standing strap-hanging with a *Wehrmacht Leutnant* jammed against me in the crush, the train lurched violently, throwing Smithson against the German. He involuntarily blurted out, 'Sorry, mate'. The German stared alarmingly at Smithson and then at me, sensing something amiss, but presumably feeling unable to do anything about it, because of the crowd pressing around him. All three of us were now fully alert, and ready to make a run for it at the next stop, where we pushed our way out through the crowded carriage, relieved to find that the German had not followed.

On another occasion, we had gone to a cinema which was showing, among other things, one of our propaganda films. Some of the audience had reacted angrily when the *Führer* had been shown in Berlin, congratulating French *Waffen SS* volunteers on their way to the Eastern Front. There had been a near-riot, and we had only just managed to get away from the cinema before the arrival of the French police. But matters reached a ridiculous level at *Les Invalides* one sunny afternoon. We had been to Napoleon's Tomb, which was thronged, as usual, with visitors. Among them, outside by the entrance, was a group of about fifty or more German soldiers, waiting to be photographed. They were arranged in three rows: the front row sitting; the second standing, and the third standing on low trestles. In front, a Frenchman was setting up a large portrait camera on a tripod. We stopped idly behind the Frenchman to watch.

'What a shower they look,' said Smithson. 'Typical, bloody conquering heroes... I don't think!'

Cook was nervous, saying, 'This is no place for us. I don't like it... let's move on.'

'Please yourself, I want to have a better look at these sods,' said Smithson. 'They don't look all that tough to me. I reckon I should get a photograph, to take home to my Mum.'

Cook and I were already moving away, when we looked back in disbelief to see Smithson move behind the photographer, who was busy under his large black camera hood, then around to his front to look back at him through the camera lens. The photographer threw back the hood, and told Smithson to clear off. The Germans remained quiet, sitting and standing impassively. Smithson waited until the photographer was again under the cloth, and then repeated his trick. This time, the photographer was really annoyed, shouting and shaking his fist at Smithson. I tried to attract the stupid youth's attention by calling to him in French, but he simply ignored me. The Germans were by now getting agitated, and talking amongst themselves. Smithson backed off, and the photographer returned to his work under the cover.

Then, very slowly, and after staring at the German group, Smithson came around to peer into the lens a third time. This time he got what he wanted. The Frenchman shouted abuse, and the Germans joined in. The uproar increased as Smithson stood absolutely still, holding his hand over the lens. He held that position until he had everyone's attention, and then took a step forward, adopted a Napoleonic pose, gave the Germans a derogatory two-fingered salute, and ran. Cook and I were already running. Smithson caught us up, laughing and bubbling with excitement.

'Did you see those stupid Krauts? Not one of them moved a bloody inch. My Dad told me the Germans always do things by numbers. He was too bloody right, for sure.'

Back at the apartment, I held a council of war. We were joined by Jean who, at first, was amused by what I called stupid and unthinking foolishness. The pattern of our life in Paris had lulled us into this unreality. What we were doing had nothing to do with the perils which could lie ahead, yet we were behaving in such a way as to jeopardise everything being done for us, as well as putting Phoenix at risk. Jean agreed emphatically with everything I said, even when I stressed that none of us would be man enough to withstand the detailed, and possibly brutal, interrogation which would certainly follow our capture. I hammered away at this point until Smithson was contrite and downcast. We finally agreed that the time had come for us to give up our meandering, and so minimise the risks. We should forego our pleasures, and stay indoors.

Then Paul Vercours arrived. We had decided that he should be told, and that, in future, we would prefer to stay in the apartment. We would never do anything so foolhardy again.

'I am glad to hear it,' he said. 'I must admit that we, too, saw the funny side of your escapade. It was dangerous, though. The Germans do not have much sense of humour, unlike you English, who prefer to behave as foolishly as possible at every opportunity.'

'How did you know about this?' I asked in amazement.

'It was quite simple, *Monsieur*. For your own good we have been watching you for some days now, ever since we discovered your fondness for going to the *Avenue Foch* to watch the Germans in the *Gestapo* Headquarters.'

How badly I had underestimated these people: I had, indeed, deliberately taken my group to the *Avenue Foch* on quite a few occasions, anxious to know its location in case it ever became necessary to seek refuge. I would probably have to go there anyway, one day, to make my final report on the success of *Kondor*. What had started as a personal reconnaissance had developed into an almost daily routine of counting the numbers of discarded *Capeaux Anglais* left outside on the pavement each night by the French as a silent protest.

'I can see that you are surprised, *Monsieur*. We have to be on our mettle at all times. Our lives depend on it. You are, no doubt, unaware that, on the last two occasions when you have visited the *Avenue Foch* and loitered outside the *Gestapo* building, you have attracted unwelcome attention. When leaving, you have been followed by someone from that building, who has trailed you for as long as possible. Each time, you have, fortunately, managed to lose him: once when he could not follow your gyrations on the *Metro* and, again this afternoon, when we had to use a little obstruction ourselves. You see, my friend, we have had the good sense also to have you followed by one of our own.'

We could not hide our surprise, and all realised just how stupid and careless we had been. Standing around in full view of those in the *Gestapo* building, not just once, but on a number of occasions, was bound to have attracted attention. I could see now that it would have been almost inevitable for us to be followed and, because we were always the same group, for us to be suspected of some mischief. On the other hand, could it be that the lines between the *Kondor* operation and the activities of the *Gestapo* in Paris had been crossed? I quickly put aside the notion that perhaps, for some reason, Kreis had decided to cut short my work, and wanted to establish contact with me. No, it could not be that. What was happening was, surely, only the direct result of our thoughtlessness.

'We have been very stupid,' I said. 'It had become something of a game for us to watch the Germans. I am truly sorry. It is all my fault.'

There was silence; no one spoke, and I ventured the obvious question.

'What do you think can happen? Who has been following us? Do you think the Germans suspect we are British, and live here?'

'I am not sure, my friend, but I think we are safe, for the moment. We have little doubt that your follower is connected with the *Gestapo*. He could well be German or, more likely, a French traitor, either a collaborator or a member of the *Milice*. For good reasons we will have to move you from here but, thankfully, we have friends in the right places, and should get ample warning if things begin to go wrong.'

'Is there anything we should do?' I asked. 'Can we help in any way?'

'No. You may not. You have caused us enough trouble already. This is none of your business. But please be more careful in future, and do not act like children.'

I could not get to sleep that night. Smithson slept soundly, apparently untroubled, while I considered every permutation of what could now develop. I wondered if I had reached the point of no return with *Kondor*; whether it would be best to break away and report to Kreis. I was now sure that Paul Vercours was in control of the Paris section of Phoenix, and could well be the overall commander. I already had a wealth of information, more than enough to destroy the operational control of Phoenix, and certainly its activities in Belgium. I, knew nothing, however, about the organisation between Paris and Spain, or of what British Intelligence were doing.

I convinced myself that, whatever the *Gestapo* was doing in Paris, it had nothing to do with *Kondor.* If their operations resulted in my arrest then, of course, they would put an end to *Kondor*. If that happened, then Phoenix would be only partly destroyed. The organisation would lick its wounds, Paul Vercours would be replaced, and the escape route would soon be back in business. I knew that I had to do my best to keep *Kondor* alive. Everyone, without exception, had to be caught in the net. *Kondor* had to be absolute; a once-and-for-all lesson for these remarkably courageous, but misguided, people.

We were a sad and sorry bunch at breakfast. Cook and Smithson got into an argument as to the reasons for the *Gestapo* shadow, and wondered if it would be best for us to take our chances, leave, and try to get to Spain on our own. I was discouraging this idea when Paul Vercours arrived. He was in no mood to waste time, and came straight to the point.

'We have worked out a plan, which will not only deal with the problem you have created, but will help us to learn more about the Germans' intentions. But I shall need your help to lead the enemy into a trap. There will be little risk to you, because we shall take care of eventualities. But we must act quickly. Do I have your support?'

We looked at each other, knowing full well that it would be nothing more than our duty in these circumstances, and agreed. Vercours then spoke to me in French.

'George, you will, of course, have to be in charge. I need to explain certain things to you, but first I want you to meet my friends ,who do not speak English, and are waiting in the next room. Please come with me.'

Vercours introduced me to two men, both dressed in very ordinary clothes such as might be worn by clerks or minor civil servants. I shook the clammy hand of Jacques Pierot, by far the bigger of the two - overweight, florid of face, with dark, oiled hair, brushed tight to his head. The other, Gustav Flamens, was younger and more agile, with a studious look and wire-rimmed spectacles. We sat at a small coffee table, and Vercours explained that my 'batch of parcels' would go to Number 84, *Avenue Foch* in the hope that the *Gestapo* shadow, once again, would follow. This time, however, we would follow Flamens, who would take up a position ahead of us, whilst Pierot would bring up the rear, following discreetly behind the 'tail'. We would have to keep Flamens in view and behave in our usual way, though following him as we looked at the sights. There would be no hurry, but we would eventually arrive at a predetermined spot where the matter would be dealt with. At no time were we to become involved in what had to be done and, at the appropriate time, we would be told when to return home.

I was asked if I understood this apparently simple plan. I did - only too well - and uppermost in my mind was the unpleasant thought that I was about to become involved in the capture and death of one of my countrymen. Vercours was impatient, and brought the briefing to a close.

'Now, to business. I want you to be on your way as soon as possible.'

It took only a few minutes to explain things to Cook and Smithson. They were enthusiastic, and recognised that there was a duty to be done, and that we had an opportunity to repay Phoenix for our transgressions of yesterday. My thoughts, however, were still in a confused whirl of divided responsibilities. I hoped that the shadower would not be German, but one of our expendable French friends, or that the *Gestapo* would simply not take the bait this morning; or even that they had given up trying to follow us home. But, no matter what befell and who the unfortunate victim was to be, I knew a harsh price was about to be paid for what I had to do to make *Kondor* a success.

We travelled into the centre of Paris by *Metro*, and came up as near the *Avenue Foch* as possible. By now, most Parisians were at work in the offices, shops and Government buildings, and we met only a few pedestrians as we walked towards Number 84. A smart, polished, black Mercedes drew up outside as we approached: two *Wehrmacht* officers got out, and were saluted by the guards as they hurried inside. We stopped for a while, on the other side of the road, to admire the vehicle, and then crossed over, noting the absence of the usual scatter of used *capotes anglaises.* Someone had obviously been out early to clean the pavement. We then walked away slowly up the *Avenue,* and it was only then that I saw Flamens, about fifty metres ahead of us.

We stopped after a while, looking around casually. No one was following us, as far as we could see. I was secretly pleased, but the others were still keen to 'hook the fish'. We found a bench in the entrance to a small park on one side of the *Avenue*, where we sat smoking, and quietly waited. Smithson, as usual, had to say something.

'This is a bloody silly caper, you know. It's daft to expect the *Gestapo* to fall for this one, just waiting for chaps like us to wander by.'

Cook snapped in reply, 'Shut up, you bloody fool, for God's sake'.

The next moment Cook grabbed my arm.

'I think we have him. Don't look back, but I'm sure I can see our Kraut friend waiting for us. He's across the road, in a doorway, lighting a cigarette. Yes, that's our man. Fawn raincoat and grey hat. If we get up now and go, I'm sure he'll follow.'

Cook was right. We finished our cigarettes, and stood for a moment or two, as if wondering what to do next. The weather was fine, and it promised to be a warm day. We began to stroll to the end of the *Avenue,* with Flamens clearly in sight. He did not hurry, and we adjusted our progress to keep him well ahead of us, and beyond the view of our shadower. We did not look back, so had no idea whether Pierot was with us or not. Flamens turned at the end of the *Avenue,* and we followed him into the residential areas. We sauntered along for more than half an hour, through streets which became meaner and dirtier, with fewer shops and cafés, and hardly anyone around. Halfway along a narrow street, with Flamens out of sight, having turned the corner at the end, Smithson stumbled and fell as he caught his foot on broken paving. As we helped him to his feet and brushed him down, Cook confirmed that our follower was still with us, and that he was carrying a small case.

At the top of the street, we turned into a still narrower one, and could see Flamens waiting for us at the wooden gate to a small church-yard. He motioned to us and went in, soon to disappear among dark ever-greens, which dominated an expanse of graves and monuments. We stopped for a moment or two at the gate to read the notices, and then entered a deeply shaded area, where the canopy of trees completely hid us from the sun. We walked along a gravel path flanked by ancient yew trees, which almost hid a small church to our right. It was a sombre place, where all was still and dead. Flamens could not be seen. We carried on along the path, which curved gradually to the right and eventually led us out of the graveyard and back into the sunshine. As we emerged, there was Flamens, waiting for us a little way ahead. We followed him for a short distance; he then stopped and beckoned us to him. He offered us each a cigarette, and helped us to light up.

'Here we shall wait,' he said.

It was not long before we saw Pierot lumbering along the street towards us. He ignored us, but spoke to Flamens. I gathered that the job had been done, and that all was well. Then, without more ado, they wished us *bonne chance,* and left us.

I had not realised that an organisation like Phoenix would, inevitably, become involved in clandestine operations other than the rel-atively straightforward business of conducting evaders along an escape route. Now, they had dealt with Conrad Weindl, and had also reacted pos-itively against the *Gestapo.* The three of us were shocked and sobered by the simple ruthless efficiency of these actions.. It showed an element of confidence which I had not expected, and which was surely a warning to me not to underestimate these people. When we got back to the apart-ment, late in the afternoon, we fully expected Jean to discuss the day's events, but he merely welcomed us home. We ate dinner with him and plied him with questions, but it was clearly evident that he knew nothing. He did, however,confirm that Phoenix was still in a state of alert and that, for reasons of prudence and safety, we were to be moved to another loca-tion, the next day.

CHAPTER TWENTY-FOUR

Our guide for this stage was none other than Emilie de Vray. I was greatly surprised and very pleased to see her again. She also seemed happy to see me, and greeted me warmly. She quickly briefed us on our next journey. We said goodbye to Jean, and left to walk to the *Metro*, travelling south to its terminus, where we changed to an omnibus train for Bouviers. At the station, Emilie made a telephone call and, after a short wait, a car arrived to take us to a large house standing in its own grounds, about two or three kilometres from Bouviers. The nameplate on the main gate told us this was the residence of a Doctor Gaillard, who met us at the door.

As we were being shown where to sleep, and how best to get away from the house in the event of a raid, I tried to learn from Emilie something about recent events. All she would say was that the matter was still being dealt with but, whatever transpired, it would probably be best if we knew nothing. It was not our concern, in any case. She did say, however, that she would probably be in the Paris area for a day or two and that, perhaps, we might meet again. I had the pleasant impression that this invitation was directed to me alone.

We settled in quickly, had lunch on our own, and then afternoon tea with Doctor and *Madame* Gaillard, a quiet, very ordinary-looking woman who said nothing at all, even when we spoke in French. She gave the impression that she barely tolerated our being in the house, and would be glad when we had moved on. Nonetheless, she played her part as hostess, and even provided us with newspapers and magazines. In the early evening, we were able to listen to the BBC, and heard a report of a truly devastating fire raid on Hamburg. If we were to believe this, the vital port had been almost completely destroyed, and thousands of its inhabitants horribly burned to death. Did I need more justification for what I was trying to do?

I was in a bitter mood when Paul Vercours and Emilie unexpectedly arrived to join us for dinner with the Gaillards. Happily, it was not long before the intimate presence of Emilie directed my thoughts to more pleasant things. I sat beside her during the meal and, very soon, we were talking together in French, mostly about ourselves and our likes and dislikes. The effect she had on me was wonderful. I almost forgot about the war, and why I was there with my enemies. We became so engrossed with one another that we were practically oblivious to the rest of the company. Before I realised it, time had flown, and the meal was finished. The Gaillards left us, and we went into the doctor's study, where Vercours told us why they had come to see us.

'I simply want to thank you, my friends, for your help. All went well with your little adventure. We now know that the *Gestapo* did, indeed, have their eyes on you, and were following you in the hope that you would lead them to us... at least, that is what a certain *Herr* Globers has told us. He was not very helpful with anything else, and what we learned of their work in Paris was no more than we knew already. You will be pleased to know that there is no sign of any German reaction and, as we have made sure that *Herr* Globers' disappearance is absolute, there is little possibility of reprisals. The *Gestapo* will never find him. They and the *Milice* will search, but we are sure that, after a few days, all will return to normal. They will accept the loss of Globers as a casualty of war, keep quiet about it, and carry on with their wretched business.'

We listened in silence. It was not pleasant to think of what Globers must have endured before he was forced to talk. Like poor Weindl, he must have longed for the blessed release of death.

'Are such incidents very frequent?' I asked Vercours, hoping that I might gain more information. 'There must be a continuous battle between you and the *Gestapo*?'

'No, there is not,' he replied quickly. 'This is the first time we have had to face such a problem, when it has been necessary to take such extreme action. We must regard this unfortunate business as being an exception. We see no evidence that the Germans are acting out of character, or that there is any new threat to us. The trigger to their activity was simply your curious interest in the *Avenue Foch*.'

'You acted very quickly, and efficiently,' I said. 'Things went well, and your men, Flamens and Pierot, were excellent.'

Vercours did not answer, but turned to Emilie. She gave me a frosty look; all the warmth had gone from her.

'No, they are not our men. It would be very stupid of us if we told you things you do not need to know. Just imagine what would happen if you were captured. The Germans would work on you, most efficiently. You cannot imagine what dreadful things they do and, in the end, you would tell them what they want to know. All we can say is that our two friends do not work directly for us, but for those who, now and then, are forced to resort to the use of violence. We ourselves have to try to avoid trouble. The very nature of what we do means that we must stay out of sight. Only when things get beyond us do we call in the experts.'

Emilie had confirmed what I had guessed to be the case: Phoenix operated alone. It must be a self-contained organisation and, most likely, its only real connections were with the British once they were in neutral territory. I took a chance at probing further.

'We have been amazed at how you work so efficiently, and help so many of us. What impresses me is how each safe house is an entity of its own, looking after us so well, but presumably receiving instructions from elsewhere?'

I sensed that I had gone too far this time. Emilie looked wary, but Vercours took up the conversation.

'What you have said is true. It must be obvious to you, and to the Germans, that organisations such as ours would not, as you say, "put all its eggs in one basket". We have survived this long because our structure allows us to carry on, even if we lose parts of it. These can be replaced without our overall work suffering. Even our leaders can be replaced in time. We would have to be destroyed from the very top to the bottom before our operations would stop, and, even then, there would always be other patriots who would come forward to continue our work.'

I sensed that my questions were bemusing both Cook and Smithson who, by their expressions, seemed annoyed that I was monopolising the conversation, which now and then lapsed into French.

'But isn't there some way that we can help,' I said, hoping to keep the discussion alive. 'We seem to have proved ourselves to you. Are there perhaps messages we can take to England for you? Is there anything we can take to the British in Spain?'

This time Emilie showed her exasperation. She tut-tutted and waggled a finger at me.

'This is not a game, George Harrison. What you are suggesting is, in any case, part of our daily business. Having you gallant RAF people trying to do our work is fatal. Let me give you an example: Only a few months ago, one of your Flight Sergeants was caught by the *Gestapo* near Toulouse. He was a very ordinary airman, brave enough to bomb the Germans every night, but no match for the *Gestapo*. He thought he was helping us by memorising the names and addresses of helpers all along the line from Liège. They tortured him so expertly that he just talked and talked. We lost many valuable friends. I also remember a really foolish man who had actually written down the names and addresses of his helpers, and was carrying a list of them in his shoe. He only wanted to remember us so that we could be thanked properly, one day. In the end, our only thanks were either the bullet, or imprisonment in German concentration camps.'

And so the evening ended. Vercours and Emilie paid their respects to the Gaillards, and left.

I spent a restless night, thinking about what I had learned of Phoenix, but also dwelling on things I could not understand. What had become of the errant British airmen? After such rough handling by the *Gestapo*, they would have stood little chance of being sent to a prisoner-of-war camp. But then, we would have been within our rights to dispose of them as spies, in accordance with the Geneva Convention. Emilie's words on retribution came back to me, again and again. But what were these concentration death camps? I had never heard of them, yet, gradually, a picture was emerging of something which had perhaps been deliberately hidden from us. The need for political concentration camps like Dachau and Ravensbrück had been established long ago, soon after the birth of the Third *Reich*. We knew there was a need to re-educate such agitators as union leaders and communists, who could work for their freedom. Then there were the malcontents such as homosexuals, gypsies and Jews who needed correction. But I had no knowledge of places where people were deliberately put to death.

We were on our way sooner than expected, saying goodbye to the Gaillards early the next morning. A man whom we had not seen before drove us, in the doctor's car, to the railway station in the centre of Bouviers. From there, we took the omnibus train to Montparnasse, changed to the *Metro*, and eventually found ourselves back at Jean's apartment. During the afternoon, in a break from his dental work, he spent a little time with us, and surprised us with the news that we would be leaving for the Pyrenees that evening. About an hour later, Emilie arrived, and told us that she would be our guide on the journey.

She gave us very comprehensive travelling instructions. We would be going to Biarritz, where she would hand us over to someone else. This time we would travel in first-class comfort on an overnight train. There were, unfortunately, no *wagon lits* or *couchettes,* but we could sleep comfortably in seats which had been booked for us. She would be in the same carriage, a few compartments from us, and would check, now and then, that all was well. All we had to do was take our seats, behave as though we were regular travellers, settle down, and try to sleep. The train would arrive at Biarritz at about eight o'clock in the morning, and we should be ready to leave it at once.

We stayed in the apartment until early evening. We double-checked our documents, and practised responses to what we might expect French officials to say. I noticed that our pink railway tickets to Biarritz had cost 597 francs. Smithson, as usual, was keyed-up and excited, fussing through his belongings time and again, and muttering atrocious French to himself in response to imagined document checks. He then turned to pressing his suit with a damp cloth and a hot flat-iron. But, in the end, I had to agree that we looked smart enough not to appear too much out of place in a first-class compartment. We ate a meal at eight o'clock. At nine-thirty, we said goodbye to Jean and left, travelling by *Metro* direct to the *Gare Austerlitz*. The Biarritz train was shunted into the departure platform just before half past ten and, at a nod from Emilie, we took our places in an empty compartment in Carriage H. Reservations had been made for us to sit three in a row, with our backs to the engine; Cook at the window, Smithson in the middle, and myself nearest the compartment door. We were facing three empty seats, which I noticed were also reserved.

The first to take one of these was a young Frenchman, who bustled in and hoisted a large expensive-looking case onto the rack, greeting us generally, and then sitting down opposite Cook, whom he addressed in a friendly way. Cook, understanding not a word, nodded to him with a smile, and then buried his head in a copy of *'Paris Soir'* which Emilie had provided. The Frenchman mumbled something, then switched on the reading light above his head, produced a heavy book and said he was going to read a very good story. I was astonished when he held up the book for Cook to see, and I recognised it as an English version of Bernard Shaw's 'Man and Superman'.

'I have to finish this tome tonight. I am studying English, among other subjects, at Orleans, and tomorrow my tutor will want to know what I have to say about this.'

The distress on Cook's face was only too apparent, so I quickly came to his rescue.

'Yes, Shaw is a master. But isn't English an odd degree course for you at this time? I thought that anything about 'perfidious Albion' was frowned on, these days.'

The student's face lit up in anticipation of a lively discussion with me, just as the compartment door was drawn back, and in came the other two passengers. They were two *Wehrmacht* officers, who took their seats, and politely wished us all a good evening. The atmosphere was electric as they surveyed us, each in turn: first me, then Smithson, then the red-faced Cook, and finally the eager Frenchman, clutching his English book. The student was bursting to speak, and once the Germans were settled in their seats, he repeated his reason for reading Shaw. They seemed to understand his French and asked, as I had expected, why he was study-ing English. He tersely rebuffed this question by saying that Shaw was not English; he was Irish.

I had to hide a smile as the Germans pondered on the Frenchman's retort. The train then started and, as we pulled away, both the Germans directed questions to the Frenchman, speaking in mixtures of poor French and English, and then in German, which was well-under-stood and spoken by the student. I joined briefly in some of the discus-sion, while Cook and Smithson switched off their reading lights and went through the motions of trying to sleep. Smithson put his copy of *'Paris Soir'* over his face and, after a while, because I had by now been almost excluded from the conversation, I too turned out my light and feigned sleep.

The discussion between the two officers and the Frenchman

ended when the student said he really had to finish reading his book. The Germans then talked between themselves, and I gathered that they were both members of the Army of Occupation, returning from leave in Germany to their places of duty in Tours. This was, thankfully, the first stop, where they quietly got out and left us supposedly asleep.

The journey continued, the compartment now almost darkened, with just one light on in the corner above the Frenchman, who was still hard at work on Shaw. He left the train at Orleans, and we were able then to stretch out and sleep, not awaking fully until it began to get light as the train was approaching Biarritz.

It was soon a beautiful morning, with the sun rising into a cloudless blue sky. As we got down from the train, we could see Emilie further along the platform in conversation with a very young, fair-haired girl. She beckoned to us and explained that she was leaving us in the care of Brigide, who would take us on to St. Jean de Luz. She kissed me lingeringly on both cheeks, ignoring the other two, and was gone. I had been too surprised to respond. Brigide did not speak English so, once again, I dominated the conversation and had to translate for the others. We waited a while for the arrival of a local train, which took us along the coast to the pretty port of St. Jean de Luz. There were no checks of any sort on the way, or when we arrived. No one even bothered to take our tickets, so we decided to keep them as souvenirs.

St. Jean seemed to be *en fête*. The little town was crowded, on what seemed to be a market day combined with some sort of religious festival. Hundreds of people thronged the streets, or clustered around the many stalls loaded with produce of all kinds. The sun was now well up, and we were beginning to feel uncomfortable in our heavy dark suits as we followed Brigide through the crowds and along the harbour road. It was with some relief that, after a few detours in the narrow streets behind the port, we arrived at a white-washed terraced house at the end of the *Rue Gambetta*. There we were met by a large, dark-skinned woman of about forty, who ushered us at once upstairs into a room where, by using signs, she made it clear we should wait.

This we did for some time, whilst a loud argument raged downstairs. The woman seemed to be in disagreement with two men. If it had anything to do with us, then all thoughts of caution had obviously been cast aside, because the argument was loud enough for anyone to hear. When she returned, she was in a vile temper. She brought with her bundles of clothes and three pairs of rope-soled sandals. She threw the clothes in a heap on the floor and, again using signs, made it clear that we were to change from our suits at once, and dress in blue denim overalls, such as those worn by most French workers. We did not argue, and she stood there, arms folded, impatiently watching our every move. When we were changed, she left the room and returned with canvas bags into which we put our suits and hats. She looked us over with obvious distaste, but finally gave each of us a Basque beret to wear.

When all was ready and packed, she hurried us downstairs to meet the two men, the younger of whom spoke to me in French with a strong accent, which I took to be Basque. He introduced himself as Claudillo, and apologised for the argument we had overheard. He said he wanted us to trust him, as we were now his responsibility, and were to go with him. I told Cook what Claudillo had said, and he agreed that there seemed little option but to do as he instructed us. Claudillo took us through the house and out into the backyard, where there were three bicycles propped against a wall. He gave us string to make slings for our canvas bags, which we hung around our shoulders, and then allocated each of us a bicycle and told us to follow him.

We soon mastered the uncomfortable machines, and set off. Claudillo and Cook went ahead, and I followed with Smithson, some distance behind. We cycled around the harbour and out of St. Jean, taking the road to the south. There was very little traffic, and we made good progress. It was now very warm, and we began to sweat, thanking Providence for the welcome change of clothes. I found the ride a pleasure. To our right were the foothills of the Pyrenees, beyond which could be seen the peaks along the frontier with Spain. The road wound for a while alongside a slow-moving river fringed with trees and brush. We eventually turned away from it, and then the going became more difficult as we left the main road and took a much smaller one leading up into the hills. It was badly maintained, and we frequently had to dismount and walk. It was a relief when, at last, we stopped at a small inn situated amongst a scattering of poor dwellings, where Claudillo bought us rough red wine and we ate bread and soft cheese.

We rested there for about an hour, and then went on our way again, even slower this time, as we were forever going uphill. At last, we reached the top, remounted, and free-wheeled most of the way down into the small town of Ascain. We sped through the narrow, almost empty, streets and on out of the town for about a kilometre, until we came to a low, white-painted farmhouse, roofed with red tiles. Swinging into the farmyard, which was out of sight of the road, we dismounted, and were greeted by a wizened, sunburnt old man who spoke to us in an unrecognisable language. Claudillo explained that this was his father, translated his greetings, and told us that this would be our refuge until the time came for us to cross the mountains.

We were settled in a small outhouse which had been adapted, in a rudimentary way, as a place to spend the night. At one end there were blankets spread out on straw and, at the other end, a water tap, stone basins, and some dirty rags hanging from a rack on the wall. Strangely, we accepted this without question, and did not even ask what we should do if things got out of hand. After a little rearranging of our bed- spaces to give each other more room, we lay down to wait. Smithson soon fell asleep. Claudillo came to us, late in the afternoon. He was worried, and looked tired.

'We were expecting to take you with us tonight, but there have been some little troubles.'

My heart sank. Was I about to be thwarted in my task at this final step? The others sensed my alarm, and were all attention.

'What's wrong?', asked Cook.

'I don't know,' I said, 'but let's be ready to move.'

Claudillo, although not understanding what had been said, sensed our anxiety.

'Don't be so alarmed, my friends. It has nothing to do with you: you are safe and, tomorrow, you will cross. But it has not been a good day for us. Some of your comrades, who were being hidden in St. Jean, have been arrested by the police. It happened this morning, on the beach, of all places, where we had told them to pass an hour or two. These three had decided to sunbathe, and one was recognised as English by a tattoo on his arm. What a fool, to be so careless.'

'Can they not be rescued?', I asked.

'No, it is impossible. It is not our police who have them now. They have been taken to Bayonne, and are in the hands of the *Gestapo*. We must fear the worst, my friends. We have warned those helping at their safe house to leave immediately, and trust in Heaven that the English will be brave, and have little to say.' Then, as an afterthought, he added, 'But then, they know very little about us, thank God.'

All I could think of was the possibility that, at this last stage in *Kondor*, I might be swept up in a *Gestapo* search of the area, never finding the key personnel in charge of the operations in the mountains. Did Claudillo know more? If we had to run for it, the only worthwhile thing to do would be to try to cross on our own, and for me to endeavour to piece the picture together in Spain, where I hoped I would meet the British.

'Was there any connection between these three men and us?' I asked.

'Very little,' replied Claudillo. 'You will remember the place where I collected you? That is the safe house in which the three men were staying. The alarm had been given just before your arrival, and the lady in charge who, as you saw, was very upset, is now a very long way from here.'

We ate that evening in the farmhouse, together with Claudillo and his father. After a strong liqueur, we went back to the out-building to sleep. Although the others wanted to talk about the morrow, I remained silent, preoccupied with my worrying thoughts. I had been trying to convince myself that I hated the English, and that it was my duty to destroy them, the escape route, and all those connected with it. But I was becoming increasingly aware that was too much of the English in me. I could not bring myself to hate them; in fact, I actually admired them. Their courage was incredible, and they were prepared to lay down their lives without hesitation. They believed implicitly in what they were fighting for, while I, on the other hand, wondered increasingly if we were still on the right path in this war. There were now things that seriously worried me, such as the sinister death camps and the relentless persecution of the Jews. The ruthlessness with which we were fighting was matched only by what the British were now doing to the Fatherland. Worst of all, the world hated us and, deep inside me, I had the uneasy feeling that we were not going to win the war.

At breakfast the next morning, Claudillo told us that we were to be taken to a place whence the final stage of our journey would commence - that very night. The *Gestapo* had been to St. Jean, and were working with the *Milice*. So far, however, there had been no unwelcome visitors at the house in the *Rue Gambetta*, which seemed to indicate that nothing had yet been learned from the three British captives. I asked Claudillo for details of our passage over the mountains, but all he would say was that we would be participating in a smuggling trip, and that he would be going with us part of the way.

We set off late in the morning, on our bicycles, belongings slung over our shoulders. We were soon into the foothills, sometimes having to dismount and push the bikes along the narrow road up towards the peaks which could be clearly seen in the distance. The weather had stayed fair, with glorious blue skies, and a refreshing light wind blowing in from the sea. Claudillo was in no hurry, and we were able to take in everything around us, and enjoy the sights of the unfamiliar countryside. We were all in good spirits, but very much on the alert.

Eventually we came to the end of the road, which petered out into a dusty track leading us ever upwards towards the mountains. Claudillo kept up an interesting flow of chatter, the significant features of which, now and then, I translated and passed on to Cook and Smithson. He had spent the whole of his life in the region, and bragged about the things he had done, but never once did he mention anything about what went on at the farm back in Ascain. He said that he had taken part in many smuggling excursions, which were a way of life with the Basques. Most of his friends were Basques, and every one of them was a smuggler of one kind or another. It was a rewarding business, and not very difficult, if you knew the ropes, and were careful. The only real dangers lay in the *Zone Interdite*, an area running two kilometres wide all along both sides of the frontier. The French, Spanish and Germans all patrolled this region, and did not stop to ask questions. Anything the least suspicious was shot at on sight. To be absolutely safe from the Germans, we would have to get well into Spain, where the worst that could happen, if we were caught, would be a long holiday in a Spanish detention camp. If we were caught by the French, or the Spaniards during the actual crossing, we would be handed over to the Germans.

We made frequent stops. At one, just after midday, Claudillo produced a leather bottle containing rough red wine, which we drank with a snack of bread and goat's cheese, while sitting among the rocks in the hot sunshine, looking far back into France. The countryside around us was open and deserted. There was no sign of cattle or sheep, nor could we see any people. Behind us, there were thickly wooded areas, stretching up towards the very tops of the mountains. Excellent evasion country, we agreed. We pressed steadily on and, in the early evening, arrived at a tumbledown farm on the very edge of the tree line. Claudillo led us into a group of rundown or derelict buildings, and showed us where to leave our bicycles in a roofless outhouse. We then joined him in what must have once been the farmhouse.

'This is where we must wait for your guide,' he said. 'Clemente will arrive very soon and then, when it is dark, you will go.'

'Who is Clemente?' I asked.

'He is a famous man,' replied Claudillo. 'There is no one like him, anywhere. He is the best smuggler between here and Barcelona, and has taken more people over the mountains than anyone else. He is my friend.'

CHAPTER TWENTY-FIVE

We waited on tenterhooks as it began to get dark. Then, suddenly, Clemente was standing in front of us. He had entered the room without a sound. We had heard nothing of his approach, and now this squat,
wizened character was staring at each of us in turn, sizing us up. Finally,
he spat on the floor, turned, and hugged Claudillo, to whom he spoke hur-
riedly in Basque. The man certainly fitted his description. He looked age-
less, but must have been in his early forties; short, with strong legs and a
stoop. His broad face was weather-beaten, and burned dark by the sun.
He wore shepherd's clothes, a light sheepskin jacket over dirty denim
overalls, rope sandals on his feet, and had two bundles slung crossways
over his shoulders. There was an earthy, animal-like smell about him. He
stank of dried sweat.

He began to prowl around. We stood motionless as he examined
the empty windows and doorway. Then, slowly, he unslung one of his
bundles, which was in fact a wine sack, and turned towards us with a
wide grin. He raised the wine sack, and expertly squirted a steam of red
wine into his mouth. He then offered it to each of us in turn, roaring with
laughter at our inability accurately to squirt the wine into our mouths, and
we joined in. The tension had been completely broken.

Someone had arrived while this was going on, I noticed a small
dark figure framed in the open doorway. All went quiet and then, to my
amazement, Emilie de Vray, of all people, came towards us. Clemente
and Claudillo greeted her with affection, and I heard Claudillo say that
all was well. The three conversed in a huddle for a short while, and then
Claudillo said *au revoir* to Emilie, and left without a word to anyone else.
I saw that she was dressed as we were, and also had a bundle slung across
her slender shoulders. She spoke to Clemente in Basque, then turned to
us with an air of authority.

'Don't be surprised, my friends. I make this passage regularly.
Someone has to make sure you reach the right people in Spain. Clemente

is the real expert. He has been doing this all his life, so we are in safe hands.'

I could see the intensity of purpose in her eyes as we grouped around her. Despite her small stature and femininity, she was undoubtedly a leader, and I felt that all was well with her in command.

'We shall be on our way as soon as it is really dark. There will be a few hours of steady walking to get us through the *Zone Interdite*, after which we still have some way to go before we are safe. Clemente and I will be in the lead, and I want you to follow closely, with George being the last man. We are almost on the edge of the forbidden zone, and the actual frontier is not far from here: in fact it is the Bidassoa, the river your Duke of Wellington had to cross with his armies on his way to Waterloo. All the fords are guarded, so we must be careful but, luckily, at this time of the year the river is low, and it is not at all difficult to swim across.'

'I can't swim,' protested Smithson. Like an elder sister, Emilie held out a comforting hand.

'There is no need to worry, my friend. Most of our RAF escapers cannot swim either, and we have taken them all safely across. I have never lost a single soul. You might not even have to swim, if we find the ford is free. You will then just wade across. But, no matter, I am sure that Mr. Cook and George can manage well, and you will be safely roped between them. That will be all right, *n'est ce pas?*'

Smithson nodded, and said nothing more.

'I want you at all times to keep in your proper order. We shall move quickly, unless Clemente tells us to stop for some reason. If he has to go forward to reconnoitre, you must not move, no matter what is happening. He will always come back and, in any case, I will tell you what has to be done.'

'What if something happens, and he does not come back?' I ventured to ask. Emilie did not hesitate.

'Then I shall decide what to do, depending on where we are. If we are still in the *Zone Interdite*, then I will get you into Spain, and to your safe house. If we get split up by some misfortune, then it is everyone for himself. You will have to get away into Spain on your own. You must not stop here in France, under any circumstances.'

I had another question: 'In that case, where do we go... can you give us the address of the next safe house in Spain?'

'No, I cannot. That would be foolish indeed. The Spaniards are as good as the *Gestapo* when it comes to torture and interrogation. If things were to get that bad, we would not dare risk the lives of other people. You would have to make your way on your own, and do your best to get well into Spain. You would have to proceed with great caution, and try to reach Pamplona. There, we have a watch kept at the entrance to the bull ring, which is in the centre of the town. We should then be able to help but, remember, once you get to Pamplona you will be safe from the Germans. The Spaniards, if they catch you, will not send you back, although you would have to spend an uncomfortable six months or so in a Spanish prison.'

Emilie asked if we had any questions, but we had none. She then spoke to Clemente in the Basque dialect, apparently telling him to make sure that all was well. He made a start with me, checking that my slung bundle was tight and secured, that my rope sandals were well-fitted and strapped, and that my beret was well down over my brow. When he was satisfied, Emilie beckoned to me to follow her outside. She walked a little way from the farmhouse, to the edge of the farmyard. It was now night, with an almost full moon climbing into a cloudless sky. Polaris and the Great Bear stood out clearly above us, and visibility was very good.

I wondered what was in the mind of this remarkable woman. She seemed to be involved in every aspect of Phoenix. Not only was she concerned with the management and organisation of the route but, now, here she was, undertaking the vital link between us and the British on the other side of the mountains. Why did she repeatedly have to make these dangerous journeys? For my part, I was keyed-up, just as I had always been when about to fly on a bombing sortie. I was prepared for the excitement of getting through the *Zone Interdite,* and then having to deal with what must surely be the last stage of this strange adventure. But then, in the moonlight, I found myself distracted by my admiration of this lovely girl beside me, who had been in my mind, off and on, ever since our first meeting in Namur. My thoughts regarding Emilie had always been honourable, unlike those which had led to so many lustful encounters with female companions in the past.

She spoke to me in her usual forthright manner.

'We have given you the code-name of *Canari*. Cook is *Alouette*, and young Smithson is *Pigeon*. We always like to know we have been successful, and so we listen to the BBC for the names of those who have safely returned to England: in your case, my dear George, they will say *'Le canari est bien rentré'*. I shall then know that all is well and that, if God so wills it, I might see you again, one day.'

Her manner had softened, but I wondered why she had not given us this information inside the farmhouse. She drew closer. There was something more important on her mind.

'We shall start soon. This is probably the last time I shall be able to talk to you before you go home to England, back to your loved ones... to your wife, perhaps?'

'I am not married, my dear Emilie.'

'But you must have many girl friends?', she asked, almost coquettishly.

'A few, I must admit. We flyers are lucky people, but there is no one serious.'

I could see in her eyes that she wanted to ask me more than she could put into words. On impulse, I tenderly clasped her in my arms and kissed her lightly on the lips. She was at first unresponsive in her surprise, and then she reacted violently, kissing me with complete abandon, with open mouth and probing tongue. I responded eagerly to her mounting passion as we pressed and struggled against each other. My hands were at her breasts, and I tried to free her clothing. Panting, she gasped, 'This is no good, my dear, dear George.' She pulled away from me, almost on the verge of tears. 'Why, oh why, did we not realise this sooner? How different things could have been.'

She drew back, frantically rearranging her clothing. She had regained her self-control, and the vibrant womanliness in her disappeared.

'We must get back inside,' she sighed, 'but please, dear God, let us be together again, sometime.'

As we walked back, I began to realise the full enormity of what would have to be done if I successfully completed *Kondor*. My revelations to the *Gestapo* would surely mean death for this lovely woman. I tried to push such horror from my mind.

Once inside, I told Cook and Smithson their code names, telling them that Emilie had been briefing me separately as leader of our team. Emilie and Clemente exchanged a few words, and we were on our way. We moved at a fast pace, made easier because we were suitably dressed, and the weather was excellent. Our sandals were comfortable, and ideal for walking. Our sacks were strapped tightly behind our shoulders, allowing free movement of both arms and legs. A routine soon established itself; Clemente in the lead, with Emilie at his shoulder, then Cook, Smithson and myself. We were now approaching the tree belt, finding it a little harder to see ahead and keep in touch with each other.

Our first emergency stop was made without a hitch. Clemente had turned and raised his hand. Without a sound, the signal was passed along the group. We crouched motionless, and then heard sheep bells and the noise of a flock being moved across the path ahead.

There were other stops and starts during the first hour as we climbed higher into the hills. We were now well amongst the trees and shrubs and, just after eleven o'clock, stopped to rest, or so I thought. All had gone well so far, and we were in good condition, and good spirits. I had difficulty in keeping my mind on the job in hand, due to the agonising knowledge that my duty would require me, eventually, to denounce Emilie. I had to admit that I had been overwhelmed by the intensity of her feelings for me, and that I was full of admiration for her... or could it be something stronger, perhaps love? But, no matter how I felt, I could not forget that she was my enemy; someone vital to the success of the escape organisation. I was dedicated to rooting this out, and she was, without any doubt, one of its most important operatives. I knew little of *Gestapo* interrogation methods, but it was certain that she would be horribly treated before being put to death. I wrestled with this dreadful dilemma, wondering if there might be some way of allowing her to escape the retribution which would descend on Phoenix once I was safely in Spain.

Clemente had gone on ahead, and was now suddenly back with us. He had news for Emilie, which they discussed before we set off again. All we were told was that we were now entering the *Zone Interdite,* as we moved on again along narrow paths shrouded by pines and shrubs. We soon began to move more quickly as the way lay downhill, and it was then that Emilie passed the word that there was a German patrol somewhere ahead. The first hint of danger was the signal from the front to stop and to get down. Ahead of us, we heard voices coming our way. Clemente quickly turned our group around and led us back along the path, and off into the scrub, where we slowly and silently picked our way through the undergrowth, continually changing direction, until we rejoined our original path, with the noisy patrol now behind us. Without further incident, we carried on down a steep descent until Clemente stopped us at the bank of a fast-flowing river. Emilie passed the word that we were at the frontier: this was the Bidassoa, and Spain was on the other side.

Clemente again left us to reconnoitre. He went off to the left along the river bank, returned, and went in the downstream direction, to the right. We waited expectantly, clustered in the riverside willows and shrubs at the water's edge. When he came back, he had a brief discussion with Emilie, and then led us upstream, about two hundred metres. Emilie told us to get ready to cross. We were at a reasonable ford, a little narrow in places, but one which had been used safely many times before. Suddenly, there was a flash of light to our right, on the other side of the river. Someone had switched on a light in a building, which we could now see in outline about fifty metres from us. Emilie whispered that this was one of the Spanish police guardhouses which were set up near the fords along the river road.

We set about preparing ourselves to cross. Our backpacks were now high on our shoulders, and Smithson was roped securely between Cook and myself, the loose end of the rope being taken up by Clemente.

We waited, eyes glued to the guardhouse. After a while, two figures walked up to it, and went inside. A minute or so later, we heard a gramophone playing and people laughing. It was then that Clemente gave us the signal to begin the crossing. We got down into the cold river, and lined ourselves up along the river bank, standing waist deep in the water, under the overhanging willows. This time Emilie had taken the lead, with Clemente close behind her.

She waited until we all ready to move, and then turned into the dark river, Clemente paying out our connecting rope behind him. Cook set off with the apprehensive Smithson close to him but, before I had even moved, I saw him go under, pulling Smithson down with him, both being carried away downstream towards the blockhouse. I naturally expected Clemente, with my help, to anchor the two unfortunates, but he had somehow lost hold of the rope. I could not hold them at my end, so, taking a deep breath, I put my head under the water and struck out towards the thrashing and spluttering pair. I reached them quickly, and grabbed Smithson by his backpack. Then, together with Cook, who was now swimming easily, we slowly made our way across, holding the terrified Smithson between us. We eventually found our feet on the other side, almost directly under the blockhouse on the road above us.

Luckily, there must have been something of a party in the blockhouse, because we could hear the voices and laughter of several people, some of them female. Their noise covered the sound of our slow and careful return under the river bank to the end of the ford, where Emilie and Clemente were waiting. We quickly slipped out of the river, crawled through the grass at the water's edge up to the road, crossed it and hurried, as fast as we could, uphill away from the river into a defile in the woods. We kept moving hard for about ten minutes, until Clemente called a halt and we stopped to regain our breath.

Emilie was relieved that we had successfully negotiated the crossing. She stressed, however, that there was still much walking to be done. We were by no means safe until we were outside the *Zone Interdite* on the Spanish side, and well into Spain. Even then, we would still have to avoid any risk until we reached the next safe house, which was quite a long way off. It was now one o'clock in the morning, and still a fine, clear night. Cook wondered whether it would not be better to get out of our wet clothes, and to change into slightly drier garments from our backpacks. When this was explained by Emilie to Clemente, he laughed scornfully, and made it clear that a little vigorous exercise would be enough to dry us.

And so we set off again, heading due west, as I could easily see from the stars, visible through the tree tops. The going was mainly through woods, which began to thin as we left the Spanish border of the *Zone Interdite*. Clemente was setting a cracking pace and, gradually, our group began to lag behind the two guides. Our drenching in the river had not helped. Although we had almost dried out, our feet were beginning to swell in the sodden sandals, and we were developing blisters, not only on our feet, but also on the skin under the arms and between our legs. Cook was really in trouble, but did his best without a single word of complaint, or any sign of the pain he was enduring. Smithson, on the other hand, was like a blown horse, limping along with his head down, moaning and groaning to himself. Bringing up the rear, I felt fit but extremely annoyed with both of them, probably because I had no reason to complain. After a while, I took their backpacks from them. Clemente carried one and I shouldered the other.

We came out into open country just before daybreak. We were still travelling westwards, and now along defined tracks. The gap between us and Emilie and Clemente had grown wider. Both Cook and Smithson appeared to be almost at their last gasp. Up ahead, I knew that Clemente was furious with us, because he had already sent Emilie back twice, to see if we could move faster. I then saw them waiting impatiently for us slowly to catch them up, on the edge of what looked like a well-used road. Emilie gave vent to her feelings.

'What a miserable trio you are. If you cannot do better than this, then all our work will be lost. Soon you will be seen and recognised as fugitives, and caught. What am I to do with you?'

She then saw the blood staining Cook's sandals, and noticed that he was trembling uncontrollably: Smithson had already collapsed. I shrugged my shoulders, and told her that, as far as I was concerned, they could stay where they were and I would go on with her. She was astounded. She turned on me, her lovely features twisted with scorn.

'How could you leave your comrades? You are strong and they are not. Can't you see they need you?'

I realised I had gone too far.

'My God, I was only joking,' I protested. 'I thought it might make them pull themselves together. But what are we to do?'

'Well, we have to say goodbye now to Clemente, in any case,' said Emilie. 'He has to get back into the hills. He must not be found in Spain. I have had this problem before, George. It is really remarkable how unfit some of you Britishers are. But we will not leave you. I have little alternative but to hide you somewhere while I go for help. Come, my friends. Be of good heart: there is a place nearby where you can remain out of sight whilst you recover your strength.'

True to her word, she persuaded us to struggle up onto the road and along it to a ditch: she ordered us to get in and then, with Clemente's help, covered us with brushwood and pieces of shrub.

'Stay there and rest,' she said. 'Sleep, by all means, but have someone on guard. I hope to return in about three hours' time.'

She said farewell to Clemente, and strode off along the narrow road, leaving us three intrepid airmen to our shame. Smithson took off his sandals and socks.

'Not a wise thing to do, Sergeant,' said Cook, turning up his nose at the sight of Smithson's filthy feet. 'We may have to run for it, and we should always be ready. Put them back on.'

'Not this airman,' Smithson said pathetically. 'I'm finished. I've had it.'

'No you haven't, you idiot,' I snapped. 'Do as you are told. Where is your pride?'

My words had their effect. Smithson hung his head and slowly replaced his sodden socks and sandals. I elected to stay on watch. Cook and Smithson soon fell asleep, snoring and grunting now and then as they lay stretched out in the bottom of the ditch. I, too, was very tired, but kept myself alert with the excitement of knowing that my long trek was almost over, and that I was on the verge of a notable success. All that remained was to get to the final safe house, the terminus of Phoenix, and learn whatever I could about the contact with the British. Then I would have to make a clean break from the place, in such a way that the *Gestapo* would have the maximum time to swing into action, and begin the mopping-up of Phoenix. Detailed information had to be passed to Paris, Brussels and Berlin in the shortest possible time, well ahead of the inevitable alert that would be flashed along the escape route, once I was found to be bogus. The decision when to make this move rested entirely in my hands; but how I was going to do it was, for the moment, beyond me.

I constantly checked my watch, finding it increasingly difficult to stay awake. The sun was now well up, and it was beginning to get warm. My whole system was crying out for food and rest. I was actually dozing when I heard the car approaching. I pushed the twigs and branches aside and peered out, surprised to see an old Renault taxi slowly coming up the road with Emilie leaning from the window, looking for our hiding place. As it went past, she saw me crawling from the ditch. The car stopped, reversed, and came back to pull up alongside us. I had to awaken the other two, who sheepishly joined me in the taxi.

'Welcome to Spain, my friends,' beamed Emilie. 'You are almost home now. The next part is easy... all downhill.'

The Spanish safe house was an attractive villa set in its own grounds, on a hillside overlooking the town of San Sebastian. It was surrounded by pines and cedars through which, about five kilometres away, one could see the inviting calm, blue seas of the Bay of Biscay. We were greeted in a most friendly way at the main door by a stout, ruddy-faced, man who ushered us inside and introduced himself as David Weatherby, a temporary expatriate, as he put it. He said he knew what we wanted most of all, and that breakfast was ready; not the Continental kind, but a man's breakfast such as we had not had for some time. When done, we could wash and bathe, and then be free to sleep for as long as we wished.

It was a simply wonderful breakfast, reminding me of my mother's daily feasts all that time ago when at school in Oxford: eggs, bacon, sausage, toast, marmalade, delightful Darjeeling tea, and even kedgeree, all placed on a sideboard, from which we helped ourselves. Being so pre-occupied with this splendid meal, I did not notice Emilie's departure. Weatherby said that she had already eaten, and was probably now in San Sebastian arranging urgent matters. We took turns to wash and shave in the single large bathroom. Clean linen and pyjamas had been laid out for us to wear. I had to help Cook, who was in a bad way. His feet were in tatters, and he had a pain in the left side of his stomach but, as usual, made no complaint. Smithson, on the other hand, seemed fully recovered, now full of his customary boyish bounce.

I was the last to use the bathroom, and could not resist taking a quick cold bath. Refreshed, and now clad in pyjamas, I rejoined the others in the breakfast room. Weatherby offered malt whiskey and cigarettes, and wanted to know if there was anything else we wanted before we slept. We were all very content, and said so.

'Good, that's fine,' said Weatherby. 'We shall not bother you with anything until later today, when you will have a visitor. Just relax and sleep. You are in safe hands. It's all over and done with, now.'

Two had to share a room. I suggested that the other two should have priority, and so it was agreed. Weatherby took me to his own bedroom, where he busied himself putting the final touches to the making-up of the bed.

'This is yours, old boy. Pleasant dreams.'

'Thank you,' I said as I got into bed, 'but could you please make sure that I am awakened in a few hours time? I want to be ready for our visitor; by the way, can you tell me what he does? What happens next?'

'Nothing to worry about, old boy. All I know is that this chap deals with some sort of formality concerning your illegal entry into Spain. You can't just wander into the country and tell the Spaniards that you are on your way home, rather than wanting to spend some time in one of their excellent prisons. I believe there is a scheme worked out with our Embassy in Madrid which straightens such things out.'

He realised that I wanted to talk, and pulled up a chair beside the bed.

'This is a funny old war, from my end. It rather passes me by, but I am only too pleased to be able to do something, even though it amounts to very little: I just seem to run a blasted hotel.'

He laughed, and took a sip at the whiskey he had brought with him.

'I stayed on after the Civil War,' he explained. 'I was out here as some sort of contact with the British Press. Strange that Franco allowed me to stay on, but then I had a Spanish wife, and she was a Nationalist, thank goodness. What goes on with this escaping business involves me very little. All the action and excitement in the hills has nothing to do with me. My only real contact is with our dear friend, Miss de Vray.'

He got up, drew the curtains, and apologised for having kept me from sleep. He left, promising to call me in good time. I lay back in bed, thinking of what he had said about the business in Madrid, and then fell into a deep sleep. I slept like a log for almost four hours. The unfamiliar large breakfast had not rested well in my stomach, and the discomfort had brought me awake. I got up, washed, and dressed in the suit and shoes that I had carried with me in the back-pack all the way from St. Jean de Luz. Someone had pressed the suit and cleaned the shoes, placing them at the foot of the bed while I had slept. Weatherby was not surprised to see me when I met him in the living room.

'Tea, old boy; I've just made a fresh pot. Best get the others up now. Oh, by the way, our visitor is already here. He's waiting for a word with you out front, on the patio.'

From now on, I had to concentrate on how best to get away from the villa and report to my contact, the German Consul in San Sebastian. I knew that there would be relatively little time to do this without causing alarm to the British, and that my interview with this visitor would inevitably start the process of revealing me as a German. The visitor was a small, insignificant-looking man, who said he was the British Consul. He had already arranged papers and forms on a garden table, and was waiting to interview me, pen poised. He began by taking note of my rank, rôle and Service details. He was content with the bare facts, and did not, at any time, embellish a question. It was clear that his Consulate dealt only with the formality of recording our arrival, and acted as a clearing house for the stream of evaders being brought in across the mountains.

In answer to my questions, this studious, carefully-spoken man explained that his only task was to prepare the way for my quick transit across Spain to Gibraltar. The detailed negotiations with the Spanish for my release would be handled by the British Embassy in Madrid, where I would have to stay for a while. When the Spaniards had accepted my paper work, I would be taken openly to Gibraltar, where I would be interrogated about my evasion by a special military unit which dealt with such matters. Only then would it be possible for news of my safety to be sent to my next-of-kin. However, until I got there, I would have to remain under the supervision of the Diplomatic Services. We had to remember that, for our early exit from Spain, the Spanish were bound by the Geneva Convention to regard us as escaped prisoners of war, and not as evaders. He thereupon produced a buff-coloured form, printed in Spanish.

'You are, for the time being, Second Lieutenant John Hoskins of the Northamptonshire Regiment. You escaped from Fallingbostel, and got to Spain more than six months ago. Will you please sign your new name, here.' I duly signed.

'What happens next?' I asked.

'Oh, things will have to take their course. There is always a wait before we can fit you in at the Embassy. In your case, you will be off to Burgos tomorrow, where we have arranged for you to stay with a good British family. When everything's ready, we will quickly get you to Madrid.'

The interview was over. He carefully put my papers into a folder. 'Now I must get on with the others,' he said.

I went back into the house to sit and think: I now knew that the breakaway would have to be made sometime that day. Although Burgos was not too far away, my departure could best be made now, while I was reasonably close to my contact point. Weatherby interrupted my thoughts by producing the whiskey bottle again, and I drank with him, this time discussing the war and the Bomber Command offensive. We were eventually joined by Cook, Smithson and the Consul, who was about to leave.

While we stood together, saying farewell, he was called to the telephone in the next room. He returned to say that he would like me to go with him to San Sebastian.

My immediate reaction was one of trepidation. Had the British already detected something wrong with my story? Possibly not, or there would have been someone a little more threatening than the British Consul to take me away. No, it was more likely something to do with my leading the group all the way from Brussels or, perhaps, there was indeed a British Intelligence presence in San Sebastian. In any case, I was feeling confident enough to deal with whatever lay ahead and, if things went badly wrong, the German Consul would be close at hand.

CHAPTER TWENTY-SIX

The British Consulate turned out to be a small office building on the edge of the town. As we parked outside, the Consul asked me if I had noticed, only about fifty metres away, the German Consulate. I looked back, but could see only a black car standing outside what I realised would be my ultimate destination. As we went in, the Consul seemed to be enjoying a private joke. With a mischievous chuckle, he said that I was indeed a lucky fellow to have someone, here in Spain, who wanted to see me after all the adventures I had gone through: when we reached his room, there was Emilie de Vray waiting for me. We greeted and embraced each other like long-lost friends. This was a very different Emilie, dressed in a well-cut suit and skirt, wearing a smart hat and carrying a fine leather handbag.

'You look surprised, my dear George. Had you forgotten our arrangement to meet again, once you were in Spain?'

No, I had certainly not forgotten. She had been in my thoughts ever since our passionate encounter at the farmhouse on the mountainside, and the cause of my questioning the justice of what I was doing: I knew also that I was in danger of letting my intense personal feelings come between me and my sworn duty. Before I could begin to make excuses, she spoke again.

'You have been placed in my care once again, George, at least for a little while. Mr Richardson has made all the arrangements, and all I have to do is make sure you get back to Weatherby's... eventually. I thought we might have dinner together. Our table is booked and, believe it or not, the bill has already been paid.'

I had never seen her so animated. All thoughts of *Kondor* had gone from my mind. I willingly surrendered to her charm, and was content to forget everything else until the time came for us to part. This woman fascinated me, and I wanted, so much, to enjoy whatever little time there was for us to share.

The restaurant was not far away. We were obviously expected, and were shown to a small table in an alcove, overlooking a courtyard filled with potted flowers, and with bougainvillea in bloom against the far wall. The place was almost empty; in fact there were only three others in the room. A young couple sat at a table in a far corner, deeply engrossed with each other and, across the room, near the serving door, sat a dapper little man with pince-nez and oiled black hair, busily devouring his food. Emilie bent towards me and pointed him out.

'That's the German Consul. We often see him. He is a nasty little man. *Heil Hitler!*' She chuckled like a naughty child, and I laughed with her.

I was more than content to let Emilie order the food and the wine. Her choices were impeccable, and she played the hostess with ease and charm. I was captivated, and allowed myself to relax into a state of dreamlike contentment, filled with thoughts of the woman with me, and of what delights might follow the meal. As we ate, we talked of many things; how we had grown up, what we enjoyed, and the people we knew. But towards the end of the meal, I began to notice that her mind was on other matters, and that she was no longer sharing my mellow mood. As the dessert was being served, the reason became clear. Glancing down at her fob-watch, her manner abruptly reverted to one of businesslike efficiency. She leant towards me and whispered:

'My dear George, how time has flown. I had no idea it was so late. I am desolate, but I must leave you.'

It took a moment for me to realise what she had said.

'What on earth do you mean?'

She looked at me, puzzled, her brows knit.

'Why are you so surprised? I have work to do; surely you must realise that. If I do not rendezvous with Clemente, at a location some way from here, before midnight, I will not be able to get back to the other side in time to make another collection from St. Jean. I have to be at Ciburne in the morning, and it will take us all night to get there.'

'My God. I don't understand, Emilie. You only arrived here, with us, this morning. Why you? Surely there must be someone else? How can you possibly do so much?'

'I do it all the time... and so does Clemente. We work together...

and there is a great deal to be done.' She pointed across the room to where the German Consul was paying his bill, and making ready to leave.

'That is the reason why,' she said angrily. 'He represents all that is evil in our world today; a monstrous tyranny which we must fight, and continue to fight, until we have won, as you in the RAF are doing.'

'My country has been invaded twice, without any reason, by these barbarians. Despite our sufferings at their hands, we shall never bow down to become part of what they now call the glorious Greater German *Reich*. You English have no idea what it is like to have your country conquered and occupied; you do not seem to realise what the Germans are trying to do with us.'

She was on the verge of tears.

'Many of us have already been killed by these swine... and there are so many more who have simply disappeared in their evil concentration camps.'

She checked herself, drew back and squared her shoulders.

'I suppose I am a soldier, just like you. I fight alongside my English comrades by doing my best to return you to the RAF, so that you can come back, again and again, to bomb the Germans until they are beaten into surrender.'

With that, our romantic dinner came to an end. My tender thoughts for her had been pushed aside by her vehement words. I realised that I was sitting opposite a bitter enemy, someone who had to be stopped and dealt with according to our rules of war. Emilie motioned to the waiter for the bill, which she initialled as having been paid. Her fury subsided as we got up to leave and, despite all she had said, I still felt admiration for this lovely, courageous woman, albeit my enemy.

'I must get you back to Richardson,' she said when we were outside, but I realised at once that this was the ideal opportunity to walk away from her and Phoenix, and end my part in Operation *Kondor*.

'There is no need, dear Emilie. You have important things to do, and I know my way back. May I not just stay with you until you leave?'

She nodded her assent, but her thoughts were elsewhere. We walked together in silence to a small pension in the harbour area, not far away. She left me at the door, saying that it would take only a few minutes for her to change, and that she would then be on her way.

'Please don't wait for me, George; I would rather say goodbye now. Let us remember this evening together, and hope that when we meet again, all will be peace.'

She fumbled in her handbag, took out an envelope and handed it to me.

'I should have given you this to read earlier, but the time went so quickly. Please do not open it until midnight, when I shall be thinking of you as I am crossing the mountains.'

We said goodbye, and kissed without emotion, or so it seemed. I walked away without a backward glance, relieved that everything had gone so easily. Now there was work to be done. I expected that Richardson would assume I was still with Emilie, and if and when he began to look for me, she would be far away, beyond contact. Weatherby, who was only on the fringe of things, would probably assume that the Consul had had good reason to keep me in town for the night. No matter what happened, I reckoned that, with reasonable luck, I had a clear run of many hours in which to put into effect the final stage of *Kondor.*

It took me less than ten minutes to reach the German Consulate, and there I found *Herr* Spiegel, the Consul, whom I had seen earlier in the restaurant, and to whom I now identified myself. He double-checked my credentials from a list of questions, provided by Berlin. He said that I had been expected, and that he had twice been warned to stand by during the past fortnight. He produced his written orders from Kreis, and showed me a telegraphic encoder which had been specially installed and tested. He had also been authorised to seek assistance from the Spaniards, if necessary. We opened the link with Berlin with the cryptic signal: "*Der Kondor ist geflogen*". I set about preparing the first transmission, which would deal with the details of the nerve centres of Phoenix in Brussels and Paris, and so forestall a general alert being broadcast throughout the route. Just as I finished, Berlin acknowledged, and confirmed they were standing by to receive my report.

My transmission listed the names and addresses of the principal members of Phoenix: Arthos and Benedict in Brussels; and Paul Vercours, Jean the dentist and Doctor Gaillard in Paris. They were to be taken out of action at once. I added that more detailed information would follow within the hour: I compiled this from the notes I had made and hidden on my person all the way from Brussels. It included the names and addresses of those managing the safe houses in which I had stayed, or which I had visited whilst helping Phoenix, as well as those of the priests in the Monastery at Namur, and of Madame Giraud in Balen. I finished with a resumé of the activity in the *Pays Basques*, and commented that the passages over the Pyrenees seemed mostly to start from Ascain and terminate at Weatherby's villa in San Sebastian. I did not mention Emilie de Vray. For the moment, I chose to consider her as a guide, to be included later in my detailed write-up.

Before I had completed my transmission, I received a congratulatory signal from Kreis, who ordered me to report as soon as possible to *Gestapo* Headquarters in Paris, where he would meet me. Spiegel said it would not be possible to do anything about getting me away until daybreak, only a few hours away: he advised me to get some rest before I left. I told him that could wait until after I had written the framework of my detailed report, which I knew would be required as soon as I arrived in Paris. Spiegel did not argue, but busied himself by completing his instructions, which included informing our Embassy in Madrid, our Consulate in Barcelona and the Spanish police.

It was not long before *Frau* Spiegel provided us with a hot breakfast, and I was able to get ready to leave. I was given a lockable attaché case, papers to get me easily out of Spain and into France, and a first-class railway voucher for the journey to Paris. Spiegel drove me to the station in Irun, on the frontier, and I found a compartment to myself on the Biarritz train. My papers were cleared before we started, and I was left alone to continue preparing my report. It was fully sketched out by the time the we reached Biarritz, where I changed to the Paris Express. Again I was able to sit alone. I had finished writing, and while putting the papers away in my case, I came across the letter that Emilie had given me to read. I opened it slowly, with deep misgivings in view of what I had just written, and read:

'My dear George, I am writing this while looking forward to being with you again for just a moment or two, before I have to return to

France. Forgive me if it disturbs you in any way, but I hope this is not the case, because what I write is of great importance to me, and I most earnestly hope that it will perhaps be the same with you. I know that it is not "correct" for a woman to write in this way, but these are desperate times, and perhaps time itself could be short for both of us. I must tell you how I feel, or I shall regret not doing so to my dying day.

I remember the very first time we met, ages ago it seems, back in Namur. Every meeting since is still fresh in my memory, and with each I have felt a growing regard for you. I cherish the hope that perhaps your feelings are the same for me. I know that you believe in God, a future for freedom, and the justice of all we are now forced to do. I am also well aware that we have only been brought together because of the war. I want you to know that I live for the day when we shall meet again. Heaven only knows where and when, if ever.

I know that you cannot answer this letter, but I hope, with all my heart, that you will never forget that I love you. ... Emilie.'

I put the letter down, and lit a cigarette. I was indeed surprised, almost baffled, by what she had written. I carefully read the letter again. I had to admit that there had been a growing bond of affection between us which, if circumstances had been different, might well have developed. But she had said that she was actually in love with me. How could this be? And did I honestly have any such regard for her? I had to admit to myself that I simply did not know. Thoughts of Emilie, and what might have been, began to torture me. There was no doubt that she was the very lifeblood of Phoenix and that, inevitably, she would be caught and dealt with by the *Gestapo*. Her death was already predestined by the report I had been so carefully compiling for the past few hours. I was now horrified at the thought, and so took the report from the case, and set about a redraft in which I made no reference to Emilie de Vray.

Kreis was already at *Gestapo* Headquarters when I arrived - tired, bedraggled, and disturbed by thoughts of what might lie ahead. Kreis, as efficient as ever, had arranged facilities for me to bathe, shave and dress, thankfully in my *Luftwaffe* uniform, which he had brought with him from Berlin. We had a light meal together, and then he told me the news.

All those I had listed in my first signal were already in custody.

The arrest of Arthos, who was in fact a Belgian nobleman and a friend of King Leopold, had caused a great stir in Belgian government circles, since he was a junior Minister. Benedict was also someone of importance. He had been picked up after having been followed to a safe house in which there were four RAF evaders. The detention of Paul Vercours had been much more difficult because, somehow, he had been alerted to the fact that something was wrong. He had been trapped in a house with two other men, one of whom had been shot and killed as he tried to escape across the rooftops. Jean de Brassey, the dentist, had been arrested while treating a patient in his surgery. Dr Gaillard had been taken in his home, together with his wife.

My second signal had been equally devastating to Phoenix, as it had dealt with the rank and file at the many safe houses. Scores of arrests had been made and, already, a large number of enemy airmen had been captured in hiding. Kreis was absolutely delighted with the success of his plan, and told me that the results were already better than expected. The meal over, we went to an office where Kreis had arranged for a stenographer to help me complete my detailed report: he sat with us as I dictated from my notes and draft report. I started from the time of my parachute drop into Belgium, and finished with my arrival at Weatherby's: Kreis did not disturb me, but constantly made notes. The only time he interrupted my dictation was when I described the death of Conrad Weindl. This distressed him, but he soon recovered his composure, and said he regretted not having had the foresight to provide each of us with a cyanide pill. I went step by step along the escape route, describing, as best I could, details of the safe houses and guides. When I had completed my dictation, the stenographer left to type the report, and Kreis turned to his notes.

'I notice, Wilhelm, that you are unable to tell us much about the guides, apart from the fact that they are usually female and good-looking. You give some general indication of where they are working, but you do not appear to know where they live. So far, we have not caught a guide... but we will. These women interest me. They are so active, and must therefore know much about the way the route works. Best of all, they will be more susceptible to expert interrogation.'

251

'It is difficult to help you there,' I lied. 'It is true that most of the guides were female, but I took little notice of them. After all, they were only involved in getting us from one place to another.'

'That may be so,' said Kreis, 'but you must try to give us some description of them. Anything will do. What did they look like? In what ways did you find them attractive? How do we catch them? Believe me, my dear Rath, no one is going to escape us this time. I am going to destroy this pestilence once and for all.'

I could not get Emilie out of my mind, and I searched hard for something to say.

'Inevitably, you are bound to catch these guides. I am sure they will not desert their organisation or abandon their work. Eventually, you will get them, either by watching the area of the safe houses or, more probably, as a result of interrogating those you have already captured. It will not be easy, because these people are fanatics, driven by patriotism and, even more, by their hatred of us and all things German. They will fight to the bitter end.'

I could see that Kreis was disconcerted by what I had said.

'I am not sure I follow you, Wilhelm. Have you been consorting with the enemy? You seem to have formed new opinions. These people certainly appear to have made an impression on you.'

I looked at my superior, knowing that he would never understand.

'Yes, *Herr Obersturmbannführer.* Indeed, they have.'

We worked together in Paris for two more days. Kreis stayed, constantly cross-examining me on what I had written, and worrying away at every detail of the rounding-up of the Phoenix organisation. He had assembled a strong team which covered every part of the line, while he master-minded their operations, keeping in touch with *Gestapo* Headquarters in Berlin. He was then called away to deal with some problem in the *Pays Basques*, and left me alone in Paris until he returned. Delighted with the progress of the operation, he decided that he was now able to leave matters in France to those in the *Avenue Foch*, and that we could work better from our base in Brussels.

The *Gestapo* purge in Belgium had gone well. Not a single detail of my report had been found negative. I was grateful to be kept out of sight of those who had been taken: I had to confirm the identities of scores of people now under interrogation in prison, from photographs taken immediately upon capture. Many were unknown to me, but all those with whom I had stayed were easily recognisable. In the cases of both Arthos and Benedict, I was called upon to verify their identities from behind a screen in the main Brussels prison. Because of their standing in Belgian circles, and their contacts with the Belgian Royal Family, the charges against them were dealt with at the highest level, and with the pretence of involving the Belgian legal system. Although the outcome was a foregone conclusion, much was made of the fact that two eminent Belgians had committed offences against the Articles of the Armistice, signed in 1940 by King Leopold.

I was now reacting badly to what I had done. The excitement which had kept my mind centred on the task of defeating Phoenix had subsided, and I was left only to witness retribution being meted out to scores of very brave people. Kreis and his team were delighted with what I had achieved, and congratulations were the order of the day, with promises of rewards to come when we returned to Berlin. Yet, to me, all this was developing into a bitter anti-climax. I had been feeling depressed and disturbed ever since my return to Paris. I was by no means proud of what I had done; in fact, I had a sense of foreboding and a feeling of shame about everything. Those I had condemned were, without exception, fine people. They had been fighting for their freedom and not, as I had once thought, settling down to fit into the framework of the Greater German *Reich*. But the die had been cast, and I had to steel myself to the knowledge that, because of me, most would pay with their lives for their brave actions.

I was then sent back to Berlin, leaving Kreis in Brussels to enjoy his success. In Berlin, my depression intensified as I was left with nothing to do but wait for Kreis to decide my future. I deliberately sought out Greta, who did her best to cheer me up, and to distract me from my problems but, particularly at night, even when I had exhausted myself in her company, my mind always returned to thoughts of Emilie de Vray.

Berlin was beginning to suffer from the results of increased British night bombing. Serious damage was being done to the city and, during the first night of my return, there was a bad raid. The next morning, I tried to contact my step-mother for news of my father, but found that the bombing had been too much for her frail resolve; she had long since left the villa for the safety of Saxony. Then, to my surprise, I was told by the *Gestapo* that *Standartenführer* Rath was in hospital in Hanover.

Kreis returned to Berlin before I could get away to see my father. His work in Belgium was now finished to his satisfaction, and he took pleasure in bringing me up-to-date with the news. This he did, sitting at ease in his office in front of a good fire, both of us making inroads into his reserve of Calvados. He was in a good mood, and I asked him first whether I might be given leave of absence to visit my father in Hanover. This he readily approved, and then told me that the famous Clemente had been trapped in the farm at Ascain, after putting up a fight in which both the farmer and his son, Claudillo, had been killed. There was little doubt that Paul Vercours had been the leader of Phoenix. He had been interrogated thoroughly but had revealed nothing. He had not been strong enough to endure this ordeal, which had been so severe that he had fallen into a coma. There being no useful purpose in keeping him alive, he had been executed at Mont Saint Marzin, together with Paul de Brassey and Doctor Gaillard. There had been other executions in accordance with International Law, but most of the remaining captives had been judged of lesser importance, and sentenced to indefinite confinement in labour camps.

I saw the other side of Kreis as we drank and talked. *Kondor* had been everything he had hoped for. His idea had at last brought a solution to the widespread traffic in *Terrorflieger*. He had earned the approbation of the High Command, and summoned to explain his work to the *Reichsführer SS* himself - Heinrich Himmler. He expected soon to be promoted and given wider responsibilities. He told me that if I wished, I could stay with him and would no doubt do well. I tried to explain that I had been extremely lucky. Unlike poor Weindl, everything had fallen into place for me, almost as if I had been blessed with guidance from above. Kreis thought otherwise: it had been good planning and preparation, backed by German resolution, that had brought about the destruction of perhaps the most important escape route of all. It was his opinion, and that of his superiors, that this type of clandestine operation would soon come to an end, particularly as so many of those involved had paid the ultimate price.

So far, I had listened quietly as a very self-satisfied man had held the stage, whilst I sat comfortably in front of the fire. We had finished the Calvados, and Kreis had opened a bottle of Cognac. I was far too relaxed to argue with him, even though I knew he was wrong in some of his theories. I realised only too well that what I had done had been devastating to the Phoenix organisation, but also guessed that it would be only a matter of time before other brave souls helped it to rise again from the ashes.

'You were right about the guides, Wilhelm,' said Kreis, as we started on the Cognac. 'It was only a matter of time before we got them.'

My heart was in my mouth as he fumbled in his pocket and took out an envelope. 'Yes, they were attractive, damned good-looking bitches, I would say.' He took some photographs from the envelope and showed them to me, one at a time. The first was a head and shoulders of Natalie.

'We caught her on the train to Paris. She had four *Terrorflieger* with her.'

He handed me another. 'This one was actually hiding in a farm which we knew was a safe house, because we had already taken away the owner and two evaders. We took your advice and kept watch. Did you ever meet either?'

'Yes, I believe the blonde was my escort from Brussels to Paris, but I have never seen the other.'

'This one is a real prize, my good friend. She was picked up by the Spanish police in the Pyrenees only a few days ago. We do not know what she was doing, but she was dressed as though she were going to war. Was she ever a guide of yours?'

I found myself staring at a photograph of Emilie de Vray. There was a heavy bruise across her lovely face, and her hair had been cut short. Yet she looked defiant. Before I could say anything, Kreis handed me the next photograph, with a chuckle.'

'Perhaps this one is more to your liking, my friend. You never told me if you *really* got to know the enemy.'

It was a photograph of all three women, standing against a wall, facing the camera, completely naked. It was all I could do to contain myself but, before I could react, Kreis dismissed the subject and turned to something else.

'These people are of little account. They can tell us nothing more than we already know.'

'What will happen to them?'

'They will probably join the others in the labour camps. With their looks, I am sure they can be made to work well.'

He took back the photographs and returned them to his pocket.

'But I have not yet told you of our finest coup. It is fantastic, Wilhelm. In all, we have rounded up more than a hundred *Terrorflieger*, one hundred and twenty-six to be exact. Just think of that in terms of the aircraft which could be back in the skies of Germany if you had not done so well.'

'And what happens to them?'

'In their case there can be no argument. All were caught in disguise, and so we are bound by International Law and by our own decrees in the way we deal with them. They are already at Buchenwald, where they are liable to summary execution as *Terrorflieger*.'

This was all too much for me. Kreis seemed oblivious to the disgust I must have shown in my face. I could think of nothing but to get away from the *Gestapo* and return to some sort of normality. I had thought long and hard before undertaking the *Kondor* operation, and had only agreed because it had seemed to offer the one chance to return to flying duties. Now I was drinking with a man who regarded me as a hero for having brought to account hundreds who, through my efforts, would be tortured and then brutally put to death: I felt sick and degraded.

I looked contemptuously at Kreis, put down my glass, and left his room without another word. I was beside myself with remorse. I really had had no idea that the *Gestapo* could be so utterly ruthless, and so devoid of human decency. I imagined the Hell facing those consigned to the concentration camps, and was shocked at the decision taken regarding the RAF evaders at Buchenwald. That was surely contrary to anything in the Geneva Convention, and also beyond the provisions set by the International Red Cross. I strove to think what I could do to get those in Buchenwald back into the hands of the *Luftwaffe*, the organisation nominally responsible for them.

It was apparent the next morning that my relationship with Kreis had changed. He said nothing of my behaviour the night before, and spoke only once as he signed my travel orders to visit my father in Hanover: I was not offered the use of a vehicle, and therefore had no alternative but to travel by train.

'Your father is in trouble, *Oberleutnant*. You are lucky that I have been able to arrange this concession, but you are to return to Berlin as quickly as possible.'

It was a slow and tedious journey to Hanover. The British had been attacking the city ever since the end of September and, in one particular raid, had caused great damage and killed many people. I got there the morning after the last raid, made during the night of 16th October. Fortunately, the weather had been bad for accurate bombing, and the enemy Pathfinders had been unable to position their target markers on the city. Most of the bombs had fallen in open country to the north and north-west, and my father's hospital was in a small village to the south.

The sight of the hospital was forbidding. There was a prison-like atmosphere about the place. A tall barbed-wire fence surrounded the grounds and the staff and nurses were uniformed. I had to report to an *SS* guard before I was escorted into the main building. There, a registrar or adjutant of sorts checked my papers, and told me that *Standartenführer* Rath was very ill, but that I could see him for just an hour, and then would have to leave. I hardly recognised the gaunt, hollow-eyed and shrunken figure as my father: I found him sitting by the window in his room, clad in a hospital smock with a blanket over his shoulders, and slippers on his feet. He had difficulty in seeing me at first but, when he did recognise me, he burst into tears. For the first time since my early youth I embraced him, putting my arms around his shuddering shoulders.

It was painfully obvious that he was very ill. We sat for a while, looking at each other, before he began to speak. He struggled for words at first and then, slowly and gradually, he found them, and a little of his old dynamism began to return. Bit by bit, I began to recognise the character of the parent I had once known. We talked about the family. He was bitter at the sudden disappearance of his wife to a place somewhere in Saxony. The marriage had not been a success and, now she had left Berlin, it seemed she had no intention of ever living with him again. With a wan smile, he asked me how I had fared with the opposite sex. Had I met someone I could marry?

A frugal lunch was brought to us, together with some beer. I could see that my visit was beginning to arouse my father: he had pulled himself together, and wanted to talk. He was fascinated with my brief account of the *Kondor* adventure, and plied me with questions about the British and the Belgians. He said that I had done well, although he expressed his surprise that I had agreed to work with the *Gestapo*. He told me that he and Kreis had discussed this point at great length before I had, at last, decided to be a part of *Kondor*. I told him that it had not been an easy decision and that, now it was over, I was unhappy at the results but, at least, would soon be free of the *Gestapo* and able to resume flying.

'I wish I could do something like that,' he said, wistfully. 'For far too long, I have been doing things in which I have had no belief. Terrible things, in fact.'

He regarded me with a pitiful look, and then straightened himself in his chair.

'I know that you have always thought much of me. I was once a good soldier, a proud one. I served my Fatherland as best I could, and hoped to do so to the end of my days. Now, my son, you are looking at a failure, a damned fool, a murderer. I am someone who has been told he has run his course. I am finished.'

What was he trying to say? Was he so ill that his mind was unhinged? He saw my astonishment and disbelief.

'No, it is only too true, my dear son. For years I have allowed myself to be drawn into something so horrible that you will have difficulty in believing what I have to say. It has been something that no true German should ever do. It is so monstrous that, surely, one day, we will all have to face retribution. I have to tell you about it so that you will understand why I am in this place, and what is going to happen to me.'

I tried to protest, but he waved me to silence, and I could only sit and listen to words which made it clear to me that he was in full command of his mental processes. He began by going back to the early days of his work in the Party, when he had been a Brownshirt and then a Storm Trooper in the *SS*. He had, at one time, enjoyed a close relationship with Adolf Hitler, until the great man had become first Chancellor and then *Führer*. My father had risen in the ranks of the *SS*, undertaking duties which were mainly political in an ever-expanding *Reich*. He had done his very best and then, at the outbreak of war, had volunteered for active service but, instead of being given command of a fighting unit, had been assigned to work with the *Gestapo* in Poland to suppress the Warsaw uprising. He had stayed there only until the Poles were defeated and then, when the *Blitzkrieg* had begun, had gone on to do similar work in Belgium and France.

Things had changed dramatically for him when we had attacked Russia. He had then been given control of the *Einsatzgruppen* operating in the Baltic area and, later, inside Russia. This was work he had heartily disliked. He had tried to get another appointment, but had been forcibly reminded of his sworn *SS* oath to the *Führer,* and his duty to deal properly with those who resisted Germany. In simple terms, this meant the elimination of guerrillas, saboteurs, agitators, Communists and Jews. He said that he had done his best to distance himself from the horror of this work. One always had to take ruthless action against subversives, so he said. Those captured in the course of guerrilla warfare could be shown no mercy but, as time went on, it was not just the Resistance he had had to deal with but the poor, persecuted dissidents and the Jews. He had become appalled by what he had done in the name of Germany. Hangings were at first the order of the day, then execution by firing squads and, finally, mass executions over open graves. Ultimately, he had been ordered to accompany Heinrich Himmler to witness an *Einsatzkommando* mass execution in Minsk. This had been such a gruesome and bloody experience that the distressed *Reichsführer* had decreed that more efficient means of dealing with the problem should be found.

I sat transfixed. At last I was learning something of what I had often suspected whilst involved with *Kondor*. But how was it that we ordinary Germans knew so little of such events? What my father was describing was almost unbelievable: he was at pains to convince me that he had striven to sever his links with the *SS*. At the end of 1941, he had been given an appointment in Berlin, where he had learned of plans for a more workable and clinical solution to disposing of the unwanted. Millions were to be transported to labour and concentration camps to ensure 'proper cleansing' of the conquered countries. At a top-level conference, held in Berlin in early 1942, it had been agreed that *die Endlösung* - the 'Final Solution' - was to be put into effect. Extermination camps were to be built in Poland, and the concentration camps in Germany, such as Belsen, Ravensbrück, Dachau and Buchenwald, were to be enlarged. A new method of elimination had been decided upon - the gas chamber: in this way, all those who were judged not to be acceptable members of the human race, such as the Jews, would be exterminated as vermin. They would be gassed, their bodies cremated, and their ashes scattered.

At this point, my father broke down in tears. I tried to console him as his body shook and trembled. He held his head in his hands, then looked up at me, as if pleading for forgiveness.

'Dear God. Do you realise that we have been responsible for the destruction of a whole section of the human race? I tried so hard to get away, but that is why I am here.'

I could find no words to console my father. He brushed away his tears and carried on.

'It was the *Reichsführer* himself who ordered me to manage the factory and working camp being built by I.G. Farben at Auschwitz Birkenau. I refused outright, to his face. He had me arrested and put in gaol. Very soon I became ill, and was brought here. They said I had contracted typhus.'

I looked with new-found affection on the old soldier who was my own flesh and blood. He had unburdened himself and, despite the air of resignation about him, had recovered his military bearing.

'I know that I am finished, my son. I have come, most unhappily, to the end of my service for Germany. There is nothing that can be done to save me, and I know that I will probably never see you again. They will never let me leave this place.'

He fumbled for something in his dressing gown pocket.

'Go with God, my son. Be true to yourself, and do your duty as best you can, as a good German officer.' He then handed me the enamelled blue cross of his *Pour le Mérite*.

The enormity of his revelations was too much for me to grasp. I simply could not understand how such dreadful things were being done, apparently without the knowledge of the majority of the German people. Could it be that our suspicions had been swept aside by the efficiency of our propaganda machine, to the point where the fate of the Jewish race was of little consequence? After all, the "Jewish programme" had started long before the war, and we had become used to the idea that Jews were different. Anti-Semitism had been brought to the fore by the Third *Reich,* and many brilliant and remarkable Jewish scientists, doctors, artists, actors, and even aviators, had been glad to get out of Germany before the war, whilst they still had the chance. Those with no alternative but to stay were caught up in the purge, and had been forced into a ghetto-like existence, How often had I seen them in their misery, forced to wear the Star of David as a shameful mark of recognition. But then, had the *Führer* not made it clear, from the outset, that the Jewish race was responsible for so many of Germany's former ills, and that international Jewry was behind the stubborn British resistance and the entry of America into the war?

All this was uppermost in my mind when I reported to Kreis on my return. He confirmed that my father was in very serious trouble, and that he would be kept in hospital for his own good. He also avowed that it was the policy of the German government to deal with the Jewish problem in the best way for the country's good. All those who were being sent to the labour camps at least had the option of working for the goal of final victory. If they could or would not work, then they would have to be "set aside", as he put it.

It was all beyond my comprehension. I could see no logic in the *Führer's* plan to rid Germany of the Jews. I closed my mind to the immense immorality of it all, and salved my conscience with the fact that, as a simple soldier, I could do nothing to change the course of history. I buried my head in the sand with the rest of Germany, and turned my thoughts to how best I could contribute to winning the war.

CHAPTER TWENTY-SEVEN

Just as Kreis had promised, I was allowed to leave the *Gestapo* and return to the *Luftwaffe*. I was interviewed at *Oberbefehlshaber der Luftwaffe* a few days later about my return to flying duties but, first, the Intelligence staff wanted to know what I had been doing whilst working with the *Gestapo*. Mine was an unusual case; there were many gaps in my career, and my file had to record the facts. I was bound by an oath of secrecy, and had been warned by Kreis to reveal nothing about *Kondor*. If pressed, I was to say that I had been working for the *Gestapo* as a special interrogator of captured British aircrew. This I did, to the apparent satisfaction of the Intelligence people but, in doing so, I could not resist breaking faith with Kreis by reporting the fact that RAF aircrew were being held in Buchenwald under sentence of death, in contravention of every rule of war. This revelation was taken up at once by the *Luftwaffe* Police, and I had to explain myself further to an outraged Air Staff General. The *Gestapo* had usurped the responsibilities of the *Luftwaffe,* and he was adamant that the British captives should quickly be removed from Buchenwald and sent to a *Luftwaffe* prisoner-of-war camp.

I returned to flying duties in November 1943, at a time when great air battles were being fought in the skies over Germany. The British continued their area attacks at night, and were now concentrating on Berlin. The Americans were operating by day, and forcing their way further and further into Germany. Both enemy air forces were taking incredible losses, but so were we. The campaign in Russia was not going well, and there were constant demands for reinforcements from all quarters. It was abundantly clear that my retraining would be short, and that I would soon see action again. I was sent first to an initial training airfield in Bavaria, where I undertook a short refresher programme on the Arado. I was rusty and, at times, strangely ill at ease with this light training aircraft. I had not been in control of an aircraft for more than three years, and it was taking time for me to settle down. It felt good, however, to be airborne again, and some of my old skills (and bad habits) began to return: it was still obvious that I had no gift whatsoever for aerobatics.

I spent a few hours flying the Siebel, and was then moved on to an operational conversion unit, where I converted to the Junkers 88. It took me a while to get used to this much heavier and faster aircraft, and I was somewhat dismayed to find that my previous experience on the similar, but slower, Heinkel proved of little help. I passed through the conversion stages, completed my day and night exercises, and then began crew training. Those allocated as my navigator and gunners were new recruits; young and enthusiastic, but inexperienced. They looked up to me, and were proud to have been selected to form a crew commanded by such a veteran as myself. We progressed through day and night cross-country flights to radar interceptions and gunnery. My old skill of flying accurately on instruments had returned, but my anxiety to do well, coupled with the fact that I had not flown for so long, often led to mistakes. I tried to hide my concern, but my former strange superstitions began to return. At times I became tense and nervous, particularly when flying in cloud or bad weather. I began to realise that I could never again be the confident, skilled pilot of yesteryear; but I kept this belief to myself, and was glad that no one else seemed to notice my misgivings.

Early in January 1944, I was posted to a *Nachtjagdgeschwader*, in constant night-fighter action against Bomber Command, which was still persisting with heavy attacks on Berlin. I was given a week of intensive flying, and then declared operational, to take my place alongside the *Experten* who were causing such havoc among the British bombers. This period was proving the most successful ever for our night-fighters. We had re-organised to meet new British tactics, and there were now four hundred crews, equipped with first-rate radio and navigational aids, effective radar to penetrate the British electronic counter-measures, and the devastating *Schräge Musik* - upward-firing cannons.

I made my first operational sortie on the night of 20th January, when a large force again attacked Berlin. Our *Nachtjagdgeschwader* was fed into the bomber stream early, and kills were made both on its way to the capital and on its return. Due either to excitement or inexperience, we achieved nothing, although, twice, we began interceptions: however, I failed to position my aircraft beneath the enemy in such a way as to 'play' *Schräge Musik*...

We operated throughout the raids on Berlin towards the end of

January, and in the final attack on 15th February, but without success. Time and again our controllers gave us targets to track, but either we lost them, or I was unable to position properly to attack. To my dismay, I was now being seized with sudden attacks of panic, the same as those which had led to my disgrace in the *Kanalkampf.* I had begun to lose weight, and there was an unsteadiness in my hands which was difficult to conceal. I could not eat a full meal, and rarely managed a full hour of sleep. On the ground, any sudden noise startled me, and it was still worse in the air. I had to steel myself to remain controlled and efficient, and to hide my confusion and distress from my crew.

Then, on the evening of 10th March, my active flying career came to an end. I was taking off in very bad conditions - driving rain mixed with sleet, and visibility down to a hundred metres or so. As we neared take-off speed, I panicked. I completely lost my head, and froze on the controls. I do not remember throttling back or trying to pull up, but the result was that we crashed through the barriers at the end of the runway, the undercarriage collapsed as we tore across a field, and we came to rest in a ditch. I was pulled unconscious from the cockpit by my crewman, just before the cannon ammunition began to explode and the aircraft caught fire and exploded.

My injuries were severe. There was serious damage to my neck and to the base of my skull. My legs were broken, as were my left collar bone and three of my ribs. Worst of all, however, was the damage to my mental stability; I needed expert medical attention for a considerable time. The repair of the physical damage to my legs and of the other broken bones was relatively straightforward. Recovery from the injuries to my neck and skull took much longer, possibly complicated by the fact that I was now a complete nervous wreck.

When I was well enough to be moved, I was transferred to a general military hospital at Bad Kreuznach, on the Rhine. For months, I drifted in and out of panic attacks and suffered periods of great depression. I was given special attention, and slowly began to emerge from the emotional confusion which had, for so long, been treated by regular doses of drugs. I began to make steady progress and, when I could find my balance and begin to walk, I was sent to a convalescent home in the Black Forest.

It was there that I was told of the death of my father. One day, I was interviewed by a member of the *SS* who demanded an account, in my own words, of my actions since visiting my father in hospital, almost nine months earlier. My conversation with my father had been secretly recorded by the hospital authorities, who therefore knew that we had discussed the future of Germany. Did I know that my father had been released from hospital? Had I had any contact with him since that visit? I assured the man that I had not: he then told me that *Standartenführer* Rath had been executed for complicity in the plan to kill the *Führer*.

This terrible news did nothing to help my state of mind. Apart from the sense of loss of a parent for whom I had once felt some affection and respect, especially during my formative years, I was filled with bitterness that such a courageous man, who had dedicated so much of his life to the service of his country, should have met his end in this way.

Soon after the British and Americans invaded Normandy, I was well enough to be examined by a Medical Board with a view to my return to active service. To my great relief, I was judged unfit for further flying of any sort, a finding based largely on the psychiatric diagnosis of my mental state. I felt I was now a tragic misfit, of no further value to my country, and it was, in fact, some time before anything was found for me to do. Then, in August, on the very day the enemy reached Paris, I was returned to Intelligence work, once more entering the portals of the *Reichsluftfartministerium: Luftwaffe* Intelligence had need of personnel to translate English documents, and to monitor the continuous broadcasts of British and American propaganda.

The work helped with my recovery. At last, the panic attacks had gone and my nervousness was under control. I settled down to work hard in the building on the *Wilhelm Strasse*, which seemed to be the aiming point of most of the Allied bombing on the capital. Then, after the failure of our last great attack in the Ardennes, the entire translation department was moved to an underground headquarters at Nordhorn. On the face of it, this was because of the intensified bombing of Berlin. More realistically, it was because the war was lost, and it seemed preferable to surrender to the British and Americans, advancing from the West, rather to the Russians, who had begun a gigantic offensive to reach Berlin.

There was little to do at Nordhorn but wait. We were caught in the middle, trusting in Providence that the Allies would reach us before the Russians. My prayers were answered during the morning of 11th April 1945, when a motorised spearhead of the 3rd United States Armoured Division reached our now gutted headquarters. Some staff had left earlier for the south, heading for Bavaria, but most of my department had thought it better to remain, and give themselves up without any resistance. I had been elected spokesman of our small group, which was paraded above ground with prominent white flags in view. A single half-track drew up, followed by a jeep armed with twin machine-guns. I moved forward and smartly saluted the American Colonel standing in the half-track. He did not bother to return my salute but glared down and shouted at us: 'Do any of you filthy bastards speak English?'

Taken aback by his anger, I blurted out, 'Yes Colonel, I do.'

'I want you and that other swine,' he pointed to a bespectacled *Major* standing near me. 'I want you two to come with me and do some explaining.'

I had no idea what he was raving about but, with the guns in the jeep trained on us, I was certainly not going to argue. I clambered into the half-track, and the *Major* was forced into the back of the jeep. The vehicles reversed, and we drove away.

We travelled at speed for about ten kilometres, towards the mountains now clearly in view to the north. I then realised that we were headed towards the Dora labour camp at Nordhausen where, I had been told, our secret war weapons were being built. It was a place I had been forbidden to visit, as it was strictly under the control of the *SS*. Even to this day, I clearly remember the revulsion and deep sense of shame that I felt when I entered what I later found to be the recuperative camp attached to the V-2 rocket factory, built nearby inside the Kohnstein mountain. I was forced to watch the futile efforts of a few American medical personnel, trying to cope with the impossible task of helping hundreds of emaciated human beings, left lying in their own excrement to die on concrete floors thinly covered with straw. They were without food or water, and were surrounded by hundreds of naked corpses, stacked neatly in piles, like firewood ready for the furnace. The American Colonel was silent as I was pushed and prodded around as though I had been personally responsible for this Hell on earth. The overpowering smell of corruption was everywhere, and I had to fight to avoid vomiting as we picked our way through the dreadful scenes of carnage.

I thanked my lucky stars that I was, for the moment, under the protection of the Colonel. American soldiers showed their disgust by spitting in my face and trying to hit me. Some even made it clear that they wanted me hanged or shot on the spot. The Colonel kept them at a distance, and ordered that I should not be touched. He said he would be dealing with me in good time and, to make his point, showed me a pile of bodies of German guards, shot out of hand by his men when they had arrived. We were distracted by the arrival of three staff cars, carrying a Brigadier General and a number of other men wearing uniforms without badges of rank. The Colonel kept me with him as he paid his respects to the Brigadier, who announced that he was taking control of the factory in the mountain. The Colonel said he was glad because he wanted to push on: he had a war to win.

The outcome of this encounter was that I was kept with the Brigadier to act as interpreter. My colleague, the *Major*, who had kept close to me, was led away by the Colonel's men: I never knew what happened to him. I stayed with the Brigadier for just a day. He was the forerunner of a special American team sent expressly to take control of our rocket development and of those scientists pioneering the project. He was glad of my expert knowledge of English and French, and used me constantly until his own scientific linguists arrived.

The Dora factory had been built deep inside the mountain, and I was able to discover that more than 6,000 missiles had already been assembled, under appalling conditions, by thousands of Germany's prisoners. Driven on by *SS* guards, deprived of food and medical care, hanged on the spot for the most trivial offences, some 60,000 people, of all nationalities, had been forced to work deep inside the mountain, building what was intended to be the weapon which would win the war for us. The place was unique; a concentration camp whose existence had been kept entirely secret.

The Americans had taken prisoner a number of *SS* officers, and I had to plead with the Brigadier not to be included with them. He was sympathetic, and I was eventually handed over to the British Army Group, which was then striking towards Bremen and on to Hamburg.

When the war ended, about a month later, I was being held safely in a British prisoner-of-war camp for officers just outside Antwerp. My English background soon brought me to the attention of the British authorities, and my talents were quickly put to use. I was segregated from the other German officers, and employed as clerk and interpreter, both within the camp and in the city, where the British were helping with the return of hundreds of Belgians. Some of the Belgians had been released from concentration camps in Germany, while others had been forced out of the extermination camps in Poland by the Russian advance, and had survived death marches to other camps in Germany. Every day, I learned more of the horrors which Germany had inflicted on Europe, and of her unbelievable attempts to wipe out the Jewish race.

In my shame, the Britishness in me began to show, as I allowed my guilt for what I had done in Germany's name to recede further into the background. It was found convenient for me to wear British khaki battledress, with a white arm-band denoting me as a POW and, merely as a convenience to the British commander, I gave my word, as an officer, that I would not attempt to escape. This set me still further apart from the other Germans, and eventually I was housed in my own lodgings, just outside the barbed wire. I was given more and more work to do of a confidential nature. Then, to my great surprise, I was moved to Brussels and attached, as a de-Nazified German, to a special International Military Tribunal, to assist in the accurate translation of documents and records of our secret intelligence organisations, and those of the French *Milice*. I was to be a member of a small team of clerks who had to check information being prepared to enable the Tribunal to decide which aspects of the German war effort could be judged as criminal.

I returned to Brussels with a sense of foreboding. It seemed as though Fate itself had taken a hand in my future, and was weaving a web in which I would surely become trapped. My desire to help even a little in clearing up the terrible chaos caused by *die Endlösung* had brought me back to the very place where I had begun my career as a spy, and whence, through my own efforts, I had indirectly caused the torture and deaths of many people. It was ironic that the organisation with which I would now have to work could well be the instrument of my own downfall. Worst of all, I was about to be placed among people, some of whom, if they had survived, would surely recognise me.

I protested vigorously , suggesting that it was wrong for a German officer to assist in the tracking down and condemning of his superiors. My protests were ignored. Such criminals were already condemned, I was told; not by the paper-shuffling of a prisoner-of-war clerk, but by the entire world. Surely the comfort of working untrammeled with the Military Tribunal was better than life in a prisoner-of-war camp? After all, I had been cleared of being a Nazi, and here I could do a little to redeem and perhaps help rebuild my country.

I considered absconding, and taking my chance amongst the drifting population of Europe's misfits. I even contemplated suicide; there was so little to live for. But, in the end, I made up my mind to brazen it out and take my chances of remaining undetected. I would, in any case, only be with the Tribunal until the trials began in Nuremberg, and then I could disappear once more, amidst my compatriots.

CHAPTER TWENTY-EIGHT

I was put to work at once in the barracks of the former *Wehrmacht* headquarters, the same place where I had been held as a hostage more than two years previously. I had to share a small room with another German, a Professor Steinbeck, who had once been a tutor at Heidelberg. Because he was a Jew, he had been sent to Auschwitz. He had worked hard, and had survived only by helping in the selection of those destined for the gas chambers; the old or those too feeble to work. He was bitterly ashamed of this. He had expected eventually to die there himself but then, as the Russians approached, he had left Auschwitz with the *SS,* and had survived the long death march to Belsen: he was there when the British liberated the place. Like me, he had been offered work in assisting in rehabilitating the survivors of *Die Endlösung.*

Our work was entirely concerned with the accurate translation of captured documents. Occasionally we were asked to concentrate on specific cases; to cross-check the background of the legal briefs being prepared by the Tribunal. We were flooded with such questions as 'What does this mean in English?' or 'Can these figures be taken as accurate?' or (and this often came up) 'Surely, this cannot be true?' Much of what we were asked to translate seemed beyond belief, and I had to leave a lot of it to Steinbeck, because my mind refused to accept the words staring at me from these German records. There was no longer any doubt in my mind that we Germans were guilty of the most horrendous crimes, and just how they had remained hidden from us, and for so long, was beyond my understanding. Most German heads had been as deep in the sand as mine, until I had seen the horrors at the Dora factory.

I worked ceaselessly in my self-imposed captivity; I never left the barracks, and kept very much to myself when not in the office with Steinbeck. I started to grow a bushy moustache, and found an old pair of steel-rimmed spectacles, which I wore at all times when out of my small bedroom. I had never fully recovered the use of my legs after the long spell in hospital, and now walked slowly, with a stoop. Altogether, I reckoned that it would take a very astute person to recognise the dashing, handsome Pilot Officer George Harrison of yesteryear.

The first actual brief we saw was that concerned with the murder of fifty RAF officers who had been executed, out of hand, by the *SS* after having escaped through an incredible tunnel, built at Stalag Luft 3 in Sagan. For a few hours, we actually worked with an RAF Wing Commander and his deputy, who were tracking down those responsible for the executions. We were able to confirm some details from documents written at the places where most had been recaptured, and to tell them something about the *Gestapo* background. I also worked with Steinbeck on a search through *Gestapo* records which carefully concealed the fate of about twenty British paratroopers, who had disappeared in Norway after a glider assault on a heavy water plant. We found nothing of value, apart from a listing of the men, some of whom had been killed when one of the gliders had crashed into a mountain, and others who had mysteriously died in hospital. Amongst these documents, I also came across a summary of British and American airmen who had been captured when safe houses had been compromised by collaborators in the Paris area. Because they had been wearing civilian clothes, they had been treated as spies and sent to Buchenwald for disposal.

It was during the course of this work that I became aware of the existence of a British Intelligence unit working with the Americans, within the Military Tribunal. It was gathering information on the escape routes, recording details of all those who had helped British and American airmen to evade capture, and listing the fates of those members of the escape organisations who had been captured by the *SS*. Fortunately, I had no direct contact with this unit, but learned more than enough about the atrocities committed by the *Gestapo* from the summaries appended to the briefs making the cases against such as the *Reichsführer SS*, Head of the *Abwehr,* and senior officials of the *Gestapo*. I desperately hoped that I would not become involved with investigations into the escape routes, and was profoundly grateful when, instead, I was given the laborious task of sifting through bundles of documents found in the ruins of Berlin.

I worked on this mass of information around the clock throughout the week before the start of the Nuremberg trials. Most of it dealt, surprisingly, with *Gestapo* activities against the German people, particularly those who had become implicated in the attempt on Adolf Hitler's life. I was fascinated to read the case against *Admiral* Canaris, and to see how the executions throughout the top levels of the Services had caused such a serious setback to morale and efficiency. With typical German thoroughness, the actual details of torture and the nature of the executions were spelled out in gory detail. All this made me wonder just how my poor father had met his end.

During the third day of this mammoth trawl, I came across some papers which referred to specific operations mounted against the Resistance organisations and, in particular, to those against the escape routes. I prepared myself for the inevitable disclosure but, when I found the report dealing with the success of *Aktion Kondor*, I was almost stunned with disbelief. I read it through and through, and could not believe my good luck. It had been compiled by Kreis's immediate superior, seemingly in the form of a citation for an award. It certainly dealt with the framework of the plan and its overall results, but made no reference to anyone in particular, except Kreis, who was credited as the author, the planner and as totally responsible. Nonetheless, whilst pleased with my good fortune, I considered the document too dangerous to be left around, and therefore took it upon myself to burn it in the coke fire in my bedroom, together with another report which distressed me. This dealt with the details of the bestial torture and death of an RAF sergeant who had escaped more than once from Stalag Luft 1 at Barth, and had been captured whilst attempting to set up an escape route, with the help of some Polish seamen, between the camp and the port of Stettin.

My work as a translator came to an end when the Commanding Officer of the Tribunal, a barrister in private life, left, with his deputy, to take part in the trials which were about to begin at Nuremberg. Steinbeck departed at the same time, for a new life in the United States as a displaced person. Left alone, I was desperately anxious to get away from Brussels, and lose myself amongst the bewildered millions of my defeated country - but this was not to be. With the departure of the Colonel to Nuremberg, command of the British element of the Tribunal devolved to a young Intelligence Corps Captain. I had spoken to him only once before, when he had made it only too clear that he did not like Germans and, furthermore, resented a German enjoying an 'easy life' with the

Tribunal. However, he now began to take a particular interest in me, initially, perhaps, because I had been at school in Yorkshire when he had been at Stowe. He confided in me that he had not wanted to become a soldier, as it had interfered with the start he had already made in the acting profession. (Because he has now become internationally famous, I will not reveal his true name, but simply refer to him by his nickname of 'Trapper').

I soon found this man repulsive: he was a homosexual, with most revolting and bizarre habits, which I discovered to my cost. His consuming passion was an ever-growing collection of pictures of German atrocities, most of them photographs taken from our captured records, showing every kind of human perversity and outrage. He took sadistic pleasure in forcing me to look at, and discuss, execution scenes, bodies hanged by the neck or impaled, parades of naked women being herded into gas chambers, and even graphic photographs of what had been done to some of those who had made an attempt on the *Führer's* life. He was obsessed with torture and death, and yet, now and then, showed a degree of pity - although always linked with his wish to see the "bloody Germans" pay for what they had done.

It was through Trapper's interest in me that I came to learn what had happened to those captured during the course of *Kondor*. He had been one of the officers involved in an exhaustive accounting of all those who had worked on escape routes in the Netherlands, Belgium and France, together with a listing of the thousands of Allied airmen who had been led to freedom. I was amazed when he made me read about the scale of this activity. More than 14,000 men, women and young people had been recorded as having helped the Allies in this way. It also surprised me to learn that almost 3,000 aircrew of Bomber Command had got back to England, but at what cost. Thousands of helpers had been killed, or had died in the concentration camps.

Trapper was in his element with me. I was the only German on whom he could vent his pent-up anger. He would not leave me alone, and constantly harangued me with the persistence of a schoolmaster dealing with an unwilling pupil. He believed that the escape routes had been something new in warfare. Their successes had played a large part in strengthening and maintaining the morale of Bomber Command, and this had been done with only negligible support from British Intelligence. Escape routes had been set up wherever shot-down aircrew were found. Many had been well-organised, but most had not survived long because of ruthless German countermeasures. There was one, however, which had become paramount, having operated throughout the war despite every German attempt to stop it: that was the Belgian route known as Phoenix.

He told me this as we sat in his office, with the early winter sun shining through the window onto his twisted face. I really began to feel that the time of my denunciation was fast approaching; that soon I would be made to pay for what I had done for my country during *Kondor*. I tried to divert the drift of conversation by telling him that I, too, had once been an evader; that I had been shot down during the *Blitzkrieg*. He listened with some interest, and asked a question or two. Then, to my relief, he switched to asking me about the years before I had gone to Heidelberg. He soon began to lose interest and, when I had finished, said that he had work to do, and that I could go. He handed me a folder as he dismissed me.

'I want you to read this carefully, to see if there is anything you don't understand: I doubt it, but we can never be sure. We'll talk about it tomorrow.'

As I walked from the room, I noticed that the title of the folder I was holding was: *"The Phoenix Line"*.

It took me a long time to complete this task because there were parts I had to read over and over again in order to refresh my memories of what exactly I had achieved in *Kondor*. I was strangely gratified to find that I had been right in telling Kreis that, although his plan had been successful, he would never stop the Belgians from striving to defeat us. I read about the catastrophic effect my subversion had caused to the Line. However, Phoenix had resumed operations, about three months after my return to Berlin - despite the terrible reprisals which had been inflicted. Paul Vercours, after prolonged torture, had been shot in the execution ground at Mont St. Marzin, strapped unconscious to a stretcher, set up against a stake between Doctor Gaillard and Jean de Brassey. Arthos and Benedict had faced the firing squad in Brussels, and there had been other executions in both Antwerp and Ghent. The *Gestapo* had rounded up scores of helpers and their charges in the many safe houses.

No one seemed to have escaped the net in any of the Brussels, Namur, Paris or *Pays Basque* areas. Even the villagers of Balen and the restaurant manager in Lille had been caught. The kindly fathers at the monastery in Namur, together with other monks, had disappeared in Germany. Doctor Klermans had been shot out of hand, and his wife and two daughters had been sent to the extermination camp at Auschwitz, simply because they were Jews. *Madame* Klermans had been condemned to the gas chamber soon after their arrival, while the two girls had been used for medical experiments: Clothilde had not survived this horror.

The most astounding revelation contained in the folder was that the real leader of Phoenix had not been Paul Vercours as I had reported, but none other than Emilie de Vray. I could not believe it; a mere slip of a girl had not only master-minded the organisation for years, but had also been its principal operative. She had started in 1941 with three British soldiers, left behind at Dunkirk, whom she had single-handedly taken across France to the British authorities in Spain. She had subsequently made the necessary contacts with British Intelligence, and had built up Phoenix to cope with the hundreds of aircrew being shot down in the British bomber offensive. After her capture by the *Gestapo*, Emilie had been suspected of being more to Phoenix than a mere guide. In a series of harrowing interrogations, over a period of more than three months, she had been subjected to systematic torture. Throughout this Hell, she had given nothing away and, in the end, had been sent to Belsen, a physical wreck, yet still resolved to fight on. When liberated by the British, she had been almost at the point of death.

Everything else in the folder was anti-climax, although I learnt that new Belgian leaders for Phoenix had been recruited from amongst those who had escaped to England. They had been quickly trained, and either parachuted back into Belgium or landed at night by aeroplane. The route had been revived, and had flourished throughout the invasion of Normandy and the advances of the Allied armies, right up until the liberation of Brussels.

What I had read about Emilie de Vray moved me profoundly. I remembered the growing feelings I had once had for her, all that time ago. I had not forgotten when I had first seen her, and how I had looked forward to meeting her as I was taken down the Line. Nor could I forget that brief moment of passion outside the farmhouse high in the Pyrenees before we had crossed into Spain; nor the confused last rendezvous in the cafe at San Sebastian, or the touching love letter which I had read on the train back to Paris. I had to admit to myself that I had certainly had warm feelings for this extraordinary woman, but she had, nonetheless, been my sworn enemy and, once I had settled back into life in the *Luftwaffe*, I had forgotten about her.

I was summoned to see Trapper early the next morning. There was a smug, self-satisfied look about him as I stood to attention in his office.

'Thank the Lord, they have made up their minds about you, my German hero. Tomorrow, you will be on your way back to what little remains of your Greater German *Reich*. We have found a place for you at one of our proper camps in Dusseldorf: they will sort you out.'

His bitter vindictiveness meant nothing but relief for me: I was overjoyed to know that, at last, I would soon be on my way back to the Fatherland. That was all that mattered; I could leave Brussels, and thus escape what might well have become my Nemesis. I handed back the Phoenix folder without showing any emotion.

'Did you not find that interesting?' he said, as I put it down in front of him. 'I marvel at how you Germans dispose of people you don't like, as though they were nothing more than cattle.'

I remained silent, but held his gaze.

'You Huns are beyond belief. I thank the Lord above that at least your masters are going to pay for the crimes you have committed. It is you "ordinary Germans" who worry me though. All the Nazis have miraculously disappeared, and we seem to be left with only those who try to convince us they knew nothing about their vile deeds, and have no shame for what has been done.'

I looked at the hatred blazing in his eyes, and had to lower my gaze. He banged his fist on the Phoenix report.

'Before you leave us, you are going to pay your respects to some of those poor souls you have been reading about. You are coming with me, this afternoon, to help the Belgians bury a few of their dead. I want you to be there to see some real people, patriots who have fought and defied you to the very end.'

A bitter wind was blowing across the small field being used as a cemetery for members of the Belgian Resistance whose bodies were being brought back to Brussels for final burial. Six coffins had been set in line, each alongside a newly-dug grave in a row behind two others occupied by those already interred. Headstones had already been set in place, and the rest of the area prepared for many more graves. Trapper made me stand beside him. I was conspicuous in a British soldier's greatcoat, a white armband denoting that I was a prisoner-of-war. I wore my spectacles, and had my head covered with a British khaki beret. I hoped to God that I would not be recognised by anyone in the crowd assembled for the burial ceremony.

A priest and a British padre together held a short service, and committed the six dead Belgians to their graves as we stood to attention. Trapper saluted with other officers as the Last Post was sounded by a Belgian soldier.

'I want you to see some of those who fought so well against you swine,' said Trapper, as he took my arm and guided me towards a small group of men and women who had been standing near the graves throughout the burial. 'You will be privileged to meet Emilie de Vray.'

I was aghast at the idea of being brought face to face with the woman who had once expressed her love for me, and whom I had ruthlessly handed over to the *Gestapo*. But Trapper's hand took a firm hold on my sleeve, and urged me forward. I began to shake, panic began to well up in me, and I feared I would completely lose my self-control. As during those terrible moments in the air when I had lost my nerve, all the soul-searching and agonising over what I had done began to erupt inside me. I was beginning to hyperventilate, and could feel the cold trickle of sweat running down my back as Trapper brought me to a halt in front of Emilie.

Fearing the worst, I lifted my eyes and saw a woman, swathed in a heavy coat, sitting hunched in a wheelchair. On the left lapel of her coat were pinned three medals, Belgium's highest honours. Her hands gripped the sides of the chair as pain seemed to surge through her body, and I saw the ugly scar tissue at the ends of her fingers, where her nails had been pulled out. 'Mademoiselle de Vray?' asked Trapper. Emilie seemed startled by the sound of her name, but lifted her head. My head swam again, and I swayed on my feet; I was sure my legs were about to give way as I looked at her. It was, indeed, Emilie's face: although very pale, she still had the skin of a younger person, but the look of an old woman. Her jaw was set firm, but at an unnatural angle where, presumably, it had healed after being broken. Her cheeks were sunken, not only from obvious under-nourishment but also, I guessed, because my countrymen had probably knocked or pulled out her teeth, one by one. *'Oui,'* she replied, as she looked about with empty eyes. *'Oui... qui est la?'* It was only then that I realised I was not to be denounced after all. Emilie was not look-ing for who was speaking, but *listening* for them. At some stage, during her appalling experiences, she had been blinded, and would never set eyes on the man responsible for her terrible fate.

Still shaking, and in the grip of a maelstrom of emotion, I was led away by Trapper. His final words to me were spoken with pure venom:

'See what you swine did to such people. That frail shell of a woman was worth a whole bloody Division of you Nazi supermen. Thank God you're finished.'

APPROXIMATE COMPARATIVE RANKS:

Luftwaffe & Wehrmacht	**RAF**
Oberst	Group Captain
Oberstleutnant	Wing Commander
Major	Squadron Leader
Hauptmann	Flight Lieutenant
Oberleutnant	Flying Officer
Leutnant	Pilot Officer
Oberfeldwebel	Flight Sergeant
Feldwebel	Sergeant
Unteroffizier	Corporal
Gefreiter	Aircraftsman First Class / Corporal

SS / SD / Gestapo	**Allied**
Reichsführer	General
Standartenführer	Colonel
Obersturmbannführer	Lieutenant Colonel
Sturmbannführer	Major
Obersturmführer	Lieutenant
Scharführer	Sergeant

GLOSSARY

Abwehr - Military Inteligence.

Aidez-moi? - Help me?

Arbeit Macht Frei - 'Labour Makes Free' - Wording which appeared over concentration camp gates, designed to indicate that their purpose was more innocuous than the fact.

Anhalter Bahnhof- Probably the railway station most used by Hitler and his government, as it was primarily for services to the East.

A.O.C. - Air Officer Commanding.

Arrét - Tram stop.

Auswärtiges Amt - Foreign Office.

Autobahn - Motorway. Hitler developed this network of very advanced roadways notionally for civil use. However, the hidden agenda was also that of being able to move troops efficiently in time of war.

Beleuchter - Aircraft used to drop flares at night to illuminate enemy bombers.

Blitzkrieg - 'Lightning war' - The tactics of rapid advance using air-craft and armour.

bonne chance - Good luck.

boutonniére - button hole - a strip of ribbon in the national colours.

capotes anglaises - prophylactics - the French objected to the term in English 'French letter' and so adopted the 'English cap (or hood)' as their slang term.

Der Kondor ist geflogen - The condor has flown

Die Endlösung - The Final Solution - The extermination of various ethnic groups, principally the Jews.

Aktion Kondor - Operation *Kondor.*

en fâte - celebrating.

Einsatzgruppe - Mobile SS Groups usually employed in the liquidation of specific groups within occupied countries.

Einsatzkommando - Individual detachments within an *Einsatzgruppe.*

Ersatzkaffee - substitute or artificial coffee.

Experten - Experts - 'Aces'.

Feldgendarmerie - Military Field Police.

Feldmütze - Field cap - soft peaked cap.

Fliegerkombi - One-piece flying overalls

Flugzeugführerabzeichen - the pilot's badge - wings

Freikorps - 'Free Corps' - Right wing para-military units which sprang up after WWI. Renegades of various nationalities were formed into *Freikorps* units during WWII, primarily for propaganda purposes.

Flak (abbr.) Flugzeugabwehrkanone - Anti-aircraft artillery.

Führer - Leader

Gau - administrative area under the *NSDAP* - as in *Gauleiter* - the Chief Executive of such an area or district

Geheim Staatspolitzei - *'Gestapo'* - Secret State police.

Geschwader - An air force Wing - comprised of three to five *Gruppen*.

Gruppe - An air force Group - comprised of three to five *Staffeln*.

'Hals- und Beinbruch' - A traditional German salutation between pilots - 'Break your neck and leg'.

Hauptquartier - Headquarters.

'Herein.' - Come in.

'Hilfe?' - Help me?

Hitler Jugend - Hitler Youth.

Internat - Boarding School.

Kampfgeschwader - Bomber wing.

Kanal Kampf - 'Channel Fight' - German reference to what we call the 'Battle of Britain'.

Kettenhunde - Chain Dogs - Field Police.

Kommandant - Commander - as in Camp Commander.

Kommandeur - Commander.

Kriegsmarine - Navy.

Kübelwagen - Jeep type utility vehicle.

Kristallnacht - 'Crystal Night' - The night of 9 November 1938 when Nazis attacked synagogues and other Jewish-owned premises. The reference to crystal is to the broken glass that littered the streets after the attacks.

L'addition - The bill.

Laissez-passer - Passport.

Luftfahrtministerium or *Reichsluftfahrtministerium* - Air Ministry - actual address *Leipziger Strasse 7,* but main frontage in *Wilhelm Strasse*. Soon to become the new Ministry of Finance building when the German government relocates to Berlin.

Luftflotte - Air Fleet.

Luftwaffe - German Air Force.

Magirus - German general purpose truck - about a 3-ton type.

Mein Kampf - Literally 'My Fight or My Struggle' - Hitler's book, written in the late 1920's, setting out his political ideology.

Milice - French Secret Police.

Nachtjagdgeschwader - Night fighter wing

NJG - abbreviation - *Nachtjagdgeschwader*

Novemberverbrecher - The November Criminals - A disparaging term used to describe those who accepted the terms of the 1918 Armistice which effectively ended WWI.

Norddeutsch - Northern German dialect.

Oberbefehlshaber der Luftwaffe - Headquarters of the Supreme Commander: *46-47 Knesebeck Strasse.*

Obersturmführer (SS) - *Oberleutnant* - Allied Lieutenant.

'Pauke Pauke!' - Literally 'Kettledrum' - Night fighter R/T code for, 'I am attacking'.

'Raus! - Abbreviation of *Heraus* - Come out.

Reichsmarschall - Title created for Hermann Göring. There is no direct equivalent in Allied terms.

Reichswehr - Army of the Weimar Republic post WWI.

RT- Radio telephony.

Reichsluftfahrtministerium - or *Luftfahrtministerium* - Air Minstry.

Reichskanzlei - *Reichs* Chancellery - *Voss Strasse* 6.

Ritterkreuz - Knight's Cross of the Iron Cross.

Schräge Musik - Literally: slanting music - upward-firing cannons which were angled slightly forward.

SD - *Sicherheitsdienst* - Security Service.

Schmeisser - MP40 machine pistol cal. 9mm

Schultzstaffel - The *SS*. Hitler's Elite Guard which later developed as the security service of the Nazis as well as having a full military capability in the *Waffen* (armed) SS

Seelöwe - Sea Lion - The planned operation to invade England in 1940.

Staffel - Squadron.

Staffelkapitän - The leader of the squadron, but more a position than a rank.

Sturmabteilung - The SA - Brown shirts - early uniformed branch of the Nazis.

'Tante Ju' - Aunty Ju. - Service nick name for the Junkers 52 3M.

Verdammte Engländers - Damned English

Verdammte Terrorflieger - Damned terror flyers.

Versailles Diktat - Treaty of Versailles. The Germans did not view the treaty as a negotiated treaty at all, but more as something imposed upon them; hence the reference commonly used at the time: the Versailles order.

Virtuti Militari - Poland's highest military decoration.

Waffen SS - The military section of the SS.

Wehrmacht - German armed forces - all three services - Army (*Heer*) - Navy (*Marine*) and Air Force (*Luftwaffe*). Often misused to describe the German Army alone.

Wilde Sau - Wild Boar. Freelance night-fighting tactics developed by *Hauptmann* (later *Oberst)* Hajo Herrman, making reference to the fierce defences mounted by a female wild boar if her progeny were threatened.

Winterübung Rügen - Winter Exercise - Codeword for German operations in Spain.

Zerstörer - Destroyers - Long range escort fighters, often the Me 110.

Zone Interdite - A zone, two kilometres wide, running all along both sides of the frontier.